Contents

Acknowledgements

Carillion would like to thank the following people for their contribution to this book: Robert Otterson, Peter Fox, Redvers Johnson, Kevin Jarvis and Ralph Need.

Harcourt would like to thank everyone at the Carillion Construction Training Centre in Sunderland for all their help at the photo shoots.

Special thanks to Chris Ledson at Toolbank for supplying some photos. Visit the Toolbank website at www.toolbank.com.

Photos

Alamy Images, p294 (top), p356 (top); Alamy Images/Charles Stirling, p140 (top); Construction Photography, p68; Corbis, p1, p35, p55 (top), p56 (top), p63, p66 (bottom), p117, p187, p205, p371; Digital Vision, p79; Dreamstime.com/Andrzej Tokarski, p126; Getty Images/Photodisc, p7, p10, p13, p16, p17, p30, p43, p45, p66 (top), p103, p237, p321, p389; Harcourt/Chris Honeywell, p55 (bottom); Harcourt/Ginny Stroud-Lewis, p56 (ear-plugs, ear defenders), p57 (top); HNT Gordon Planemakers, Australia/Terry Gordon, p138 (bottom); iStockPhoto/Guy Erwood, p67; Maria Joannou, p121 (bottom), p142 (bottom), p146 (bottom), p158 (top left), p161, p342 (bottom), p344 (bottom left), p345 (top), p346 (bottom left, bottom right), p347 (top), p353 (frame fixings), p354 (top left), p368 (bottom), p369 (top); Masterfile/Jon Lee, p25; Photographers Direct, p145 (bottom); Photographers Direct/Andrew Arthurs, p352 (bottom); Photographers Direct/Martyn F. Chillmaid, p354 (bottom middle); Photographers Direct/Quayside Graphics, p83; Photographers Direct/Andy Smith, p408 (bottom); Photos.com, p369 (bottom); Rockwool, p309 (bottom); Shout, p51 (bottom); Toolbank, p56 (boots), p57 (bottom), p120 (top), p122 (top), p123 (top), p128, p130 (top), p131 (bottom), p133 (bottom), p404 (bottom); Rachael Williams, p2, p107 and p341 (bottom).

All other photos copyright Gareth Boden/Harcourt Ltd.

Carpentry and Joinery

www.heinemann.co.uk

✓ Free online support
✓ Useful weblinks
✓ 24 hour online ordering

01865 888058

Inspiring generations

Heinemann, Halley Court, Jordan Hill, Oxford OX2 8EJ
Heinemann is the registered trademark of Harcourt Ltd

© Carillion Construction Ltd

First published 2006

11 10 09 08 07 06
10 9 8 7 6 5 4 3 2 1

British Library Cataloguing in Publication Data is available
from the British Library on request.

10-digit ISBN: 0 435 32570 1
13-digit ISBN: 978 0 435325 70 1

Designed by HL Studios
Layout by HL Studios
Printed in the UK by Scotprint
Illustrated by HL Studios

Cover design by GD Associates
Cover photo: © Harcourt Ltd/Gareth Boden and Photodisc

Websites

Please note that the examples of websites suggested in this book were up-to-date at the
time of writing. We have made all links available on the Heinemann website at
www.heinemann.co.uk/hotlinks. When you access the site, the express code is 5701P.

*The information and activities in this book have been prepared according to the standards
reasonably to be expected of a competent trainer in the relevant subject matter. However,
you should be aware that errors and omissions can be made and that different employers
may adopt different standards and practices over time. Therefore, before doing any practical
activity, you should always carry out your own Risk Assessment and make your own
enquiries and investigations into appropriate standards and practices to be observed.*

About this book

This book has been written based on a concept used within Carillion Training Centres for many years. That concept is about providing learners with the necessary information they need to support their studies and at the same time ensuring it is presented in a style which they find both manageable and relevant.

The content of this book has been put together by a team of instructors, each of whom have a wealth of knowledge and experience in both training for NVQs and Technical Certificates and their trade.

This book has been produced to help the learner build a sound knowledge and understanding of all aspects of the NVQ and Technical Certificate requirements associated with their trade. It has also been designed to provide assistance when revising for Technical Certificate end tests and NVQ job knowledge tests.

Each chapter of this book relates closely to a particular unit of the NVQ or Technical Certificate and aims to provide just the right level of information needed to form the required knowledge and understanding of that subject area.

This book provides a basic introduction to the tools, materials and methods of work required to enable you to complete work activities effectively and productively. Upon completion of your studies, this book will remain a valuable source of information and support when carrying out your work activities.

For further information on how the content of this student book matches to the unit requirements of the NVQ and Intermediate Construction Award, please visit www.heinemann.co.uk and follow the FE and Vocational link, followed by the Construction link, where a detailed mapping document is available for download.

Information about the use of and safety regulations relating to the use of circular saws is also available for download. Follow the links as above to access this document.

How this book can help you

You will discover a variety of features throughout this book, each of which have been designed and written to increase and improve your knowledge and understanding. These features are:

- **Photographs** – many photographs that appear in this book are specially taken and will help you to follow a step-by-step procedure or identify a tool or material.

- **Illustrations** – clear and colourful drawings will give you more information about a concept or procedure.

- **Definitions** – new or difficult words are picked out in **bold** in the text and defined in the margin.

- **Remember** – key concepts or facts are highlighted in these margin boxes.

- **Find out** – carry out these short activities and gain further information and understanding of a topic area.

- **Did you know?** – interesting facts about the building trade.

- **Safety tips** – follow the guidance in these margin boxes to help you work safely.

- **FAQs** – frequently asked questions appear in all chapters along with informative answers from the experts.

- **On the job scenarios** – read about a real-life situation and answer the questions at the end. What would you do? (Answers can be found in the Tutor Resource Disc that accompanies this book.)

- **End of chapter knowledge checks** – test your understanding and recall of a topic by completing these questions.

- **Glossary** – at the end of this book you will find a comprehensive glossary that defines all the **bold** words and phrases found in the text. A great quick reference tool.

- **Links to useful websites** – any websites referred to in this book can be found at www.heinemann.co.uk/hotlinks. Just enter the express code 5701P to access the links.

chapter 1

The construction industry

OVERVIEW

Construction means creating buildings and services. These might be houses, hospitals, schools, offices, roads, bridges, museums, prisons, train stations, airports, monuments – and anything else you can think of that needs designing and building! What about an Olympic stadium? The 2012 London games will bring a wealth of construction opportunity to the UK and so it is an exciting time to be getting involved.

In the UK, 2.2 million people work in the construction industry – more than in any other – and it is constantly expanding and developing. There are more choices and opportunities than ever before and pay and conditions are improving all the time. Your career doesn't have to end in the UK either – what about taking the skills and experience you are developing abroad? Construction is a career you can take with you wherever you go. There's always going to be something that needs building!

This chapter will cover the following:

- Understanding the industry
- Communication
- Getting involved in the construction industry
- Sources of information and advice.

Understanding the industry

Find out

Think of an example of a small, medium and large construction company. Do you know of any construction companies that have only one member of staff?

The construction industry is made up of countless companies and businesses that all provide different services and materials. An easy way to divide these companies into categories is according to their size.

- A small company is defined as having between 1 and 49 members of staff.

- A medium company consists of between 50 and 249 members of staff.

- A large company has 250 or more people working for it.

A business might only consist of one member of staff (a sole trader).

The different types of construction work

There are four main types of construction work:

1. New work – this refers to a building that is about to be or has just been built.

New work is just one type of construction area

2. Maintenance work – this is when an existing building is kept up to an acceptable standard by fixing anything that is damaged so that it does not fall into disrepair.

3. Refurbishment/renovation work – this generally refers to an existing building that has fallen into a state of disrepair and is then brought up to standard by repair. It also refers to an existing building that is to be used for a different purpose, for example, changing an old bank into a pub.

4. Restoration work – this refers to an existing building that has fallen into a state of disrepair and is then brought back to its original condition or use.

These four types of work can fall into one of two categories depending upon who is paying for the work:

1. Public – the government pays for the work, as is the case with most schools and hospitals etc.

2. Private – work is paid for by a private client and can range from extensions on existing houses to new houses or buildings.

Job and careers

Jobs and careers in the construction industry fall mainly into one of four categories:

- building

- civil engineering

- electrical engineering

- mechanical engineering.

Building involves the physical construction (making) of a structure. It also involves the maintenance, restoration and refurbishment of structures.

Civil engineering involves the construction and maintenance of work such as roads, railways, bridges etc.

Electrical engineering involves the installation and maintenance of electrical systems and devices such as lights, power sockets and electrical appliances etc.

Mechanical engineering involves the installation and maintenance of things such as heating, ventilation and lifts.

The category that is the most relevant to your course is building.

Carpenters are building craft workers

Job types

The construction industry employs people in four specific areas:

1. professionals
2. technicians
3. building craft workers
4. building operatives.

Professionals

Professionals are generally of graduate level (i.e. people who have a degree from a university) and may have one of the following types of job in the construction industry:

- architect – someone who designs and draws the building or structure
- structural engineer – someone who oversees the strength and structure of the building
- surveyor – someone who checks the land for suitability to build on
- service engineer – someone who plans the services needed within the building, for example, gas, electricity and water supplies.

Technicians

Technicians link professional workers with craft workers and are made up of the following people:

- architectural technician – someone who looks at the architect's information and makes drawings that can be used by the builder

- building technician – someone who is responsible for estimating the cost of the work and materials and general site management

- quantity surveyor – someone who calculates ongoing costs and payment for work done.

Building craft workers

Building craft workers are the skilled people who work with materials to physically construct the building. The following jobs fall into this category:

- carpenter or joiner – someone who works with wood but also other construction materials such as plastic and iron. A carpenter primarily works on site while a joiner usually works off site, producing components such as windows, stairs, doors, kitchens, and **trusses**, which the carpenter then fits into the building

- bricklayer – someone who works with bricks, blocks and cement to build the structure of the building

- plasterer – someone who adds finish to the internal walls and ceilings by applying a **plaster skim**. They also make and fix plaster **covings** and plaster decorations

- painter and decorator – someone who uses paint and paper to decorate the internal plaster and timberwork such as walls, ceilings, windows and doors, as well as **architraves** and **skirting**

- electrician – someone who fits all electrical systems and fittings within a building, including power supplies, lights and power sockets

- plumber – someone who fits all water services within a building, including sinks, boilers, water tanks, radiators, toilets and baths. The plumber also deals with lead work and rainwater fittings such as guttering

- slater and tiler – someone who fits tiles on to the roof of a building, ensuring that the building is watertight

Definition

Trusses – prefabricated components of a roof which spread the load of a roof over the outer walls and form its shape

Plaster skim – a thin layer of plaster that is put on to walls to give a smooth and even finish

Covings – a decorative moulding that is fitted to the top of a wall where it meets the ceiling

Architraves – a decorative moulding, usually made from timber, that is fitted around door and window frames to hide the gap between the frame and the wall

Skirting – a decorative moulding that is fitted at the bottom of a wall to hide the gap between the wall and the floor

- woodworking machinist – someone who works in a machine shop, converting timber into joinery components such as window sections, spindles for stairs, architraves and skirting boards, amongst other things. They use a variety of machines such as lathes, bench saws, planers and sanders.

Building operatives

There are two different building operatives working on a construction site.

1. Specialist building operative – someone who carries out specialist operations such as dry wall lining, asphalting, scaffolding, floor and wall tiling and glazing.

2. General building operative – someone who carries out non-specialist operations such as kerb laying, concreting, path laying and drainage. These operatives also support other craft workers and do general labouring. They use a variety of hand tools and power tools as well as **plant**, such as dumper trucks and JCBs.

Definition

Plant – industrial machinery

The building team

Constructing a building or structure is a huge task that needs to be done by a team of people who all need to work together towards the same goal. The team of people is often known as the building team and is made up of the following people.

Clients

The client is the person who requires the building or refurbishment. This person is the most important person in the building team because they finance the project fully and without the client there is no work. The client can be a single person or a large organisation.

Architect

The architect works closely with the client, interpreting their requirements to produce contract documents that enable the client's wishes to be realised.

Clerk of works

Selected by the architect or client to oversee the actual building process, the clerk of works ensures that construction sticks to agreed deadlines. They also monitor the quality of workmanship.

Local Authority

The Local Authority is responsible for ensuring that construction projects meet relevant planning and building legislation. Planning and building control officers approve and inspect building work.

Quantity surveyor

The quantity surveyor works closely with the architect and client, acting as an accountant for the job. They are responsible for the ongoing evaluation of cost and interim payments from the client, establishing whether or not the contract is on budget. The quantity surveyor will prepare and sign off final accounts when the contract is complete.

The building team is made up of many different people

Specialist engineers

Specialist engineers assist the architect in specialist areas, such as civil engineering, structural engineering and service engineering.

Health and safety inspectors

Employed by the Health and Safety Executive (HSE), health and safety inspectors ensure that the building contractor fully implements and complies with government health and safety legislation. For more information on health and safety in the construction industry, see Chapter 2 (page 35).

Building contractors

The building contractors agree to carry out building work for the client. Contractors will employ the required workforce based on the size of the contract.

Estimator

The estimator works with the contractor on the cost of carrying out the building contract, listing each item in the bill of quantities (e.g. materials, labour and plant). They calculate the overall cost for the contractor to complete the contract, including further costs as overheads, such as site offices, management administration and pay, not forgetting profit.

Site agent

The site agent works for the building contractor and is responsible for the day-to-day running of the site such as organising deliveries etc.

Suppliers

The suppliers work with the contractor and estimator to arrange the materials that are needed on site and ensure that they are delivered on time and in good condition.

General foreman

The general foreman works for the site manager and is responsible for co-ordinating the work of the ganger (see below), craft foreman and subcontractors. They may also be responsible for the hiring and firing of site operatives. The general foreman also liaises with the clerk of works.

Craft foreman

The craft foreman works for the general foreman organising and supervising the work of particular crafts. For example, the carpentry craft foreman will be responsible for all carpenters on site.

Ganger

The ganger supervises general building operatives.

Chargehand

The chargehand is normally employed only on large build projects, being responsible for various craftsmen and working with joiners, bricklayers, and plasterers.

Operatives

Operatives are the workers who carry out the building work, and are divided into three subsections:

1. Craft operatives are skilled tradesman such as joiners, plasterers, bricklayers.

2. Building operatives include general building operatives who are responsible for drain laying, mixing concrete, unloading materials and keeping the site clean.

3. Specialist operatives include tilers, pavers, glaziers, scaffolders and plant operators.

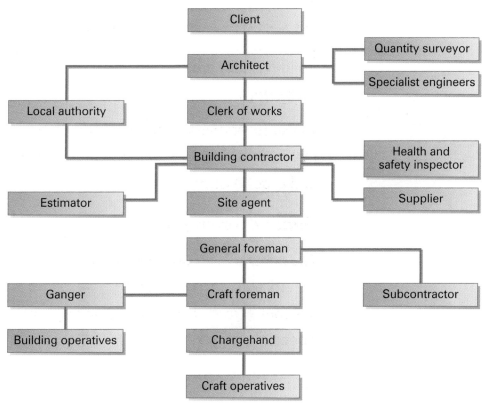

Figure 1.1 The building team

The different types of building

There are of course lots of very different types of building, but the main types are:

- residential – houses and flats etc.

- commercial – shops and supermarkets etc.

- industrial – warehouses and factories etc.

These types of building can be further broken down by the height or number of storeys that they have (one storey being the level from floor to ceiling):

- low rise – a building with one to three storeys

- medium rise – a building with four to seven storeys

- high rise – a building with seven storeys or more.

Buildings can also be categorised according to the number of other buildings they are attached to:

- detached – a building that stands alone and is not connected to any other building

- semi-detached – a building that is joined to one other building and shares a dividing wall, called a party wall

- terraced – a row of three or more buildings that are joined together, of which the inner buildings share two party walls.

A low rise residential building

Building requirements

Every building must meet the minimum requirements of the *Building Regulations*, which were first introduced in 1961 and then updated in 1985. The purpose of building regulations is to ensure that safe and healthy buildings are constructed for the public and that **conservation** is taken into account when they are being constructed. Building regulations enforce a minimum standard of building work and ensure that the materials used are of a good standard and fit for purpose.

What makes a good building?

When a building is designed, there are certain things that need to be taken into consideration, such as:

- security
- warmth
- safety
- light
- privacy
- ventilation.

A well-designed building will meet the minimum standards for all of the considerations above and will also be built in line with building regulations.

Identifying the different parts of a building

All buildings consist of the following two main parts:

1. the substructure

2. the superstructure.

The substructure consists of all building work below the ground level, including the foundations, up to the **damp proof course**. The purpose of the substructure is to spread the load of the building.

The superstructure consists of all the building work above the substructure and its purpose is to provide shelter and divide space.

The things that make up the substructure or superstructure can be divided into four different sections:

1. Primary elements – these include the main parts of the building that provide support, protection, floor-to-floor access and the division of space. Examples of primary elements are foundations, walls, floors, roofs and stairs.

2. Secondary elements – these include the non-essential and non-load bearing parts that are used to close off openings or to provide a finish. Examples of secondary elements are doors, windows, skirting and architraves.

3. Finishing elements – these include the final parts required to complete a component and can be superficial or necessary to complete the job. Examples of finishing elements are paint, wallpaper, plaster or face brickwork.

4. Services – these are the electrical, mechanical and specialist installations that are normally piped or wired into the building. Examples of services are running water and electricity.

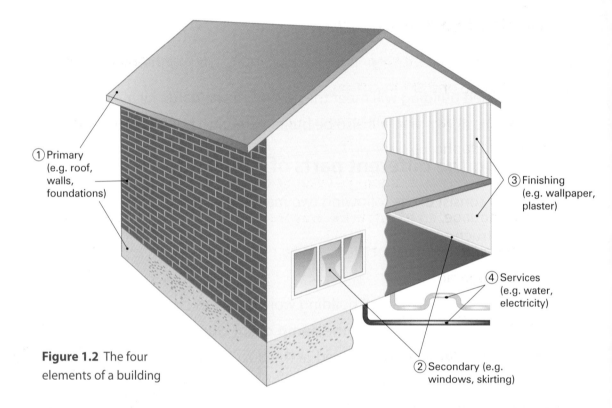

① Primary (e.g. roof, walls, foundations)

③ Finishing (e.g. wallpaper, plaster)

④ Services (e.g. water, electricity)

② Secondary (e.g. windows, skirting)

Figure 1.2 The four elements of a building

Communication

Communication, in the simplest of terms, is a way or means of passing on information from one person to another. Communication is very important in all areas of life and we often do it without even thinking about it. You will need to communicate well when you are at work, no matter what job you do. What would happen if someone couldn't understand something you had written or said? If we don't communicate well, how will other people know what we want or need and how will we know what other people want?

Companies that do not establish good methods of communicating with their workforce or with other companies, will not function properly and will end up with bad working relationships. Good working relationships can *only* be achieved with co-operation and good communication.

Methods of communication

There are many different ways of communicating with others and they all generally fit into one of these three categories:

1. speaking (verbal communication), for example talking face to face or over the telephone

2. writing, for example sending a letter or taking a message

3. body language, for example the way we stand or our facial expressions.

Each method of communicating has good points (advantages) and bad points (disadvantages).

Verbal communication

Verbal communication is the most common method we use to communicate with each other. If two people don't speak the same language or if someone speaks very quietly or not very clearly, verbal communication cannot be effective. Working in the construction industry you may communicate verbally with other people face to face, over the telephone or by radio/walkie-talkie.

Verbal communication is probably the method you will use most

Advantages

Verbal communication is instant, easy and can be repeated or rephrased until the message is understood.

Disadvantages

Verbal communication can be easily forgotten as there is no physical evidence of the message. Because of this it can be easily changed if passed to other people. Someone's accent or use of slang language can sometimes make it difficult to understand what they are saying.

Written communication

Written communication can take the form of letters, faxes, messages, notes, instruction leaflets, text messages, faxes, drawings and emails, amongst others.

Messages

To . Andy Rodgers . . . .

Date . . Tues 10 Nov . . . . . .   Time . 11.10 am . . . .

Message: . Mark from Stokes called with a . . . . query about the recent order. Please phone . . . . asap. (tel 01234 567 890) . . . .

. . . .

. . . .

Message taken by: . . . .   Lee Barber . . . .

Figure 1.3 A message is a form of written communication

Advantages

There is physical evidence of the communication and the message can be passed on to another person without it being changed. It can also be read again if it is not understood.

Disadvantages

Written communication takes longer to arrive and understand than verbal communication and body language. It can also be misunderstood or lost. If it is handwritten, the reader may not be able to read the writing if it is messy.

Body language

It is said that, when we are talking to someone face to face, only 10 per cent of the communication is verbal. The rest of the communication is body language and facial expression. This form of communication can be as simple as the shaking of a head from left to right to mean 'no' or as complex as the way someone's face changes when they are happy or sad or the signs given in body language when someone is lying.

We often use hand gestures as well as words to get across what we are saying, to emphasise a point or give a direction. Some people communicate entirely through a form of body language called sign language.

Advantages

If you are aware of your own body language and know how to use it effectively, you can add extra meaning to what you say. For example, say you are talking to a client or a work colleague. Even if the words you are using are friendly and polite, if your body language is negative or unfriendly, the message that you are giving out could be misunderstood. By simply maintaining eye contact, smiling and not folding your arms, you have made sure that the person you are communicating with has not got a mixed or confusing message.

Try to be aware of your body language

Body language is quick and effective. A wave from a distance can pass on a greeting without being close, and using hand signals to direct a lorry or a load from a crane is instant and doesn't require any equipment such as radios.

Disadvantages

Some gestures can be misunderstood, especially if they are given from very far away, and gestures that have one meaning in one country or culture can have a completely different meaning in another.

Which type of communication should I use?

Of the many different types of communication, the type you should use will depend upon the situation. If someone needs to be told something formally, then written communication is generally the best way. If the message is informal, then verbal communication is usually acceptable.

The way that you communicate will also be affected by who it is you are communicating with. You should of course always communicate in a polite and respectful manner with anyone you have contact with, but you must also be aware of the need to sometimes alter the style of your communication. For example, when talking to a friend, it may be fine to talk in a very informal way and use slang language, but in a work situation with a client or a colleague, it is best to alter your communication to a more formal style in order to show professionalism. In the same way, it may be fine to leave a message or send a text to a friend that says 'C U @ 8 4 work', but if you wrote this down for a work colleague or a client to read, it would not look very professional and they may not understand it.

Communicating with other trades

Communicating with other trades is vital because they need to know what you are doing and when, and you need to know the same information from them. Poor communication can lead to delays and mistakes, which can both be costly. It is quite possible for poor communication to result in work having to be stopped or redone. Say you are decorating a room in a new building. You are just about to finish when you find out that the electrician, plumber and carpenter have to finish off some work in the room. This information didn't reach you and now the decorating will have to be done again once the other work has been finished. What a waste of time and money. A situation like this can be avoided with good communication between the trades.

You will work with people from other trades

Common methods of communicating in the construction industry

A career in construction means that you will often have to use written documents such as drawings, specifications and schedules. These documents can be very large and seem very complicated but, if you understand what they are used for and how they work, using such documents will soon become second nature.

For more detailed information see Chapter 7 Drawings page 187.

Drawings

Drawings are done by the architect and are used to pass on the client's wishes to the building contractor. Drawings are usually done to scale because it would be impossible to draw a full-sized version of the project. A common scale is 1:10, which means that a line 10 mm long on the drawing represents 100 mm in real life. Drawings often contain symbols instead of written words to get the maximum amount of information across without cluttering the page. See Chapter 7 pages 196 and 197 for more information.

Specifications

Specifications accompany a drawing and give you the sizes that are not available on the drawing, as well as telling you the type of material to be used and the quality that the work has to be finished to.

Schedules

A schedule is a list of repeated design information used on big building sites when there are several types of similar room or house. For example, a schedule will tell you what type of door must be used and where. Another form of schedule used on building sites contains a detailed list of dates by which work must be carried out and materials delivered etc.

Other documents

As well as drawings, specifications and schedules there are some other important types of documents you will come across that are not specifically about the building or structure you are working on. Rather they are about your day-to-day tasks and your job. We will now look at a selection of these documents.

Timesheet

A timesheet is used to record the hours you have worked and where the work was carried out. Failure to complete your timesheet accurately and submit it on time may result in a loss of wages.

P. Gresford Building Contractors

Timesheet _____

Employee _____   **Project/site** _____

Date	Job no.	Start time	Finish time	Total time	Travel time	Expenses
M						
Tu						
W						
Th						
F						
Sa						
Su						
Totals						

Employee's signature _____

Supervisor's signature _____

Date _____

Figure 1.4 A typical timesheet

Jobsheet/Day worksheet

A job sheet is used to record work to be done. A day worksheet is used to record work done that wasn't originally planned and shown in the jobsheet.

P. Gresford Building Contractors

Jobsheet

Customer   Chris MacFarlane

Address   1 High Street

               Any Town

               Any County

Work to be carried out

Hang internal door in kitchen

Special conditions/instructions

Fit with door closer

3 × 75mm butt hinges

Figure 1.5 A typical jobsheet

P. Gresford Building Contractors

Day worksheet

Customer _Chris MacFarlane_   **Date** _____

Description of work being carried out _____

Hang internal door in kitchen.

_____

Labour	Craft	Hours	Gross rate	TOTALS
Materials	**Quantity**	**Rate**	**% addition**	
Plant	**Hours**	**Rate**	**% addition**	

Comments

Signed _____   **Date** _____

Site manager/foreman signature _____

Figure 1.6 A typical day worksheet

Requisition form

A requisition form (also known as an order form) is used when you require plant, materials or equipment. Once you have worked out what you need and how much of it you need, a requisition form can then be filled in and sent to the relevant supplier.

P. Gresford Building Contractors

Requisition form

Supplier _____   Order no. _____

_____   Serial no. _____

Tel no. _____   Contact _____

Fax no. _____   Our ref _____

Contract/Delivery address/Invoice address   Statements/applications

_____   for payments to be sent to

_____   _____

Tel no. _____   _____

Fax no. _____   _____

Item no.	Quantity	Unit	Description	Unit price	Amount

Total £ _____

Payment terms _____   Date _____

Originated by _____

Authorised by _____

Figure 1.7 A typical requisition form (order form)

Remember

Make sure you have all the tools and equipment you need before you go to do a job. You will need to plan ahead and fill in a requisition form early!

Delivery note

A delivery note is sent by a supplier along with an order. It lists the materials delivered and the quantity. If you receive a delivery, you must check the delivery note against the tools, equipment or materials delivered. If everything matches, then you can sign the note. If anything is missing or damaged, you should not sign the note and must inform your supervisor.

Delivery Note

Bailey & Sons Ltd

Building materials supplier

Tel: 01234 567890

Your ref: AB00671

Our ref: CT020

Date: 17 Jul 2006

Order no: 67440387

Invoice address:
Carillion Training Centre,
Deptford Terrace, Sunderland

Delivery address:
Same as invoice

Description of goods	Quantity	Catalogue no.
OPC 25kg	10	OPC1.1

Comments:

Date and time of receiving goods:

Name of recipient (caps):

Signature:

Figure 1.8 A typical delivery note

Work programme

A work programme is a method of showing very easily what work is being carried out on a building and when. Used by many site agents or supervisors, a work programme is a bar chart that lists the tasks that need to be done down the left side and shows a timeline across the top (see Figure 1.9). A work programme is used to make sure that the relevant trade is on site at the correct time and that materials are delivered when needed. A site agent or supervisor can quickly tell from looking at the chart if work is keeping to schedule or falling behind.

Time in days							
Activity	1	2	3	4	5	6	7
A	█						
B	█	█	█				
C		█	█				
D			█	█	█		
E		█	█	█	█	█	█
F				█	█	█	█
G						█	█

Figure 1.9 A work programme

Getting involved in the construction industry

There are many ways of entering the construction industry, but the most common way is as an apprentice.

Apprenticeships

You can become an apprentice by:

1. being employed directly by a construction company who will send you to college

2. being employed by a training provider, such as Carillion, which combines construction training with practical work experience.

On 1 August 2002, the construction industry introduced a mandatory induction programme for all apprentices joining the industry. The programme has four distinct areas:

1. apprenticeship framework requirements

2. the construction industry

3. employment

4. health and safety.

An apprenticeship will give you on-the-job training and experience

Apprenticeship frameworks are based on a number of components designed to prepare people for work in a particular construction occupation.

Construction frameworks are made up of the following mandatory components:

- NVQs

- technical certificates (construction awards)

- key skills.

However, certain trades require additional components. Bricklaying, for example, requires abrasive wheels certification.

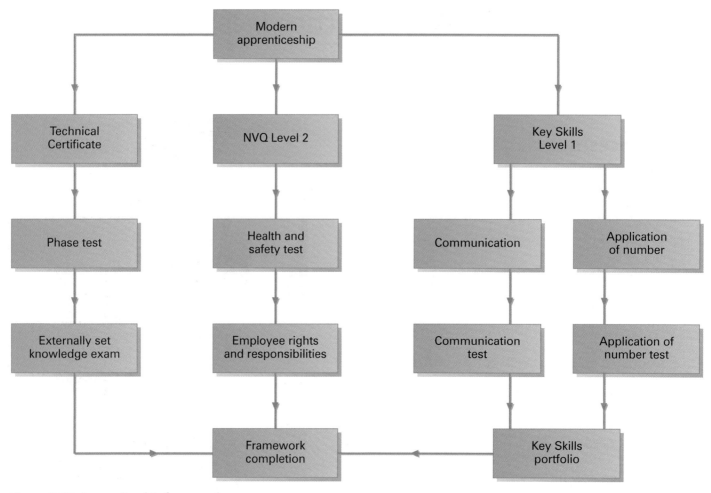

Figure 1.10 Apprenticeship framework

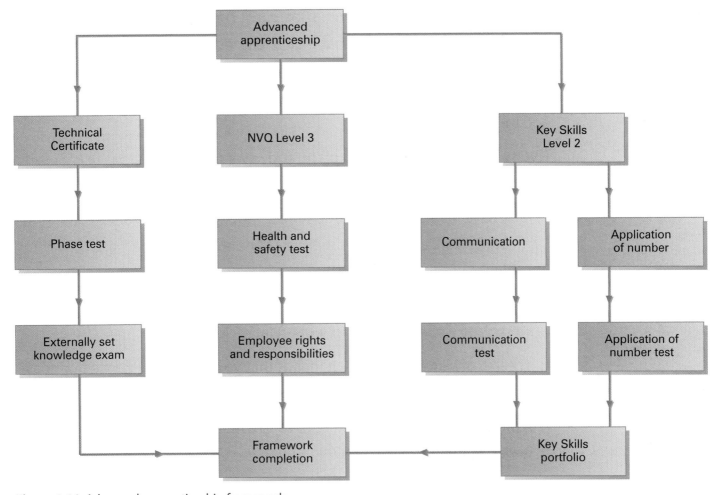

Figure 1.11 Advanced apprenticeship framework

National Vocational Qualifications (NVQs)

NVQs are available to anyone, with no restrictions on age, length or type of training, although learners below a certain age can only perform certain tasks. There are different levels of NVQ (e.g. 1, 2 , 3), which in turn are broken down into units of competence. NVQs are not like traditional examinations in which someone sits an exam paper. An NVQ is a 'doing' qualification, which means it lets the industry know that you have the knowledge, skills and ability to actually 'do' something.

The Construction Industry Training Board (CITB) is the national training organisation for construction in the UK and is responsible for setting training standards. NVQs are made up of both mandatory and optional units and the number of units that you need to complete for an NVQ depends on the level and the occupation.

NVQs are assessed in the workplace, and several types of evidence are used:

- Witness testimony consists of evidence provided by various individuals who have firsthand knowledge of your work and performance relating to the NVQ. Work colleagues, supervisors and even customers can provide evidence of your performance.

- Your natural performance can be observed a number of times in the workplace while carrying out work-related activities.

- The use of historical evidence means that you can use evidence from past achievements or experience, if it is directly related to the NVQ.

- Assignments or projects can be used to assess your knowledge and understanding of a subject.

- Photographic evidence showing you performing various tasks in the workplace can be used, providing it is authenticated by your supervisor.

Technical certificates

Technical certificates are often related to NVQs. A certificate provides evidence that you have the underpinning knowledge and understanding required to complete a particular task. An off-the-job training programme, either in a college or with a training provider, may deliver technical certificates. You generally have to sit an end-of-programme exam to achieve the full certificate.

Key skills

Some students have key skills development needs, so learners and apprentices must achieve key skills at Level 1 or 2 in both Communications and Application of number. Key skills are signposted in each level of the NVQ and are assessed independently, so you will need to be released from your training to attend a key skills test.

Employment

Conditions of employment are controlled by legislation and regulations. The Department of Trade and Industry (DTI) publishes most of this legislation. To find out more about your working rights, visit the DTI website. A quick link has been made available at www.heinemann.co.uk/hotlinks – just enter the express code 5701P.

The main pieces of legislation that will apply to you are:

- The Employment Act 2002 which gives extra rights to working parents and gives new guidance on resolving disputes, amongst other things.

- The Employment Relations Act 1999 covers areas such as trade union membership and disciplinary and grievance proceedings.

- The Employment Rights Act 1996 details the rights an employee has by law, including the right to have time off work and the right to be given notice if being dismissed.

- The Sex Discrimination Acts of 1975 and 1986 state that it is illegal for an employee to be treated less favourably because of their sex, for example, paying a man more than a woman or offering a woman more holiday than a man, even though they do the same job.

- The Race Relations Act 1976 states that it is against the law for someone to be treated less favourably because of their skin colour, race, nationality or ethnic origin.

- The Disability Discrimination Act 1995 makes it illegal for someone to be treated less favourably just because they have a physical or mental disability.

- The National Minimum Wage Act 1998 makes sure that everyone in the UK is paid a minimum amount. How much you must be paid depends on how old you are and whether or not you are on an Apprenticeship Scheme. The national minimum wage is periodically assessed and increased so it is a good idea to make sure you know what it is. At the time of writing, under 18s and those on Apprenticeship Schemes do not qualify for the minimum wage. For those aged 18–21, the minimum wage is £4.25 per hour and for adult workers aged 22 or over, the minimum wage is £5.05 per hour.

The Race Relations Act protects people of all skin colours, races and nationalities

Find out

What is the national minimum wage at the moment? You can find out from lots of different places, including the DTI website. You can find a link to the site at www.heinemann.co.uk/ hotlinks – just enter the express code 5701P

Contract of employment

Within two months of starting a new job, your employer must give you a contract of employment. This will tell you the terms of your employment and should include the following information:

- job title

- place of work

- hours of work

- rates of pay

- holiday pay

- overtime rates

- statutory sick pay

- pension scheme

- discipline procedure

- termination of employment

- dispute procedure.

If you have any questions about information contained within your contract of employment, you should talk to your supervisor before you sign it.

When you start a new job, you should also receive a copy of the safety policy and an employee handbook containing details of the general policy, procedures and disciplinary rules.

Discrimination in the workplace

Discrimination means treating someone unjustly, and in the workplace it can range from bullying, intimidation or harassment to paying someone less money or not giving them a job. Discriminating against people within the working environment is against the law. This includes discrimination on the grounds of:

- sex, gender or sexual orientation

- race, colour, nationality or ethnic origin

- religious beliefs

- disability.

The law states that employment, training and promotion should be open to all employees regardless of any of the above. Pay should be equal for men and women if they are required to do the same job.

Men and women must be treated equally at work

Sources of information and advice

There are many places you can go to get information and advice about a career in the construction industry. If you are already studying, you can speak to your tutor, your school or college careers adviser or you can get in touch with Connexions for careers advice especially for young people. Visit www.heinemann.co.uk/hotlinks and enter the express code 5701P for a link to Connexions' website. You can also find their telephone number in your local phonebook.

Organisations such as those listed below are very good sources of careers advice specific to the construction industry.

- CITB (Construction Industry Training Board) – the industry's national training organisation

- City and Guilds – a provider of recognised vocational qualifications

- The Chartered Institute of Building Services Engineers

- The Institute of Civil Engineers

- Trade unions such as GMB (Britain's General Union), UCATT (Union of Construction, Allied Trades and Technicians), UNISON (the public services union), Amicus (the manufacturing union, previously MSF).

Links to all these organisations' websites can be found by visiting www.heinemann.co.uk/hotlinks and entering the express code 5701P.

FAQ

Why do I need to learn about different trades?

It is very important that you have some basic knowledge of what other trades do. This is because you will often work with people from other trades and their work will affect yours and vice versa.

What options do I have once I have gained my NVQ Level 2 qualification?

Once you are qualified, there is a wide range of career opportunities available to you. For example, you could progress from a tradesman to a foreman and then to a site agent. There may also be the opportunity to become a clerk of works, an architect or a college lecturer. Some tradesmen are happy to continue as tradesmen and some start up their own businesses.

Knowledge check

1. How many members of staff are there in a small company, a medium company and a large company?

2. Give an example of a public construction project. Who pays for public work?

3. Name a job in each of the four construction employment areas: professional; technician; building craft worker; building operative.

4. Why is the client the most important member of the building team?

5. Explain the meaning of the following building types: residential; low rise; semi-detached.

6. What is the substructure of a building?

7. What are the three different methods of communication?

8. What information might a schedule give you?

9. What does NVQ stand for?

10. What information must be in your contract of employment?

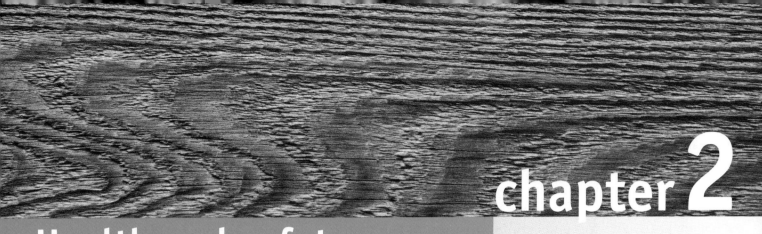

chapter 2

Health and safety

OVERVIEW

Every year in the construction industry over 100 people are killed and thousands more are seriously injured as a result of the work that they do. There are thousands more who suffer from health problems, such as dermatitis, asbestosis, industrial asthma, vibration white finger and deafness. You can therefore see why learning as much as you can about health and safety is very important.

This chapter will cover:

- Health and safety legislation

- Health and welfare in the construction industry

- Manual handling

- Fire and fire-fighting equipment

- Safety signs

- Personal protective equipment (PPE)

- Reporting accidents

- Risk assessment.

Health and safety legislation

Definition

Employer – the person or company you work for

While you are at work, in whatever location or environment that may be (e.g. on a building site or in a client's home), you need to be aware of some important laws that are there to protect you from harm. The laws state how you should be protected and what your **employer** has to do to keep you safe, i.e. their responsibilities.

Health and safety legislation not only protects you, but also states what your responsibilities are in order to keep others safe. It is very important that you follow any guidance given to you regarding health and safety and that you know what your responsibilities are.

What is legislation?

Did you know?

The average fine for breaking a health and safety law in the year 2003/04 was £9,858. The largest fine was £700,000

The word legislation generally refers to a law that is made in Parliament and is often called an act. For our purposes, health and safety acts state what should and shouldn't be done by employers and employees in order to keep work places safe. If an employer or an employee does something they shouldn't, or just as importantly, doesn't do something they should, they could face paying a large fine or even a prison sentence.

Health and safety legislation you need to be aware of

There are a lot of different pieces of legislation and regulations that affect the construction industry. Over the next few pages are just a few of those that you need to be aware of. Some of these are dealt with in more detail later on in this chapter.

Health and Safety at Work Act 1974

The Health and Safety at Work Act 1974 applies to all places of work, not just construction environments. It not only protects employers and employees but also any member of the public who might be affected by the work being done. The act outlines what must be done by employers and employees to ensure that the work they do is safe.

The main objectives of the Health and Safety at Work Act are:

- to ensure the health, safety and welfare of all persons at work
- to protect the general public from work activities
- to control the use, handling, storage and transportation of explosives and highly flammable substances
- to control the release of **noxious** or offensive substances into the atmosphere.

The Health and Safety at Work Act is **enforced** by the **Health and Safety Executive** (HSE). HSE inspectors have the power to:

- enter any premises to carry out investigations
- take statements and check records
- demand seizure, dismantle, neutralise or destroy anything that is likely to cause immediate serious injury
- issue an improvement notice, which gives a company a certain amount of time to sort out a health and safety problem
- issue a prohibition notice, which stops all work until the situation is safe.
- give guidance and advice on health and safety matters
- **prosecute** people who break the law, including employers, employees, self-employed manufacturers and suppliers.

As we learnt at the beginning of this chapter, employers and employees have certain responsibilities under health and safety legislation. These are often referred to as 'duties' and are things that should or shouldn't be done by law. If you do not carry out your duties, you are breaking the law and you could be prosecuted.

Definition

Noxious – harmful or poisonous

Find out

Will you be working with any highly flammable, explosive or noxious substances? What are they?

Definition

Enforced – making sure a law is obeyed

Prosecute – to accuse someone of committing a crime, which usually results in being taken to court and, if found guilty, being punished

Duties of the employer

Under the Health and Safety at Work Act employers must:

- provide a safe entrance and exit to the workplace

- provide a safe place to work

- provide and maintain safe machinery and equipment

- provide employees with the necessary training to be able to do their job safely

- have a written safety policy

- ensure safe handling, transportation and storage of machinery, equipment and materials

- provide personal protective equipment (PPE)

- involve trade union safety representatives, where appointed, in all matters relating to health and safety.

Duties of the employee

Under the Health and Safety at Work Act employees must:

- take care at all times and ensure that they do not put themselves or others at risk by their actions

- co-operate with employers with regard to health and safety

- use any equipment and safeguards provided by their employer

- not misuse or interfere with anything that is provided for their safety.

You have a legal duty to work safely at all times

Control of Substances Hazardous to Health Regulations 2002 (COSHH)

The COSHH regulations state how employees and employers should work with, handle, move and dispose safely of potentially dangerous substances. A substance hazardous to health is anything that might negatively affect your health, for example:

- dust or small particles from things like bricks and wood and fumes from chemicals

- chemicals in things like paint, **adhesives** and cement

- explosive or flammable chemicals or material.

The main aim of the COSHH regulations is to ensure that any risks due to working with hazardous substances or being exposed to them are assessed. Action must then be taken to eliminate or control the risks.

There are three different ways in which hazardous substances can enter the body:

1. Inhalation – breathing in the dangerous substance

2. Absorption – when the hazardous substance enters the body through the skin

3. Ingestion – taking in the hazardous substance through the mouth.

The COSHH regulations are as follows.

1. You should know exactly what products and substances you are using. You should be told this information by your employer.

2. Any hazards to health from using a substance or being exposed to it must be assessed by your employer.

3. If a substance is associated with any hazards to health, your employer must eliminate or control the hazard by either using a different substance or by making sure the substance is used according to guidelines (i.e. used outside or only used for short periods of time). Your

Definition

Adhesive – glue

Find out

Will you be working with any substances hazardous to health? What precautions and safety measures do you think should be taken for each?

Remember

It is not always possible to see a harmful substance so, if you are given any PPE or instructions about how to use/move/dispose of something, use them. Don't think that just because you can't see a hazardous substance, it isn't there

employer must also provide you with appropriate PPE and make sure that all possible precautions are taken.

4. Your employer must ensure that people are properly trained and informed of any hazards. All staff should be trained to recognise identifiable hazards and should know the correct precautions to take.

5. In order to make sure precautions are up to date, your employer has to monitor all tasks and change any control methods when required.

6. In case anyone ever needs to know what happened in the past, a record of all substances used by employees must be kept.

Provision and Use of Work Equipment Regulations 1998 (PUWER)

The PUWER regulations cover all working equipment such as tools and machinery. Under the PUWER regulations, employers must make sure that any tools and equipment they provide are:

- suitable for the job

- maintained (serviced and repaired)

- inspected (a regular check that ensures the piece of equipment and its parts are still in good working condition).

Employers also have to make sure that any risk of harm from using the equipment has been identified and all precautions and safety measures have been taken. Employers must also ensure that anyone who uses the equipment has been properly trained and instructed in how to do so.

Under PUWER, all tools and equipment must be regularly serviced and repaired

The Manual Handling Operations Regulations 1992

These regulations cover all work activities in which a person does the lifting instead of a machine. The correct and safe way to lift, which reduces the risk of injury, is covered later on in this chapter (see page 00).

The Control of Noise at Work Regulations 2005

In the course of your career in construction, it is likely that you will be at some time working in a noisy environment. The Control of Noise at Work Regulations are there to protect you against the consequences of being exposed to high levels of noise, which can lead to permanent hearing damage.

Damage to hearing can be caused by:

- the volume of noise (measured in decibels)
- the length of time exposed to the noise (over a day, over a lifetime etc.).

The regulations give guidance on the maximum period of time someone can be safely exposed to a decibel level, and your employer has to follow it.

If you have access to the internet, you might wish to visit the Health and Safety Executive website and find out what it is like to have hearing loss caused by long-term exposure to noise. A link to the web page has been made available at www.heinemann.co.uk/hotlinks – just enter the express code 5701P.

The Work at Height Regulations 2005

It is not at all unusual for a construction worker to carry out their everyday job high up off the ground, for example, on scaffolding, on a ladder, or on the roof of a building. The Work at Height Regulations make sure that your employer does all that they can to reduce the risk of injury or death from working at height. Your employer has a duty to:

- avoid work at height where possible
- use equipment that will prevent falls
- use equipment and other methods that will minimise the distance and consequences of a fall.

As an employee, under the regulations you must follow any training that has been given to you, report any hazards to your supervisor and use any safety equipment that is made available to you.

The Electricity at Work Regulations 1989

The Electricity at Work Regulations cover any work that involves the use of electricity or electrical equipment. Your employer has a duty to make sure that electrical systems you may come into contact with are safe and regularly maintained. They also have to make sure that they have done everything the law states to reduce the risk of an employee coming into contact with a live electrical current.

The Personal Protective Equipment at Work Regulations 1992

There are certain situations in which you will need to wear personal protective equipment (PPE). The Personal Protective Equipment at Work Regulations detail the different types of PPE that are available and states when they should be worn. Your employer has to ensure appropriate PPE is available for certain tasks (e.g. gloves when working with solvents, face masks when cutting bricks, safety goggles when using a circular saw).

The different types of PPE available are covered in more detail later on in this chapter (see page 55).

Reporting of Injuries, Diseases and Dangerous Occurrences Regulations 1995 (RIDDOR)

Employers have duties under RIDDOR to report accidents, diseases or dangerous occurrences. This information is used by the HSE to identify where and how risk arises and to investigate serious accidents.

Several other regulations exist which cover very specific things such as asbestos, pressure equipment and lead paint. If you want to find out more about these regulations, or any others, ask your tutor or employer for more information or visit the Health and Safety Executive website (go to www. heinemann.co.uk/hotlinks and enter the express code 5701P for a quick link).

Health and welfare in the construction industry

Jobs in the construction industry have one of the highest injury and accident rates and as a worker you will be at constant risk unless you adopt a good health and safety attitude. By following the rules and regulations set out to protect you and by taking reasonable care of yourself and others, you will become a safe worker and thus reduce the chance of any injuries or accidents.

The most common risks to a construction worker

What do you think these might be? Think about the construction industry you are working in and the hazards and risks that exist.

The most common health and safety risks a construction worker faces are:

- accidents
- ill health.

Remember

Health and safety laws are there to protect you and other people. If you take shortcuts or ignore the rules, you are placing yourself and others at serious risk

Accidents

We often hear the saying 'accidents will happen', but when working in the construction industry, we should not accept that accidents just happen sometimes. When we think of an accident, we quite often think about it as being no one's fault and something that could not have been avoided. The truth is that most accidents are caused by human error, which means someone has done something they shouldn't have done or, just as importantly, not done something they should have done.

Accidents can happen if your work area is untidy

Accidents often happen when someone is hurrying, not paying enough attention to what they are doing or they have not received the correct training.

If an accident happens, you or the person it happened to may be lucky and will not be injured. More often, an accident will result in an injury which may be minor (e.g. a cut or a bruise) or possibly major (e.g. loss of a limb). Accidents can also be fatal. The most common causes of fatal accidents in the construction industry are:

- falling from scaffolding
- being hit by falling objects and materials
- falling through fragile roofs
- being hit by forklifts or lorries
- electrocution.

Ill health

While working in the construction industry, you will be exposed to substances or situations that may be harmful to your health. Some of these health risks may not be noticeable straight away and it may take years for **symptoms** to be noticed and recognised.

Ill health can result from:

- exposure to dust (such as asbestos), which can cause breathing problems and cancer
- exposure to solvents or chemicals, which can cause **dermatitis** and other skin problems
- lifting heavy or difficult loads, which can cause back injury and pulled muscles
- exposure to loud noise, which can cause hearing problems and deafness
- using vibrating tools, which can cause **vibration white finger** and other problems with the hands.

Everyone has a responsibility for health and safety in the construction industry but accidents and health problems still happen too often. Make sure you do what you can to prevent them.

Definition

Symptom – a sign of illness or disease (e.g. difficulty breathing, a sore hand or a lump under the skin)

Dermatitis – a skin condition where the affected area is red, itchy and sore

Vibration white finger – a condition that can be caused by using vibrating machinery (usually for very long periods of time). The blood supply to the fingers is reduced which causes pain, tingling and sometimes spasms (shaking)

Staying healthy

As well as keeping an eye out for hazards, you must also make sure that you look after yourself and stay healthy. One of the easiest ways to do this is to wash your hands on a regular basis. By washing your hands you are preventing hazardous substances from entering your body through ingestion (swallowing). You should always wash your hands after going to the toilet and before eating or drinking.

Always wash your hands to prevent ingesting hazardous substances

Other precautions that you can take are ensuring that you wear **barrier cream**, the correct PPE and only drink water that is labelled as drinking water. Remember that some health problems do not show symptoms straight away and what you do now can affect you much later in life.

Welfare facilities

Welfare facilities are things such as toilets, which must be provided by your employer to ensure a safe and healthy workplace. There are several things that your employer must provide to meet welfare standards and these are:

- Toilets – the number of toilets provided depends upon the amount of people who are intended to use them. Males and females can use the same toilets providing there is a lock on the inside of the door. Toilets should be flushable with water or, if this is not possible, with chemicals.

- Washing facilities – employers must provide a basin large enough to allow people to wash their hands, face and forearms. Washing facilities must have hot and cold running water as well as soap and a means of drying your hands. Showers may be needed if the work is very dirty or if workers are exposed to **corrosive** and **toxic** substances.

Definition

Barrier cream – a cream used to protect the skin from damage or infection

Definition

Corrosive – a substance that can damage things it comes into contact with (e.g. material, skin)

Toxic – poisonous

- Drinking water – there should be a supply of clean drinking water available, either from a tap connected to the mains or from bottled water. Taps connected to the mains need to be clearly labelled as drinking water and bottled drinking water must be stored in a separate area to prevent **contamination**.

- Storage or dry room – every building site must have an area where workers can store the clothes that they do not wear on site, such as coats and motorcycle helmets. If this area is to be used as a drying room then adequate heating must also be provided in order to allow clothes to dry.

- Lunch area – every site must have facilities that can be used for taking breaks and lunch well away from the work area. These facilities must provide shelter from the wind and rain and be heated as required. There should be access to tables and chairs, a kettle or urn for boiling water and a means of heating food, such as a microwave.

When working in an occupied house, you should make arrangements with the client to use the facilities in their house.

On the job: Manual handling

Glynn and Frankie are unloading bags of plaster from a wheelbarrow. While handling a bag of plaster, Glynn gets a sharp pain in his back and drops the bag. Frankie goes and tells their supervisor, who comes over to where Glynn is sitting in a great deal of pain. What do you think should happen next? Do you think this incident could have been prevented?

Manual handling

Manual handling means lifting and moving a piece of equipment or material from one place to another without using machinery. Lifting and moving loads by hand is one of the most common causes of injury at work. Most injuries caused by manual handling result from years of lifting items that are too heavy, are awkward shapes or sizes, or from using the wrong technique. However, it is also possible to cause a lifetime of back pain with just one single lift.

Poor manual handling can cause injuries such as muscle strain, pulled ligaments and hernias. The most common injury by far is spinal injury. Spinal injuries are very serious because there is very little that doctors can do to correct them and, in extreme cases, workers have been left paralysed.

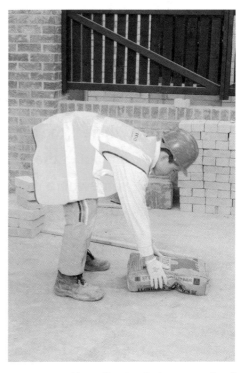

Poor manual handling techniques can lead to serious permanent injury

What you can do to avoid injury

The first and most important thing you can do to avoid injury from lifting is to receive proper manual handling training. Kinetic lifting is a way of lifting objects that reduces the chance of injury and is covered in more detail on the next page.

Before you lift anything you should ask yourself some simple questions:

* Does the object need to be moved?

* Can I use something to help me lift the object? A mechanical aid such as a forklift or crane or a manual aid such as a wheelbarrow may be more appropriate than a person.

* Can I reduce the weight by breaking down the load? Breaking down a load into smaller and more manageable weights may mean that more journeys are needed, but it will also reduce the risk of injury.

- Do I need help? Asking for help to lift a load is not a sign of weakness and team lifting will greatly reduce the risk of injury.

- How much can I lift safely? The recommended maximum weight a person can lift is 25 kg but this is only an average weight and each person is different. The amount that a person can lift will depend on their physique, age and experience.

- Where is the object going? Make sure that any obstacles in your path are out of the way before you lift. You also need to make sure there is somewhere to put the object when you get there.

- Am I trained to lift? The quickest way to receive a manual handling injury is to use the wrong lifting technique.

Lifting correctly (kinetic lifting)

When lifting any load it is important to keep the correct posture and to use the correct technique.

The correct posture before lifting:

- feet shoulder width apart with one foot slightly in front of the other
- knees should be bent
- back must be straight
- arms should be as close to the body as possible
- grip must be firm using the whole hand and not just the finger tips.

The correct technique when lifting:

- approach the load squarely facing the direction of travel
- adopt the correct posture (as above)
- place hands under the load and pull the load close to your body
- lift the load using your legs and not your back.

When lowering a load you must also adopt the correct posture and technique:

- bend at the knees, not the back

- adjust the load to avoid trapping fingers

- release the load.

Remember

Even light loads can cause back problems so, when lifting anything, always take care to avoid twisting or stretching

Think before lifting

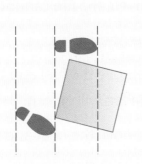

Adopt the correct posture before lifting

Get a good grip on the load

Adopt the correct posture when lifting

Move smoothly with the load

Adopt the correct posture and technique when lowering

Fire and fire-fighting equipment

Fires can start almost anywhere and at any time but a fire needs three things to burn. These are:

1. fuel

2. heat

3. oxygen.

Figure 2.1 The triangle of fire

This can be shown in what is known as 'the triangle of fire'. If any of the sides of the triangle are removed, the fire cannot burn and it will go out.

Remember:

• Remove the fuel and there is nothing to burn so the fire will go out.

• Remove the heat and the fire will go out.

• Remove the oxygen and the fire will go out as fire needs oxygen to survive.

Fires can be classified according to the type of material that is involved:

• Class A – wood, paper, textiles etc.

• Class B – flammable liquids, petrol, oil etc.

• Class C – flammable gases, liquefied petroleum gas (**LPG**), propane etc.

• Class D – metal, metal powder etc.

• Class E – electrical equipment.

Find out

What fire risks are there in the construction industry? Think about some of the materials (fuel) and heat sources that could make up two of the sides of 'the triangle of fire'

Fire-fighting equipment

There are several types of fire-fighting equipment, such as fire blankets and fire extinguishers. Each type is designed to be the most effective at putting out a particular class of fire and some types should never be used in certain types of fire.

Fire extinguishers

A fire extinguisher is a metal canister containing a substance that can put out a fire. There are several different types and it is important that you learn which type should be used on specific classes of fires. This is because if you use the wrong type, you may make the fire worse or risk severely injuring yourself.

Fire extinguishers are now all one colour (red) but they have a band of colour which shows what substance is inside.

Water

The coloured band is red and this type of extinguisher can be used on Class A fires. Water extinguishers can also be used on Class C fires in order to cool the area down.

Water fire extinguisher

A water fire extinguisher should **never** be used to put out an electrical or burning fat/oil fire. This is because electrical current can carry along the jet of water back to the person holding the extinguisher, electrocuting them. Putting water on to burning fat or oil will make the fire worse as the fire will 'explode', potentially causing serious injury.

Foam

The coloured band is cream and this type of extinguisher can also be used on Class A fires. A foam extinguisher can also be used on a Class B fire if the liquid is not flowing and on a Class C fire if the gas is in liquid form.

Foam fire extinguisher

Carbon dioxide (CO_2) extinguisher

Carbon dioxide (CO_2)

The coloured band is black and the extinguisher can be used on Class A, B, C and E fires.

Dry powder

The coloured band is blue and this type of extinguisher can be used on all classes of fire. The powder puts out the fire by knocking down the flames.

Fire blankets

Fire blankets are normally found in kitchens or canteens as they are good at putting out cooking fires. They are made of a fireproof material and work by smothering the fire and stopping any more oxygen from getting to it, thus putting it out. A fire blanket can also be used if a person is on fire.

It is important to remember that when you put out a fire with a fire blanket, you need to take extra care as you will have to get quite close to the fire.

Definition

Induction – a formal introduction you will receive when you start any new job, where you will be shown around, shown where the toilets and canteen etc. are, and told what to do if there is a fire

Dry powder extinguisher

A fire blanket

What to do in the event of a fire

During **induction** to any workplace, you will be made aware of the fire procedure as well as where the fire assembly points (also known as **muster points**) are and what the alarm sounds like. On hearing the alarm you must stop what you are doing and make your way to the nearest muster point.

This is so that everyone can be accounted for. If you do not go the muster point or if you leave before someone has taken your name, someone may risk their life to go back into the fire to get you.

When you hear the alarm, you should not stop to gather any belongings and you must not run. If you discover a fire, you must only try to fight the fire if it is blocking your exit or if it is small. Only when you have been given the all-clear can you re-enter the site or building.

Remember

Fire and smoke can kill in seconds so think and act clearly, quickly and sensibly

Safety signs

Safety signs can be found in many areas of the workplace and they are put up in order to:

- warn of any **hazards**
- prevent accidents
- inform where things are
- tell you what to do in certain areas.

Types of safety sign

There are many different safety signs but each will usually fit into one of four categories:

1. Prohibition signs – these tell you that something MUST NOT be done. They always have a white background and a red circle with a red line through it.

Definition

Hazard – a danger or risk

Figure 2.2 A prohibition sign

Figure 2.3 A mandatory sign

2. Mandatory signs – these tell you that something MUST be done. They are also circular but have a white symbol on a blue background.

3. Warning signs – these signs are there to alert you to a specific hazard. They are triangular and have a yellow background and a black border.

4. Information signs – these give you useful information like the location of things (e.g. a first aid point). They can be square or rectangular and are green with a white symbol.

Figure 2.4 A warning sign

Figure 2.5 An information sign

Remember

Make sure you take notice of safety signs in the workplace – they have been put up for a reason!

Figure 2.6 A safety sign with both symbol and words

Most signs only have symbols that let you know what they are saying. Others have some words as well, for example, a no smoking sign might have a cigarette in a red circle, with a red line crossing through the cigarette and the words 'No smoking' underneath.

Personal protective equipment (PPE)

Personal protective equipment (PPE) is a form of defence against accidents or injury and comes in the form of articles of clothing. This is not to say that PPE is the only way of preventing accidents or injury. It should be used together with all the other methods of staying healthy and safe in the workplace (i.e. equipment, training, regulations and laws etc.).

PPE must be supplied by your employer free of charge and you have responsibility as an employee to look after it and use it whenever it is required.

Types of PPE

There are certain parts of the body that require protection from hazards during work and each piece of PPE must be suitable for the job and used properly.

Head protection

There are several different types of head protection but the one most commonly used in construction is the safety helmet (or hard hat). This is used to protect the head from falling objects and knocks and has an adjustable strap to ensure a snug fit. Some safety helmets come with attachments for ear defenders or eye protection. Safety helmets are meant to be worn directly on the head and must not be worn over any other type of hat.

Eye protection

Eye protection is used to protect the eyes from dust and flying debris. The three main types are:

1. Safety goggles – made of a durable plastic and used when there is a danger of dust getting into the eyes or a chance of impact injury.

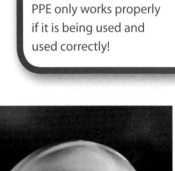

Remember

PPE only works properly if it is being used and used correctly!

A safety helmet

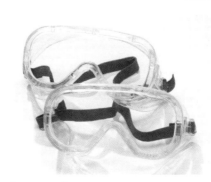
Safety goggles

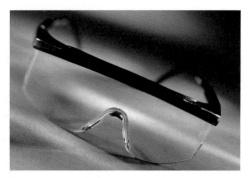

Safety spectacles

2. Safety spectacles – these are also made from a durable plastic but give less protection than goggles. This is because they don't fully enclose the eyes and so only protect from flying debris.

3. Facemasks – again made of durable plastic, facemasks protect the entire face from flying debris. They do not, however, protect the eyes from dust.

Safety boots

Foot protection

Safety boots or shoes are used to protect the feet from falling objects and to prevent sharp objects such as nails from injuring the foot. Safety boots should have a steel toe-cap and steel mid-sole.

Ear-plugs

Ear defenders

Hearing protection

Hearing protection is used to prevent damage to the ears caused by very loud noise. There are several types of hearing protection available but the two most common types are ear-plugs and ear defenders.

1. Ear-plugs – these are small fibre plugs that are inserted into the ear and used when the noise is not too severe. When using ear-plugs, make sure that you have clean hands before inserting them and never use plugs that have been used by somebody else.

2. Ear defenders – these are worn to cover the entire ear and are connected to a band that fits over the top of the head. They are used when there is excessive noise and must be cleaned regularly.

Respiratory protection

Respiratory protection is used to prevent the worker from breathing in any dust or fumes that may be hazardous. The main type of respiratory protection is the dust mask.

Dust masks are used when working in a dusty environment and are lightweight, comfortable and easy to fit. They should be worn by only one person and must be disposed of at the end of the working day. Dust masks will only offer protection from non-toxic dust so, if the worker is to be exposed to toxic dust or fumes, a full respiratory system should be used.

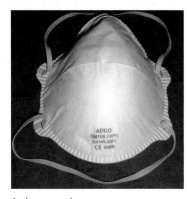

A dust mask

Hand protection

There are several types of hand protection and each type must be used for the correct task. For example, wearing lightweight rubber gloves to move glass will not offer much protection so leather gauntlets must be used. Plastic–coated gloves will protect you from certain chemicals and Kevlar® gloves offer cut resistance. To make sure you are wearing the most suitable type of glove for the task, you need to look first at what is going to be done and then match the type of glove to that task.

Safety gloves

Reporting accidents

When an accident occurs, there are certain things that must be done. All accidents need to be reported and recorded in the accident book and the injured person must report to a trained first aider in order to receive treatment. Serious accidents must be reported under the Reporting of Injuries, Diseases and Dangerous Occurrences Regulations 1995 (RIDDOR). Under RIDDOR your employer must report to the HSE any accident that results in:

- death

- major injury

- an injury that means the injured person is not at work for more than three consecutive days.

The accident book

The accident book is completed by the person who had the accident or, if this is not possible, someone who is representing the injured person.

The accident book will ask for some basic details about the accident, including:

- who was involved

- what happened

- where it happened

- the day and time of the accident

- any witnesses to the accident

- the address of the injured person

- what PPE was being worn

- what first aid treatment was given.

As well as reporting accidents, 'near misses' must also be reported. This is because near misses are often the accidents of the future. Reporting near misses might identify a problem and can prevent accidents from happening in the future. This allows a company to be **proactive** rather than **reactive**.

Definition

Proactive – taking action *before* something happens (e.g. an accident)

Reactive – taking action *after* something happens

Report of an Accident, Dangerous Occurrence or Near Miss

Date of incident _____ **Time of incident** _____

Location of incident _____

Details of person involved in accident

Name _____ Date of birth _____ Sex _____

Address _____

_____

_____ Occupation _____

Date off work (if applicable) _____ **Date returning to work** _____

Nature of injury _____

Management of injury   ☐ First Aid only   ☐ Advised to see doctor

                                 ☐ Sent to casualty   ☐ Admitted to hospital

Account of accident, dangerous occurrence or near miss
(Continued on separate sheet if necessary)

Witnesses to the incident
(Names, addresses and occupations)

Was the injured person wearing PPE? If yes, what PPE? _____

_____

Signature of person completing form _____

Occupation _____ **Date** _____

Figure 2.7 A typical accident book page

Risk assessments

A risk assessment is where the dangers of an activity are measured against the likelihood of accidents taking place. People carry out risk assessments hundreds of times each day without even knowing it. For example, every time we cross the road we do a risk assessment without even thinking about it.

In the construction industry, risk assessments are done by experienced people who are able to identify what risks each task has. They are then able to put measures in place to control the risks they have identified. At some point in your career, you will have to carry out a risk assessment. You will be given proper training in how to do this but, until then, it is still important that you understand how risk assessments work. Below is an example of an everyday situation (crossing the road) and how a risk assessment would be carried out for this.

Step 1

Identify the hazards (the dangers) – in this situation the hazards are vehicles travelling at speed.

Step 2

Identify who will be at risk – the person crossing the road will be at risk, as will any drivers on the road who might have to swerve to avoid that person.

Step 3

Calculate the risk from the hazard against the likelihood of an accident taking place – the risk from the hazard is quite high because if an accident were to happen, the injury could be very serious. However, the likelihood of an accident happening is low because the chances of the person being hit while crossing are minimal.

Step 4

Introduce measures to reduce risk – in this case crossing the road at traffic lights or pedestrian crossings reduces risk.

Step 5

Monitor the risk – changes might need to be made to the risk assessment if there are any changes to the risks involved. In our example, changes might be traffic lights being out of order or an increase in the speed limit on the road.

On the job: Scaffold safety

Ralph and Vijay are working on the second level of some scaffolding clearing debris. Ralph suggests that, to speed up the task, they should throw the debris over the edge of the scaffolding into a skip below. The building Ralph and Vijay are working on is on a main road and the skip is not in a closed off area. What do you think of Ralph's idea? What are your reasons for this answer?

Knowledge check

1. Name five pieces of health and safety legislation that affect the construction industry.

2. What does HSE stand for? What does it do?

3. What does COSHH stand for?

4. What does RIDDOR stand for?

5. What might happen to you or your employer if a health and safety law is broken?

6. What are the two most common risks to construction workers?

7. State two things that you can do to avoid injury when lifting loads using manual handling techniques.

8. What three elements cause a fire and keep it burning?

9. What class(es) of fire can be put out with a carbon dioxide (CO_2) extinguisher?

10. What does a prohibition sign mean?

11. Describe how you would identify a warning sign.

12. Name the six different types of PPE.

13. Who fills in an accident report form?

14. Why is it important to report 'near misses'?

15. Briefly explain what a risk assessment is.

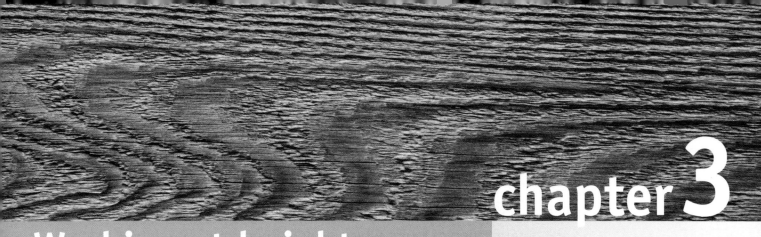

chapter 3

Working at height

OVERVIEW

Most construction trades require frequent use of some type of working platform or access equipment. Working off the ground can be dangerous and the greater the height the more serious the risk of injury. This chapter will give you a summary of some of the most common types of access equipment and provide information on how they should be used, maintained and checked to ensure that the risks to you and others are minimal.

This chapter will cover the following:

- General safety considerations
- Stepladders and ladders
- Roof work
- Trestle platforms
- Hop-ups
- Scaffolding.

General safety considerations

You will need to be able to identify potential hazards associated with working at height, as well as hazards associated with equipment. It is essential that access equipment is well maintained and checked regularly for any deterioration or faults, which could compromise the safety of someone using the equipment and anyone else in the work area. Although obviously not as important as people, equipment can also be damaged by the use of faulty access equipment. When maintenance checks are carried out they should be properly recorded. This provides very important information that helps to prevent accidents.

Risk assessment

Before any work is carried out at height, a thorough risk assessment needs to be completed. Your supervisor or someone else more experienced will do this while you are still training, but it is important that you understand what is involved so that you are able to carry out an assessment in the future.

For a working at height risk assessment to be valid and effective a number of questions must be answered:

1. How is access and **egress** to the work area to be achieved?

2. What type of work is to be carried out?

3. How long is the work likely to last?

4. How many people will be carrying out the task?

5. How often will this work be carried out?

6. What is the condition of the existing structure (if any) and the surroundings?

7. Is adverse weather likely to affect the work and workers?

8. How competent are the workforce and their supervisors?

9. Is there a risk to the public and work colleagues?

Definition

Egress – an exit or way out

Duties

Your employer has a duty to provide and maintain safe plant and equipment, which includes scaffold access equipment and systems of work.

You have a duty:

- to comply with safety rules and procedures relating to access equipment

- to take positive steps to understand the hazards in the workplace and report things you consider likely to lead to danger, for example a missing handrail on a working platform

- not to tamper with or modify equipment.

Stepladders and ladders

Stepladders

A stepladder has a prop, which when folded out allows the ladder to be used without having to lean it against something. Stepladders are one of the most frequently used pieces of access equipment in the construction industry and are often used every day. This means that they are not always treated with the respect they demand. Stepladders are often misused – they should only be used for work that will take a few minutes to complete. When work is likely to take longer than this, a sturdier alternative should be found.

When stepladders are used, the following safety points should be observed:

- Ensure the ground on which the stepladder is to be placed is firm and level. If the ladder rocks or sinks into the ground it should not be used for the work.

- Always open the steps fully.

- Never work off the top tread of the stepladder.

- Always keep your knees below the top tread.

- Never use stepladders to gain additional height on another working platform.

- Always look for the kitemark, which shows that the ladder has been made to British Standards.

> **Did you know?**
>
> Only a fully trained and competent person is allowed to erect any kind of working platform or access equipment. You should therefore not attempt to erect this type of equipment unless this describes you!

Figure 3.1 British Standards Institution Kitemark

A number of other safety points need to be observed depending on the type of stepladder being used.

Wooden stepladder

Before using a wooden stepladder:

- Check for loose screws, nuts, bolts and hinges.

- Check that the tie ropes between the two sets of **stiles** are in good condition and not frayed.

- Check for splits or cracks in the stiles.

- Check that the treads are not loose or split.

Never paint any part of a wooden stepladder as this can hide defects, which may cause the ladder to fail during use, causing injury.

Wooden stepladder

Aluminium stepladder

Before using an aluminium stepladder:

- Check for damage to stiles and treads to see whether they are twisted, badly dented or loose.

- Avoid working close to live electricity supplies as aluminium will conduct electricity.

Definition

Stiles – the side pieces of a stepladder into which the steps are set

Safety tip

If any faults are revealed when checking a stepladder, it should be taken out of use, reported to the person in charge and a warning notice attached to it to stop anyone using it

Aluminium stepladder

Fibreglass stepladder

Before using a fibreglass stepladder, check for damage to stiles and treads. Once damaged, fibreglass stepladders cannot be repaired and must be disposed of.

Ladders

A ladder, unlike a stepladder, does not have a prop and so has to be leant against something in order for it to be used. Together with stepladders, ladders are one of the most common pieces of equipment used to carry out work at heights and gain access to the work area.

As with stepladders, ladders are also available in timber, aluminium and fibreglass and require similar checks before use.

Ladder types

Pole ladder

These are single ladders and are available in a range of lengths. They are most commonly used for access to scaffolding platforms. Pole ladders are made from timber and must be stored under cover and flat, supported evenly along their length to prevent them sagging and twisting. They should be checked for damage or defects every time before being used.

Extension ladder

Extension ladders have two or more interlocking lengths, which can be slid together for convenient storage or slid apart to the desired length when in use.

Find out

What are the advantages and disadvantages of each type of stepladder?

Did you know?

Stepladders should be stored under cover to protect from damage such as rust or rotting

Pole ladder

Aluminium extension ladder

Extension ladders are available in timber, aluminium and fibreglass. Aluminium types are the most favoured as they are lightweight yet strong and available in double and triple extension types. Although also very strong, fibreglass versions are heavy, making them difficult to manoeuvre.

Erecting and using a ladder

The following points should be noted when considering the use of a ladder:

- As with stepladders, ladders are not designed for work of long duration. Alternative working platforms should be considered if the work will take longer than a few minutes.

- The work should not require the use of both hands. One hand should be free to hold the ladder.

- You should be able to do the work without stretching.

- You should make sure that the ladder can be adequately secured to prevent it slipping on the surface it is leaning against.

Pre-use checks

Before using a ladder check its general condition. Make sure that:

- no rungs are damaged or missing

- the stiles are not damaged

- no **tie-rods** are missing

- no repairs have been made to the ladder.

In addition, for wooden ladders ensure that:

- they have not been painted, which may hide defects or damage

- there is no decay or rot

- the ladder is not twisted or warped.

Erecting a ladder

Observe the following guidelines when erecting a ladder:

- Ensure you have a solid, level base.

- Do not pack anything under either (or both) of the stiles to level it.

- If the ladder is too heavy to put it in position on your own, get someone to help.

- Ensure that there is at least a four-rung overlap on each extension section.

- Never rest the ladder on plastic guttering as it may break, causing the ladder to slip and the user to fall.

- Where the base of the ladder is in an exposed position, ensure it is adequately guarded so that no one knocks it or walks into it.

- The ladder should be secured at both the top and bottom. The bottom of the ladder can be secured by a second person, however this person must not leave the base of the ladder whilst it is in use.

- The angle of the ladder should be a ratio of 1:4 (or 75°). This means that the bottom of ladder is 1 m away from the wall for every 4 m in height (see Figure 3.2).

- The top of the ladder must extend at least 1 m, or 5 rungs, above its landing point.

Remember

You must carry out a thorough risk assessment before working from a ladder. Ask yourself, 'Would I be safer using an alternative method?'

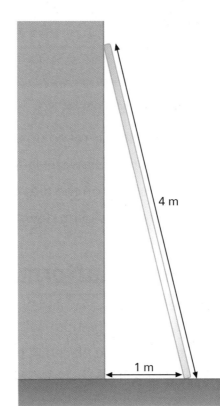

4 m

1 m

Figure 3.2 Correct angle for a ladder

Roof work

When carrying out any work on a roof, a roof ladder or **crawling board** must be used. Roof work also requires the use of edge protection or, where this is not possible, a safety harness.

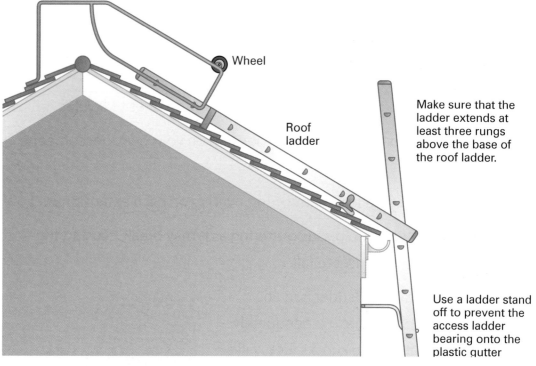

Figure 3.3 Roof work equipment

The roof ladder is rolled up the surface of the roof and over the ridge tiles, just enough to allow the ladder to be turned over and the ladder hook allowed to bear on the tiles on the other side of the roof. This hook prevents the roof ladder sliding down the roof once it is accessed.

Trestle platforms

A trestle is a frame upon which a platform or other type of surface (e.g. a table top) can be placed. A trestle should be used rather than a ladder for work that will take longer than a few minutes to complete. Trestle platforms are composed of the frame and the platform (sometimes called a stage).

Frames

A-frames

These are most commonly
used by carpenters and painters.
As the name suggests, the frame
is in the shape of a capital A
and can be made from timber,
aluminium or fibreglass. Two
are used together to support a
platform (a scaffold or staging
board). See Figure 3.4.

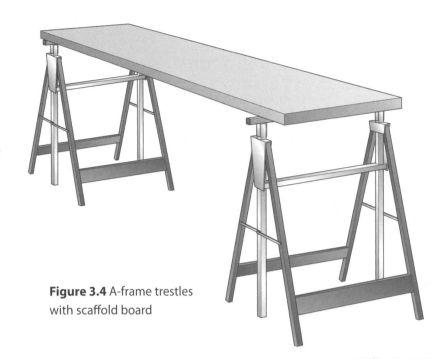

Figure 3.4 A-frame trestles
with scaffold board

When using A-frames:

* they should always be opened fully and, in the same way as stepladders,
  must be placed on firm, level ground

* the platform width should be no less than 450 mm thick

* the overhang of the board at each end of the platform should be not
  more than four times its thickness.

> **Safety tip**
>
> A-frame trestles should
> never be used as
> stepladder as they are not
> designed for this purpose

Steel trestles

These are sturdier than A-frame
trestles and are adjustable in height.
They are also capable of providing a
wider platform than timber trestles
– see Figure 3.5. As with the A-frame
type, they must be used only on firm
and level ground but the trestle itself
should be placed on a flat scaffold
board on top of the ground.
Trestles should not be placed more
than 1.2 m apart.

Figure 3.5 Steel trestle with staging board

Platforms

Scaffold boards

To ensure that scaffold boards provide a safe working platform, before using them check that they:

- are not split
- are not twisted or warped
- have no large knots, which cause weakness.

Staging boards

These are designed to span a greater distance than scaffold boards and can offer a 600 mm wide working platform. They are ideal for use with trestles.

Hop-ups

Also known as step-ups, these are ideal for reaching low-level work that can be carried out in a relatively short period of time. A hop-up needs to be of sturdy construction and have a base of not less than 600 mm by 500 mm. Hop-ups have the disadvantage that they are heavy and awkward to move around.

Scaffolding

Tubular scaffold is the most commonly used type of scaffolding within the construction industry. There are two types of tubular scaffold:

1. Independent scaffold – free-standing scaffold that does not rely on any part of the building to support it (although it must be tied to the building to provide additional stability).

2. Putlog scaffold – scaffolding that is attached to the building via the entry of some of the poles into holes left in the brickwork by the bricklayer. The poles stay in position until the construction is complete and give the scaffold extra support.

No one other than a qualified **carded scaffolder** is allowed to erect or alter scaffolding. Although you are not allowed to erect or alter this type of scaffold, you must be sure it is safe before you work on it. You should ask yourself a number of questions to assess the condition and suitability of the scaffold before you use it:

- Are there any signs attached to the scaffold which state that it is incomplete or unsafe?

- Is the scaffold overloaded with materials such as bricks?

- Are the platforms cluttered with waste materials?

- Are there adequate guardrails and scaffold boards in place?

- Does the scaffold actually *look* safe?

- Is there the correct access to and from the scaffold?

- Are the various scaffold components in the correct place (see Figure 3.6)?

- Have the correct types of fittings been used (see Figure 3.7)?

Definition

Carded scaffolder – someone who holds a recognised certificate showing competence in scaffold erection

Did you know?

It took 14 years of experimentation to finally settle on 48 mm as the diameter of most tubular scaffolding poles

Remember

If you have any doubts about the safety of scaffolding, report them. You could very well prevent serious injury or even someone's death

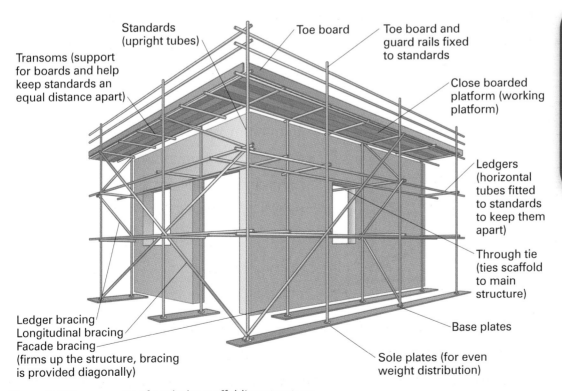

Figure 3.6 Components of a tubular scaffolding structure

Standards (upright tubes)

Toe board

Toe board and guard rails fixed to standards

Transoms (support for boards and help keep standards an equal distance apart)

Close boarded platform (working platform)

Ledgers (horizontal tubes fitted to standards to keep them apart)

Through tie (ties scaffold to main structure)

Base plates

Sole plates (for even weight distribution)

Ledger bracing
Longitudinal bracing
Facade bracing
(firms up the structure, bracing is provided diagonally)

Right angle coupler – load bearing; used to join tubes at right angles

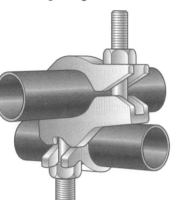

Universal coupler – load bearing; also used to join tubes at right angles

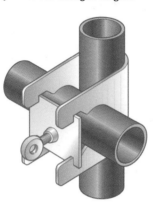

Swivel coupler – load bearing; used to join tubes at various angles e.g. diagonal braces

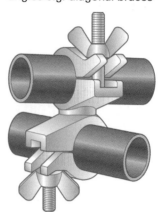

Adjustable base plate or base plate used at the base of standards to allow even weight distribution

Figure 3.7 Types of scaffold fittings

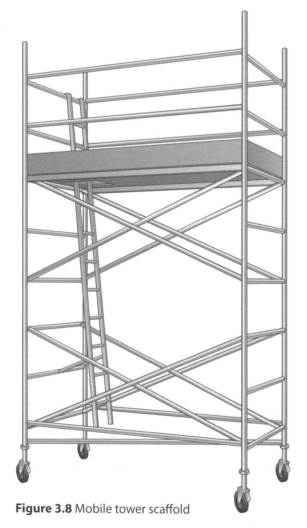

Figure 3.8 Mobile tower scaffold

Mobile tower scaffolds

Mobile tower scaffolds are so called because they can be moved around without being dismantled. Lockable wheels make this possible and they are used extensively throughout the construction industry by many different trades. A tower can be made from either traditional steel tubes and fittings or aluminium, which is lightweight and easy to move. The aluminium type of tower is normally specially designed and is referred to as a 'proprietary tower'.

Low towers

These are a smaller version of the standard mobile tower scaffold and are designed specifically for use by one person. They have a recommended working height of no more than 2.5 m and a safe working load of 150 kg. They are lightweight and easily transported and stored.

These towers require no assembly other than the locking into place of the platform and handrails. However, you still require training before you use one and you must ensure that the manufacturer's instructions are followed when setting up and working from this type of platform.

Figure 3.9 Low tower scaffold

Erecting a tower scaffold

It is essential that tower scaffolds are situated on a firm and level base. The stability of any tower depends on the height in relation the size of the base:

- For use inside a building, the height should be no more than three-and-a-half times the smallest base length.

- For outside use, the height should be no more than three times the smallest base length.

The height of a tower can be increased providing the area of the base is increased **proportionately**. The base area can be increased by fitting outriggers to each corner of the tower.

For mobile towers, the wheels must be in the locked position whilst they are in use and unlocked only when they are being repositioned.

There are several important points you should observe when working from a scaffold tower:

- Any working platform above 2 m high must be fitted with guardrails and toe boards. Guard rails may also be required at heights of less than 2 m if there is a risk of falling on to potential hazards below, i.e. reinforcing rods. Guardrails must be fitted at a minimum height of 950 mm.

- If guardrails and toe boards are needed, they must be positioned on all four sides of the platform.

- Any tower higher than 9 m must be secured to the structure.

- Towers must not exceed 12 m in height unless they have been specifically designed for that purpose.

- The working platform of any tower must be fully boarded and be at least 600 mm wide.

- If the working platform is to be used for materials then the minimum width must be 800 mm.

- All towers must have their own access and this should be by an internal ladder.

FAQ

Am I protected from electrocution if I am working on a wooden stepladder?

No. If you are working near a live current on a wooden stepladder, if any metal parts of the ladder, such as the tie rods, come into contact with the current, they will conduct the flow of electricity and you may be electrocuted. Take every precaution possible in order to avoid the risk of electrocution – the simplest precaution is turning off the electricity supply.

What determines the type of scaffolding used on a job?

As you will have read in this chapter, only a carded scaffolder is allowed to erect or alter scaffolding. They will select the scaffolding to be used according to the ground condition at the site, whether or not people will be working on the scaffolding, the types of materials and equipment that will be used on the scaffolding and the height to which access will be needed.

On the job:
Attending to fascia boards

Pete has been asked by a client to take a look at all the fascia boards on a two-storey building. Depending on the condition of the fascia boards, they will need either repairing or replacing. The job will probably take Pete between two and six hours, depending on what he has to do.

What types of scaffolding do you think might be suitable for Pete's job? Can you think of anything Pete will have to consider while he prepares for and carries out this task? Think about things like egress and exit points, whether or not the area is closed off to the public and how long Pete will be working at height etc.

Knowledge check

1. Name four different methods of gaining height while working.

2. What must be done before any work at height is carried out?

3. What are your three health and safety duties when working at height?

4. As a rule, what is the maximum time you should work from a ladder or stepladder?

5. How should a wooden stepladder be checked before use?

6. When storing a wooden pole ladder, why does it need to be evenly supported along its length?

7. Explain the 1:4 (or 75°) ratio rule which should be observed when erecting a ladder.

8. When should a trestle platform be used?

9. What two types of board can be used as a platform with a trestle frame?

10. Why should you only use a specially designed hop-up?

11. There are two types of tubular scaffolding – what are they and how do they differ?

12. What are the eight questions you should ask yourself before using scaffolding?

13. In order to increase the height of a tower scaffold, what else has to be increased and by how much?

14. How high should scaffold guardrails be?

15. What is the only way you should access scaffolding?

chapter 4

Timber technology

OVERVIEW

This chapter is designed to give you an overview of the different types of timber materials you can expect to be working with during your working life as a carpenter and joiner. It will also help to build your knowledge and understanding of the way in which timber is processed, preserved and protected.

This chapter will cover the following:

- Classification of timber
- Identification of timber
- Conversion of timber
- Seasoning of timber
- Timber defects
- Timber decay
- Preservation and protection
- Manufactured boards.

Classification of timber

Timber is classified as either hardwood or softwood. This can sometimes be confusing, as not all hardwoods are physically hard or soft woods soft. For example, the balsa tree is classed as a hardwood although it is very soft and light. The wood of a yew tree, classified as softwood timber, is harder than most hardwoods.

Hardwood and softwood refer to the **botanical** differences and not to the strength of the timber. Generally speaking, hardwood trees are **deciduous**, broad-leafed, with an encased seed. Softwood trees are usually **evergreen** with needles and cone-shaped seeds.

Definition

Botanical – the classification of trees based upon scientific study

Deciduous – the name given to a type of tree that sheds its leaves every year

Evergreen – a type of tree that keeps its leaves all year round

Identification of timber

One of the best ways of becoming familiar with, and being able to identify, a reasonably wide range of timber species, is to form a personal collection. Small, matchbox-size samples are ideal for this.

The key to learning and memorising timber species is colour. Once timbers have been grouped together, identification becomes a process of elimination. Tables 4.1 (softwoods) and 4.2 (hardwoods) outline the general appearance, distribution and uses of timber species most commonly used.

Name	Main sources	Description	Main uses
Douglas fir	Canada, USA	Pinkish-brown timber with distinct grain and a clean, sweet smell	Good quality joinery, strip flooring, stairs and plywood veneers
Larch	Europe, including UK	Strong, resinous reddish-brown timber with a good straight grain	Gates, fences etc.

Table 4.1 Commonly used softwoods *(continued overleaf)*

Name	Main sources	Description	Main uses
Pitch pine	Southern USA	Hard, tough, heavy timber, very distinct grain, generally pink to brown; easily recognised by its resinous, turpentine smell	Shipbuilding, polished softwood joinery and church furniture
Redwood (commonly known as Pine)	Europe	Pinkish-white timber with distinct orange/red grain; clean pine smell	General purpose joinery
Whitewood (also known as European Spruce)	Europe	Similar to redwood but paler and lacks the resinous pine smell	Joists, rafters, floorboards etc.
Western red cedar	Canada, USA	Light, soft, spongy timber with a woolly texture; pink to reddish-brown, darkening to grey when exposed to the weather	Externally for good quality timber buildings, saunas etc.

Table 4.1 Commonly used softwoods (cont'd)

Name	Main sources	Description	Main uses
Ash	Europe	Creamy, white timber with occasional dark steaks (black heart), generally straight grained but can be quite coarse	Furniture, boat building, sports equipment etc.
Oak	Europe	English oak is generally acknowledged to be the toughest, whilst Polish or Slovenian oak is usually the least tough and is easily worked. The timber is a pale yellowish-brown, with a distinct darker figure of 'silver grain'	High-class joinery, panelling, doors etc.

Table 4.2 Commonly used hardwoods *(continued overleaf)*

Name	Main sources	Description	Main uses
Beech	Europe	Cream to pale brown timber which darkens a little on exposure to air and has an attractive dark fleck running through it	Furniture, kitchen utensils, wood block floors etc.
Mahogany	Africa	Reddish-brown timber with grey tinges; very attractive grain with a tendency to woolliness	High-class joinery, furniture, boat building and plywood veneers
Mahogany	Spain, Cuba	Superb timber, usually variable and deep in colour, from yellowish-brown to deep rich red, with curling grain	As for African Mahogany but considered to be superior
Maple	Canada, North East USA	Medium dark, reddish-brown timber with a close, even texture, similar to sycamore to which it is closely related	Hardwood strip flooring etc.
Sapele	West Africa	Medium dark, reddish-brown timber with a pronounced stripe; when carefully cleaned it will give a superb finish	Furniture, veneers etc.
Teak	India, Java, Thailand	Outstanding timber to use, this golden brown timber, often with a distinct dark figure, has a greasy, oily texture	High-class joinery, furniture, boat building etc.
Walnut	Europe	Purplish-brown with very attractive dark figure, sometimes with a curl or burr; valuable timber much sought after by cabinet makers and veneer manufacturers	Furniture, veneers etc.

Table 4.2 Commonly used hardwoods (cont'd)

Conversion of timber

Conversion is the sawing of a log into board or planks ready for use by the carpenter or joiner. How the timber is converted directly affects its usefulness.

Softwoods are nearly always sawn in their country of origin, while hardwoods are often imported in log form and converted by the timber merchant, sometimes to customer requirements.

Methods of conversion

There are four main methods of conversion:

- through and through
- tangential
- quarter
- boxed heart.

Through and through sawn timber

Also known as flat slab or slash sawing, through and through sawing is the simplest and most economical method of converting timber. See Figure 4.1. Although there is very little wastage with this method, the majority of the boards produced are prone to a large amount of shrinkage and distortion.

Tangential sawn timber

The tangential sawn timber method of conversion is used to provide floor joists and beams, as it gives the strongest timber. See Figure 4.2. It is also used on pitch pine and douglas fir for decorative purposes to produce 'flame figuring' or 'fiery grain'.

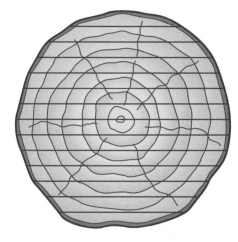

Figure 4.1 Through and through sawn timber

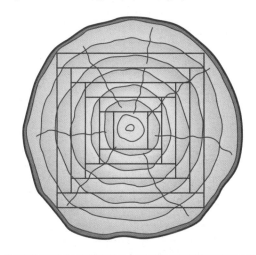

Figure 4.2 Tangential sawn timber

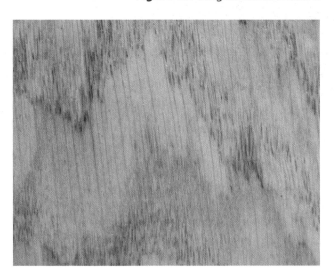

Flame figuring

Quarter sawn timber

Quarter sawn timber, shown in Figure 4.3, produces the best quality timber. However, it is also the most expensive, both in time involved and material wastage. It produces the greatest quantity of 'rift' or 'radial sawn' boards, which are generally superior for joinery purposes.

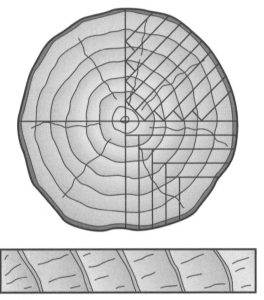

Figure 4.3 Quarter sawn timber

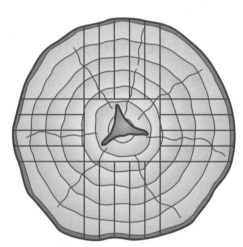

Figure 4.4 Boxed heart sawn timber

Boxed heart sawn timber

Boxed heart sawn timber is a type of radial sawing that is used when the heart of the tree is rotten or badly shaken. It is sometimes known as floor boarding sawing, as the boards are ideal for this purpose because they are hard-wearing and do not distort. See Figure 4.4.

Seasoning of timber

Timber from newly felled trees contains a high proportion of water in the form of sap, which is made up of water and minerals drawn up from the soil. Most of this water has to be removed by some form of drying, which is called seasoning.

Did you know?

Timber contains millions of tiny cells which normally contain a mixture of air, water and other chemicals

The main reasons for seasoning are:

- to make sure that shrinkage occurs before the timber is used
- to make sure that the moisture content of the timber is below the 'dry rot' safety line of 20 per cent (discussed later in this chapter)
- to make sure that dry timber is used
- dry timber is stronger
- seasoned timber is less likely to split or distort
- wet timber will not accept glue, paint or polish.

The timber should be dried to a moisture content that is similar to the surrounding atmosphere in which it will be used. See Table 4.3.

Timber location	Moisture content (per cent)
Carcasing timber (joists etc.)	18–20
External joinery	16–18
Internal timber where there is a partial intermittent heating system	14–16
Internal timber where there is a continuous heating system	10–12
Internal timber placed directly over, or near, sources of heat	7–10

Table 4.3 Moisture content table

There are two main methods of seasoning timber:

1. natural, normally called 'air seasoning'
2. artificial, normally called 'kiln seasoning'.

Air seasoning

For air drying the timber is stacked in a pile in open-sided, covered sheds, which protect the timber from rain but still allow a free circulation of air. A moisture content of between 18–20 per cent can be achieved in a period of 2–12 months.

Kiln seasoning

Most timber that is used is kiln seasoned. If done correctly the moisture content of the timber can be reduced without causing any timber defects.

Depending on the size of the timber, the length of time the timber needs to stay in the kiln varies between two days and six weeks.

There are two types of kiln in general use:

1. compartment kiln

2. progressive kiln.

A compartment kiln is shown in Figure 4.5. It is usually a brick or concrete structure, in which the timber remains stationary during the drying process. The drying of the timber depends on three factors:

* air circulation supplied by fans

* heat, usually supplied by heating coils

* humidity, which is raised by steam sprays.

In a progressive kiln the timber is stacked on trolleys, which pass slowly through a long chamber, with gentle changes to heat and humidity as it moves from one end of the chamber to the other.

There are three clear advantages of using kiln, as opposed to air, drying:

1. the speed at which the seasoning can be completed

2. the facility to dry timber to any desired moisture content

3. the sterilising effect of the heated air upon fungi and insects in the timber, lessening the likelihood of fungal or insect attack.

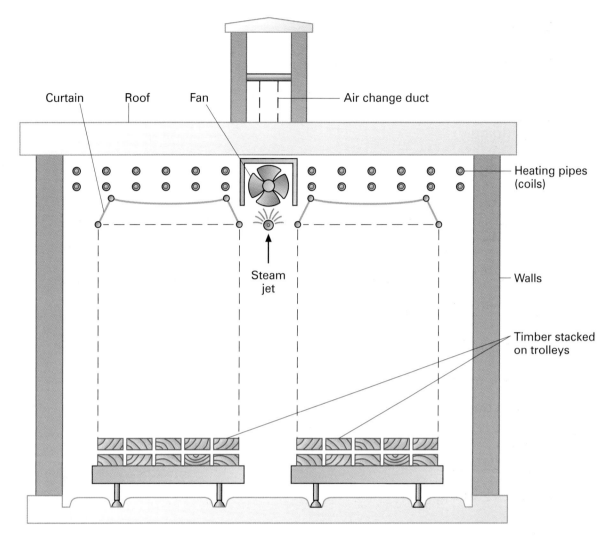

Figure 4.5 Compartment kiln

Timber defects

Defects are faults that are found in timber. Some present a serious structural weakness in the timber, others do little more than spoil its appearance.

Defects can be divided into two groups:

1. seasoning defects
2. natural defects.

Seasoning defects

Seasoning defects can be further divided into:

- bowing
- springing
- winding (or twist)
- cupping
- shaking
- collapse
- case hardening.

Bowing

Bowing is usually caused by poor stacking during seasoning. It is a serious defect, causing good timber to be suitable only for use in short lengths. See Figure 4.6.

Figure 4.6 Bowing

Springing

Springing is an edgeways curvature of a board. It is usually caused by the release of internal stresses during seasoning. See Figure 4.7.

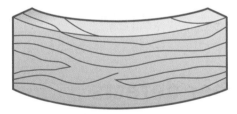

Figure 4.7 Springing

Winding (or twist)

Winding, also known as twist, is very serious as it restricts the use of the timber to short lengths. It is caused by poor seasoning and poor stacking. See Figure 4.8.

Figure 4.8 Winding (or twist)

Cupping

Cupping is very common in flat sawn boards. It occurs through shrinkage of the timber when drying. See Figure 4.9.

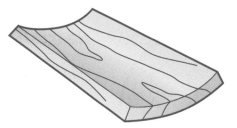

Figure 4.9 Cupping

Shaking

Shaking is caused by the board being dried too rapidly. It is particularly common at the ends of boards, spreading along the grain. See Figure 4.10.

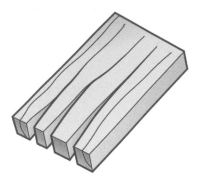

Figure 4.10 Shaking

Collapse

Collapse is a rare defect caused by too rapid drying in the early stages of seasoning. The moisture is drawn out too rapidly causing dehydrated cells to collapse. See Figure 4.11.

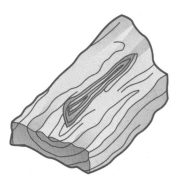

Figure 4.11 Collapse

Case hardening

Case hardening is caused by too rapid drying, resulting in the outside cells of the timber drying and hardening, sealing off the moisture in the central part of the board. See Figure 4.12.

Natural defects

Natural defects can be further divided into:

- heart shakes
- cup shakes
- star shakes
- knots.

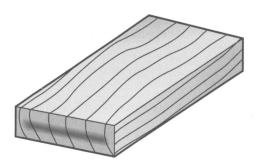

Figure 4.12 Case hardening

Heart shakes

Heart shakes are usually the result of disease or over-maturity of the tree. The shakes radiate from the centre of the log and are caused by internal shrinkage. See Figure 4.13.

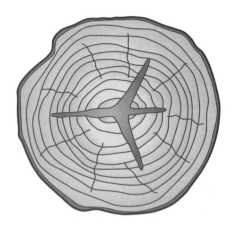

Figure 4.13 Heart shakes

Cup or ring shakes

Cup shakes, also known as ring shakes, are caused by a separation of the annual rings and are usually due to a lack of nutrient or twisting of the tree in high winds. In bad cases economic conversion of the log is very difficult. See Figure 4.14.

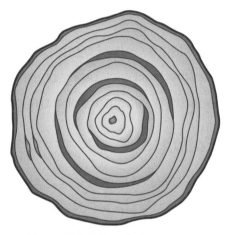

Figure 4.14 Cup shakes

Did you know?

Each season trees grow a new layer of wood, which shows as a ring when we cut the trunk, the thickness varies depending on growing conditions that year. Rings on trees from tropical areas rarely show because there is little seasonal variation

Figure 4.15 Star shakes

Star shakes

Star shakes are radial cracks which occur around the outside of the log. They are caused by shrinkage at the outside of the log whilst the middle remains stable. This is usually because the log has been left too long before conversion. See Figure 4.15.

Knots

Knots mainly occur in softwood and mark the origin of a branch in the tree. Knots are termed either 'dead' or 'live' depending on the condition of the branch which caused it. Dead knots are often loose. Small live knots are no real problem. Small dead knots and large knots, either dead or live, are a serious structural weakness.

Types of knot are shown in Figures 4.16 to 4.19.

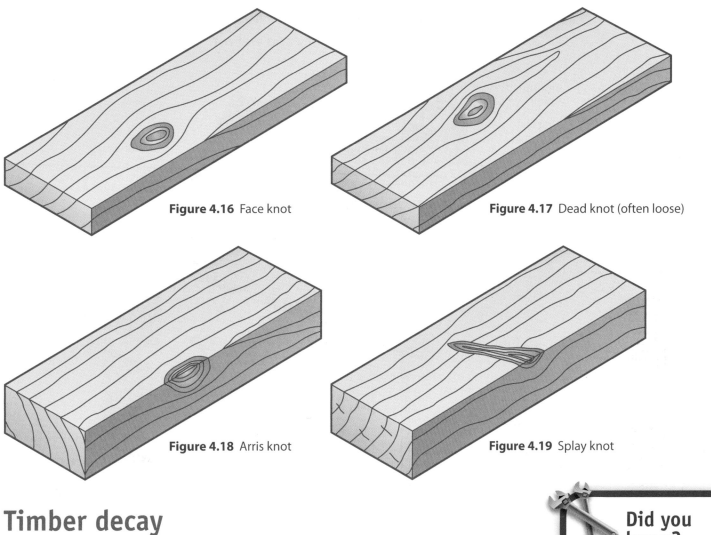

Figure 4.16 Face knot

Figure 4.17 Dead knot (often loose)

Figure 4.18 Arris knot

Figure 4.19 Splay knot

Timber decay

The decay of timber is caused by one or both of the following:

- wood-destroying fungi
- wood-boring insects.

Wood-destroying fungi

There many forms of fungi which, under suitable conditions, will attack timber until it is destroyed. They mainly fall into two groups:

1. dry rot
2. wet rot.

Did you know?

Arris, as in an arris knot, means edge

Both types can be a serious hazard to constructional timbers. Figure 4.20 shows some possible causes of dry and wet rot.

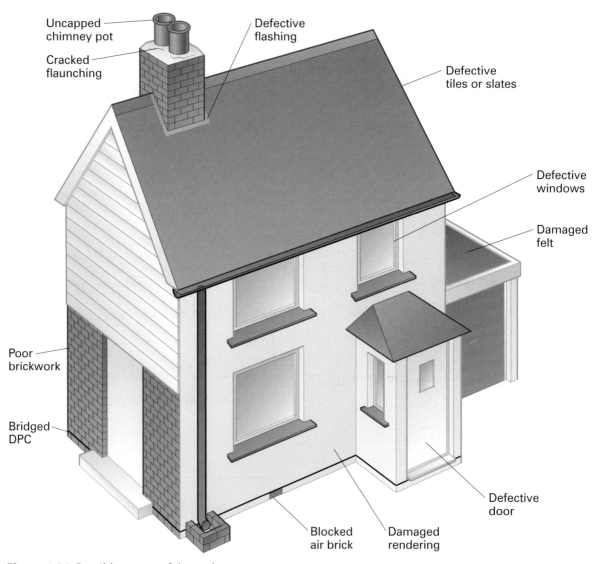

Figure 4.20 Possible causes of dry and wet rot

Dry rot

This is the most common and most serious of wood-destroying fungi. The fungus does most damage to softwoods but also attacks hardwoods, particularly when they are close to softwoods already infected. If left undetected or untreated it can destroy much of the timber in a building.

Dry rot is so called because of the dry, crumbly appearance of the infected timber. It is, however, excessive moisture that is the main cause of the decay. If the wood is kept dry and well ventilated there should be little chance of dry rot occurring.

The main conditions for an attack of dry rot are:

- damp timber, with a moisture content above 20 per cent (known as the **dry rot safety line**)

- poor, or no, ventilation (i.e. no circulation of fresh air).

The attack of dry rot takes place in three stages, which are shown in Figures 4.21 to 4.23:

- The spores (seeds) of the fungus germinate and send out hyphae (roots) which bore into the timber.

- The hyphae branch out and spread through the timber. A fruiting body now starts to grow.

- The fruiting body, which resembles a large, fleshy pancake, starts to ripen. When fully ripened it discharges millions of red spores into the air. The spores attach to fresh timber and the cycle starts again.

Definition

Dry rot safety line – when the moisture content of damp timber reaches 20 per cent. Dry rot is likely if the moisture content exceeds this

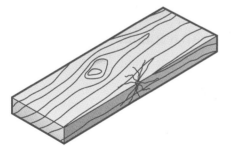

Figure 4.21 Dry rot stage one

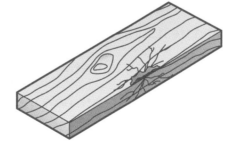

Figure 4.22 Dry rot stage two

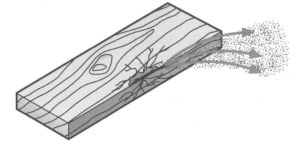

Figure 4.23 Dry rot stage three

Identification of dry rot

Dry rot can be identified by:

- an unpleasant, musty smell

- visible distortion of infected timber; warped, sunken and/or shrinkage cracks

- probing to test the timber for softening or crumbling

- the appearance of fruiting bodies

- presence of fine, orange-red dust on the floorboards and other parts of the structure

- presence of whitish-grey strands on the surface of the timber.

Eradication of dry rot

Dry rot is eradicated by carrying out the following actions:

- Eliminate all possible sources of dampness, such as blocked air bricks, bridged damp proof course, leaking pipes etc.

- Determine the extent of the attack.

- Remove all infected timber.

- Clean and treat surrounding walls, floors etc. with a suitable fungicide.

- Treat any remaining timber with a preservative.

- Replace rotted timber with new treated timber.

- Monitor completed work for signs of further attack.

Wet rot

This is a general name given to another type of wood-destroying fungus. The conditions where wet rot is found are usually wet rather than damp. Although wet rot is capable of destroying timber it is not as serious a problem as dry rot and, if the source of wetness is found, the wet rot can be halted.

The most likely places to find wet rot are:

- badly maintained external joinery, where water has penetrated
- ends of rafters and floor joists
- fences and gate posts
- under leaking sinks or baths etc.

Identification of wet rot

The signs to look for to identify wet rot are:

- timber becomes darker in colour with cracks along the grain
- decay usually occurs internally leaving a thin layer of relatively sound timber on the outside
- localised areas of decay close to wetness
- a musty, damp smell.

Eradication of wet rot

As wet rot is not as serious a problem as dry rot, less extreme measures are normally involved. It is usually sufficient to remove the rotted timber, treat the remaining timber with a fungicide and replace any rotted timber with treated timber. Lastly, if possible, the source of any wetness should be rectified.

Wood-boring insects

There are three common species of insects which attack timber in buildings in the British Isles. These are the Common Furniture Beetle, the Death Watch Beetle and the Powder Post Beetle. In addition, in certain parts of Surrey and neighbouring areas the House Longhorn Beetle causes significant damage.

Figure 4.24 shows how the beetles damage the wood by laying their eggs in the timber. These hatch into grubs, which are responsible for destruction of the timber.

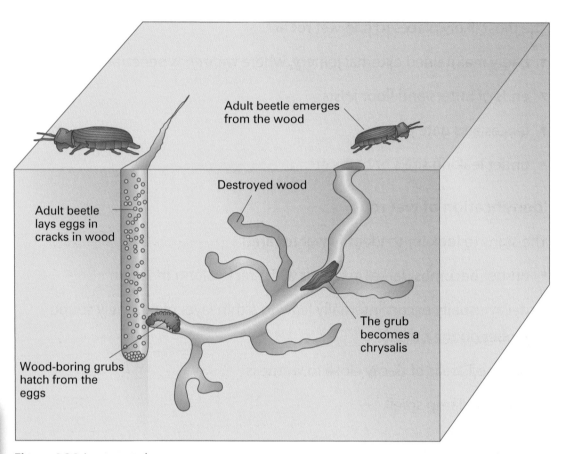

Figure 4.24 Insect attack

Eradication of insects

If the insect attack is confined to a small area the infected timbers can be cut out and replaced. If the attack is over a large area it is better to pass the work to a specialist firm.

Preservation and protection

Not only do we need to protect timber from fungal and insect attack but also, where timber is exposed, it needs protecting from the weather. Preservation extends the life of timber and greatly reduces the cost of maintenance.

Remember

Contact a professional for advice where load bearing timbers have been attacked, as there may be a need to prop or shore up to prevent collapse of the structure

Types of preservative

Timber preservatives are divided into three groups:

- tar oils
- water-borne
- organic solvents.

Tar oils

Tar oils are derived from coal tar, are very effective and relatively cheap. However, they give off a very strong odour which may contaminate other materials. Creosote is the most common type of this preservative.

Water-borne

Water-borne preservatives are mainly solutions of copper, zinc, mercury or chrome. Water is used to carry the chemical into the timber and then allowed to evaporate, leaving the chemical in the timber. They are very effective against fungi and insects and are able to penetrate into the timber. They are also easily painted over and relatively inexpensive.

Organic solvents

Organic solvents are the most effective, but also the most costly of the preservatives. They have excellent penetrating qualities and dry out rapidly. Many of this type are proprietary brands such as those manufactured by Cuprinol™.

Methods of application

Preservative can be applied in two ways:

1. non-pressure methods – brushing, spraying, dipping or steeping
2. pressure methods – empty cell, full cell or double vacuum.

Non-pressure methods

Although satisfactory results can be achieved, there are disadvantages with using non-pressure methods. The depth of penetration is uneven and, with certain timbers, impregnation is insufficient to prevent leaking out (leaching). Table 4.4 lists non-pressure methods and how and where to employ them.

Method	How and where to employ it
Brushing	The most commonly used method of applying preservative, it is important to apply the preservative liberally and allow it to soak in
Spraying	Usually used where brushing is difficult to carry out, in areas such as roof spaces
Dipping	Timbers are submerged in a bath of preservative for up to 15 minutes
Steeping	Similar to dipping only the timber is left submerged for up to two weeks

Table 4.4 Non-pressure methods

Pressure methods

Pressure methods generally give better results with deeper penetration and less leaching. Table 4.5 lists pressure methods and how and where to employ them.

Method	How and where to employ it
Empty cell	Preservative is forced into the timber under pressure. When the pressure is released the air within the cells expands and blows out the surplus for re-use. This method is suitable for water-borne and organic solvent preservatives.

Table 4.5 Pressure methods *(continued overleaf)*

Method	How and where to employ it
Full cell	Similar to empty cell, but prior to impregnation a vacuum is applied to the timber. The preservative is then introduced under pressure to fill the cells completely. Suitable for tar oils and water-borne preservatives.
Double vacuum	A vacuum is applied to remove air from the cells, the preservative introduced, the vacuum released and pressure applied. The pressure is released and a second vacuum applied to recover surplus preservative. This method is used for organic solvent preservatives.

Table 4.5 Pressure methods (cont'd)

Safety tip

All preservatives are toxic and care should be taken at all times. Protective clothing should always be worn when using preservatives

Manufactured boards

The most common types of wood-based manufactured boards are:

- plywood
- laminated board
- chipboard (particle board)
- fibre board.

Plywood

Plywood is made from thin layers of timber called **veneers**. The veneers are glued together to form boards. There is normally an odd number of veneers with the grain alternating across and along the sheet, which gives both strength and stability to the board. See Figure 4.25.

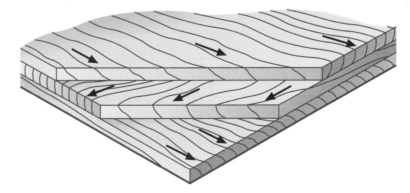

Figure 4.25 Plywood section showing grain direction

Stamp	Grade	Use
INT	Interior	Internal use only – has low resistance to humidity or dampness
MR	Moisture resistant	Has a fair resistance to humidity and dampness
BR	Boil resistant	Has a fairly high resistance in exposed conditions
WBP	Weather and boil proof	Can be used in extreme conditions under continuous exposure (boats, buildings etc.)

Table 4.6 Plywood grade table

Plywood is graded according to the type of glue used in its manufacture and also according to the situation in which it will be used. The grade is usually stamped on the board by the manufacturer. A list of grades is shown in Table 4.6.

Blockboard
Strips are up to 25 mm wide. Good quality hardwood veneers are sometimes used.

Laminboard
Strips are 7-8 mm wide. This produces a better quality board.

Battenboard
Strips are up to 75 mm wide, producing a poorer quality board.

Figure 4.26 Laminated boards

Laminated boards

Laminated boards are made from strips of wood laminated together and sandwiched between two veneers. Three common varieties are shown in Figure 4.26.

Chipboard

Chipboard is made from compressed wood chips and wood flakes bonded with a synthetic resin glue. See Figure 4.27. There are various grades, which include those used to make floor panels etc.

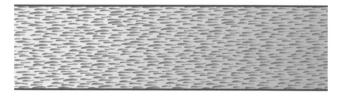

Figure 4.27 Chipboard

Fibreboard

Fibreboard is made from pulped wood that is mixed with an adhesive and pressed into sheets. It usually comes in three forms:

1. hardboard
2. insulation board (or softboard)
3. medium density fibreboard (**MDF**).

Hardboard

Hardboard is manufactured from sugar cane pulp and available in sheets from 3–6 mm in thickness. Oil tempered hardboard offers a reasonable resistance to moisture. See Figure 4.28.

Hardboard is also manufactured with various finishes, which include:

- plastic faced
- reeded
- perforated
- enamelled.

Figure 4.28 Hardboard

Insulation board (or softboard)

Also called softboard, insulation board is made from the same material as hardboard but not compressed. It is used as a wall and ceiling covering to give very good insulation. See Figure 4.29.

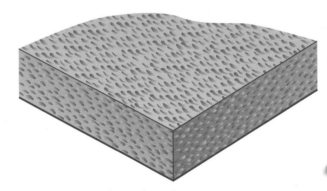

Figure 4.29 Insulation board

Medium density fibreboard (MDF)

Medium density fibreboard (MDF) is now used to form skirting boards, and mouldings such as architraves etc. It is easy to work with both hand and powered tools. It is mainly used internally but moisture resistant sheets are available.

Did you know?

Architrave is a name for mouldings around windows and doors

Safety tip

Dust extraction or a respirator should be worn when cutting or sanding any timber, but particularly some tropical hardwoods and MDF, which can be harmful

FAQ

How do I choose between hardwood and softwood for a job?

The type of timber you should use for a job is usually detailed in the specifications. There are a number of reasons why one type of wood is chosen over another. Hardwood is usually more expensive and long-lasting than softwood. Often grown in the hot climates of equatorial countries (e.g. African and South American countries), hardwood is used for jobs where the wood will be visible (i.e. high-class joinery). Softwood is usually grown in countries with cooler climates. It is often cheaper than hardwood and used for jobs where the wood will be concealed (e.g. floorboards and rafters).

On the job: Twisted timber

Wayne goes to the store to get some timber for a job. When Wayne lifts the timber from the shelf, he notices that the wood is in wind (i.e. twisted). How could this have happened? What could have been done to prevent it from happening? Do you think Wayne can still use the timber? Give reasons for your answer.

Knowledge check

1. What is meant by timber conversion?

2. How can dry rot be eradicated?

3. Name four types of insects that attack timber.

4. How is plywood manufactured?

5. Name three non-pressure methods of applying preservatives.

6. Briefly describe the differences between hardwood and softwood.

7. Name four examples of seasoning defects.

8. Name four examples of natural defects.

9. What does MDF stand for?

10. What do the words 'deciduous' and 'evergreen' mean?

chapter 5

Handling and storage of materials

OVERVIEW

Work in any building trade involves handling and storing materials, tools and equipment, sometimes under difficult conditions. The cost of injuries from poor or careless handling practice is enormous and careless storage risks damage, loss and theft of materials and equipment. This can cause delays and unnecessary cost to contractors.

These risks to oneself and others can be minimised by following a few simple guidelines and applying a level of common sense when moving and storing materials and equipment.

The following topics will be covered in this chapter:

- Safe handling

- Wood and sheet materials

- Ironmongery

- Adhesives

- Doors, door frames and window frames

- Wall and floor units

- Materials associated with other trades.

Safe handling

Definition

Manual handling
– using the body to lift, carry, push or pull a load

Chapter 2 Health and safety explains safe **manual handling** methods in more detail – see page 47–49. When handling any materials or equipment, always think about the health and safety issues involved and remember manual handling practices explained to you during your induction.

You are not expected to remember everything but basic common sense will help you to work safely.

- Always wear your safety helmet and boots at work.

- Wear gloves and ear defenders when necessary.

- Keep your work areas free from debris and materials, tools and equipment not being used.

- Wash your hands before eating.

- Use barrier cream before starting work.

- Always use correct lifting techniques.

Ensure you follow instructions given to you at all times when moving any materials or equipment. The main points to remember are:

- always try to avoid manual handling (or use mechanical means to aid the process)

- always assess the situation first to establish the best method of handling the load

- always reduce any risks as much as possible (e.g. split a very heavy load, move obstacles from your path before lifting)

- tell others around you what you are doing

- if you need help with a load, get it. Do not try to lift something beyond what you can manage.

Did you know?

In 2004/05 there were over 50,000 injuries while handling, lifting or carrying in the UK (source: Health and Safety Executive)

Wood and sheet materials

As a carpenter or joiner, wood and sheet materials such as plywood are the materials you will use the most. It is therefore important that you know how to store them correctly.

Carcassing timber

Carcassing timber is wood used for non-load-bearing jobs such as ceiling and floorboard supports, stud wall partitions and other types of framework. It should normally be stored outside under a covered framework. It should be placed on timber bearers clear of the ground. The ground should be free of vegetation and ideally covered over with concrete. This reduces the risk of absorption of ground moisture, which can damage the timber and cause wet rot. Piling sticks or cross-bearers should be placed between each layer of timber, about 600 mm apart, to provide support and allow air circulation. Tarpaulins or plastic covers can be used to protect the timber from the elements, however, care must be taken to allow air to flow freely through the stack. See Figure 5.1.

Remember

The storage racks used to store wood must take account of the weight of the load. Access to the materials being stored is another important consideration

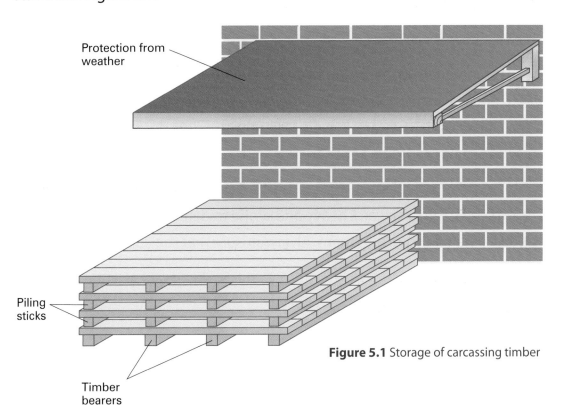

Protection from weather

Piling sticks

Timber bearers

Figure 5.1 Storage of carcassing timber

Joinery grade and hardwoods

These timbers should be stored under full cover wherever possible, preferably in a storage shed. Good ventilation is needed to avoid build-up of moisture through absorption. This type of timber should also be stored on bearers on a well-prepared base.

Plywood and other sheet materials

All sheet materials should be stored in a dry, well-ventilated environment. Specialised covers are readily available to give added protection for most sheet materials, helping to prevent condensation caused when non-specialised types of sheeting are used.

Sheet materials should be stacked flat on timber cross-bearers, spaced close enough together to prevent sagging. Alternatively, where space is limited, sheet materials can be stored on edge in purpose-made racks which allow the sheets to rest against the backboard. There should be sufficient space around the plywood for easy loading and removal. The rack should be designed to allow sheets to be removed from either the front or the ends.

Leaning sheets against walls is not recommended, as this makes them bow, which is difficult to correct.

For sheet materials with faces or decorative sides, the face sides should be placed against each other to minimise the risk of damage due to friction of the sheets when they are moved. Different sizes, grades and qualities of sheet materials should be kept separate with off-cuts stacked separately from the main stack.

Sheet materials are awkward, heavy and prone to damage so extra care is essential when transporting them. Always ensure that the correct PPE is worn.

Find out

What are the PPE requirements when moving sheet materials?

Safety tip

Due to the size, shape and weight of sheet materials, always get help to lift and carry them. If possible, use a purpose-made plywood trolley which will transport the load for you

Storage of sheet materials

Ironmongery

Ironmongery includes not just fittings and fixtures made of iron, but also hardware made from other materials including brass, chrome, porcelain and glass. Items you might come across include door handles, hooks, locks, hinges, window fittings, screws and bolts.

Door furniture

Door furniture such as locks, bolts, letter boxes, knockers and handles etc. are 'desirable' items, which means that they are very likely to be stolen unless stored securely. A store person is usually responsible for the storage and distribution of such items and keeps a check on how many are given out and to whom.

Examples of door furniture

In addition to being stored securely, door furniture should also be kept in separate compartments of a racking storage system or at least on shelving. Where possible all door furniture should be retained in the manufacturer's packaging until needed. This prevents damage and loss of components such as screws and keys. Large heavy items should be stored on lower shelves to avoid unnecessary lifting.

Fixings

Each type of fixing is designed for a specific purpose and includes items such as nails, screws, pins, bolts, washers, rivets and plugs. As with door furniture, fixings tend to disappear if their storage is not supervised and controlled by a store person.

Fixings must be stored appropriately to keep them in good condition and to make them easy to find. Where possible, they should be kept in bags or boxes clearly marked with their size and type. Storing them in separate

Safety tip

Carelessly discarded fixings, such as nails, can be costly, but can also create health and safety hazards

Remember

Broken fixings should be disposed of carefully

Different types of fixings should be stored separately

compartments is the most convenient method of storage. This enables easy and fast selection when required and prevents the wrong fixing being used. Time taken to sort out different types and sizes of fixings that have become mixed up is a waste of your time and your employer's time.

Adhesives

Adhesives are substances used to bond (stick) surfaces together. Because of their chemical nature, there are a number of potentially serious risks connected with adhesives if they are not stored, used and handled correctly.

All adhesives should be stored and used in line with the manufacturer's instructions. This usually involves storing them on shelving, with labels facing outward, in a safe, secure area (preferably a lockable store room). It is important to keep the labels facing outwards so that the correct adhesive can be selected.

The level of risk associated with adhesive use is dependent on the type of adhesive. Some of the risks include:

- explosion

- poisoning

- skin irritation

- disease.

Adhesives should be stored according to the manufacturer's instructions

As explained in Chapter 2 Health and safety, these types of material are closely controlled by COSHH, which aims to minimise the risks involved with their storage and use.

All adhesives have a recommended **shelf life**. This must be taken into account when storing to ensure the oldest stock is stored at the front and used first. Remember to refer to the manufacturer's guidelines as to how long the adhesive will remain fit for purpose once opened. Adhesives can be negatively affected by poor storage, including loss in adhesive strength and extended setting time.

Doors, door frames and window frames

Timber doors, door frames and window frames should stored flat on timber bearers under full cover to protect them from exposure to the weather. There should be adequate space between the doors or frames to enable access.

Wall and floor units

Kitchen wall and floor units should be stacked no more than two units high against a solid surface such as a wall. Protective sheeting may be used to prevent damage and staining.

Materials associated with other trades

As a carpenter or joiner, you will often work closely with people in many other trades, for example bricklayers and painters and decorators. Understanding storage of their materials will help you in your own work.

Wall and roofing materials

These materials include items such as bricks, blocks and tiles. They may be supplied loose or packaged, shrink-wrapped in plastic and sometimes on timber pallets.

When these materials are supplied in loose form they should be off-loaded manually. They should never be tipped as this inevitably damages them. They should be stacked on edge in rows, on level and well-drained ground.

The stack height should be no more than 1.8 m. Protection against rain and frost should be provided with a tarpaulin or polythene sheet covering, which should be weighted down at the bottom.

Sand, gravel and crushed rock

Sand, gravel and crushed rock are known as **aggregates** and are normally supplied in bulk by tipper lorries. Small amounts are usually supplied bagged. Each type should be stored separately in bays to prevent mixing and contamination. They should also be stored as near to the mixing point as possible. Storage areas should have hard, concrete-based floors, laid on a slight slope so that water will drain away.

Loose bricks should be handled manually

Tarpaulins or plastic covers can be used to protect stockpiles from leaves, rubbish and the weather.

Paints and varnishes

These are supplied in:

- 1-, 2.5-, 5- and 10-litre containers
- bulk/trade 25-litre containers.

They should be stored on shelves, in a secure store, at an even temperature. Each shelf and container should be marked with its contents. Large containers should be placed on lower shelves to avoid unnecessary lifting.

Storage of paints

Highly flammable liquids

Liquefied Petroleum Gas (LPG), petrol, cellulose thinners, methylated spirits, chlorinated rubber paint and white spirit are all highly flammable liquids. These materials require special storage in order to ensure they do not risk injury to workers.

- Containers should only be kept in a special storeroom which has a floor made of concrete that slopes away from the storage area. This is to prevent leaked materials from collecting under the containers.

- The actual storeroom should be built of concrete, brick or some other fireproof material.

- The roof should be made from an easily shattered material in order to minimise the effect of any explosion.

- Doors should be at least 50 mm thick and open outwards.

- Any glass used in the structure should be wired and not less than 6 mm thick.

- The standing area should have a sill surrounding it that it is deep enough to contain the contents of the largest container stored.

- Containers should always be stored upright.

- The area should not be heated.

- Electric lights should be intrinsically safe.

- Light switches should be flameproof and should be on the outside of the store.

- The building should be ventilated at high and low levels and have at least two exits.

- Naked flames and spark producing materials should be clearly prohibited, including smoking.

- The storeroom should be clearly marked with red and white squares and 'Highly Flammable' signage.

Did you know?

'Inflammable' means the same thing as flammable, i.e. if something is inflammable it means that it is easily lit and capable of burning rapidly

Figure 5.2 Storage of highly flammable liquids

Definition

FIFO – first in first out (a system of using stock whereby the oldest material is used first so that it doesn't perish)

Bagged materials

Bagged materials, such as cement, plaster and sand, should be stored in a ventilated, waterproof shed, with a sound (good condition) dry floor. They should be clear of the walls and piles should be no more than eight to ten bags high.

Bags should be used in the same order as they were delivered, known as 'first in first out' (**FIFO**).

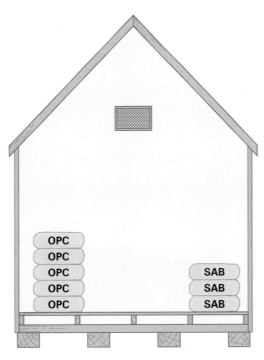

- Dry, ventilated shed
- Stock must be rotated so that old stock is used before new
- Not more than five bags high
- Clear of walls
- Off floor

Figure 5.3 Storage of bagged materials

Glass

Glass should be stored vertically in racks. The conditions for glass storage should be:

- clean – storing glass in dirty or dusty conditions can cause discoloration

- dry – if moisture is allowed between the sheets of glass it can make them stick together, which may make them difficult to handle and more likely to break.

If only a small number of sheets of glass are to be stored, they can be leant against a stable surface, as shown in the photo below.

Storage of glass

FAQ

What happens if there is a delivery of timber but there is no room in the wood store?

It is probably best to remove some of the old stock from the wood store and either store it flat on timber cross-bearers or on edge in racks. This timber should be used first and as soon as possible. The new timber can now be stored in the wood store.

What should I do if I notice a leakage in the LPG store?

Leaking LPG should be treated as a very dangerous situation. Don't turn on any lights or ignite any naked flames, for example a cigarette lighter. Any kind of spark could ignite the LPG. Report the situation immediately and don't attempt to clear up the spillage yourself.

On the job: Unloading timber

Damon and Molly are helping to unload some timber that has just been delivered. They are carrying it from the lorry to the joinery shop and placing it in the wood store. While Damon is walking through the joinery shop with some timber, he trips over a hammer someone has left on the floor. Meanwhile, Molly is in the store with a sheet of plywood. She can't see any room on the shelves for the sheet of wood so she leans it against the wall. She has heard that it is OK to store sheet material on edge, so it should be fine.

Before Damon and Molly started bringing the timber into the shop, what should they have done to avoid Damon's accident? What do you think of Molly's storage of the plywood sheet? Would you have done the same thing?

Knowledge check

1. List some of the basic common-sense things you can do to stay safe when handling materials.

2. What is carcassing timber and how should it be stored?

3. Why is it important to ensure that timber is not exposed to moisture during storage?

4. What might happen if you store sheet materials leaning against a wall?

5. What is the best way to store door furniture?

6. Name the four risks associated with adhesive materials.

7. How should aggregates be stored?

8. How can you reduce the amount of lifting needed when storing materials such as paint?

9. Describe the characteristics of a special storeroom used to store highly flammable liquids.

10. What are the ideal conditions for glass storage? Why?

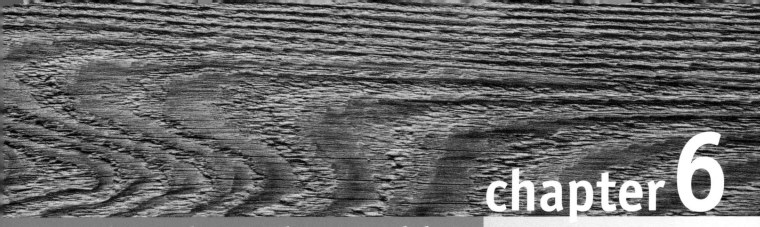

chapter 6

Hand tools and portable power tools

OVERVIEW

Whatever type of work is involved, the quality of the finished product depends upon the skill of the operator in selecting and using the correct tools to cut, shape and assemble the materials for the task. There is a wide range of tools available and this chapter looks at the main hand and portable power tools that the carpenter and joiner should be able to use and maintain properly. We will also look at the importance of safety and the precautions you should take when using tools. Issues relating to the protection and maintenance of tools will also be addressed.

This chapter will cover the following:

- Hand tools
- Portable power tools.

Some additional information about the use of and safety regulations relating to the use of circular saws is available for download. To access this document, please visit www.heinemann.co.uk and follow the FE and Vocational link, followed by the construction link.

Hand tools

Although portable power tools are increasingly being used, and can complete many tasks much faster than hand tools, the good carpenter and joiner will still need to use a wide range of hand tools.

It is essential to have a basic set of hand tools. It is also good practice to extend your tool kit by purchasing good tools, as and when needed for a particular job, so building up a set of high-quality tools over time.

In this section we will look at each type of hand tool in turn, including where and how to use them. We will also address general safety measures and recommendations. Finally we will look at how to protect and maintain tools, so that they give long and efficient service.

Definition

PPE – personal protective equipment, which might include a helmet, safety glasses and gloves

Safety first

The following are general safety rules when using any hand tools:

- Wear the correct **PPE** for the task, particularly good quality safety glasses if there is any danger of fast-flying objects.

- Do not wear loose clothing or jewellery that could catch on tools.

- Secure all work down before working on it.

- Keep hands well away from the sharp edges of tools, especially saw teeth, chisels and drill bits.

- Never use a tool to do a job for which it was not designed.

- Make sure that tools are kept sharp and stored properly when not in use.

- Never force the tool – the tool should do the work.

- Never place any part of your body in front of the cutting edge.

- Keep work areas clean.

Summary of hand tool types

Hand tools can be grouped in the following categories, each of which is covered separately below, with illustrations:

- measuring and marking out tools
- sawing tools
- cutting tools
- planing tools
- shaping tools
- drilling or boring tools
- percussion tools
- screwdrivers
- holding and clamping tools
- lever tools
- tools for levelling
- jigs and guides.

Measuring and marking out

The main tools for measuring and marking out are:

- folding rules
- retractable steel tape measures
- metal steel rules
- pencils
- marking knife
- tri-square
- sliding bevel

- mitre square

- combination square

- gauges.

Folding rules

Folding rules are used in the joiner's shop or on site. They are normally one metre long when unfolded and made of wood or plastic. They can show both metric and imperial units.

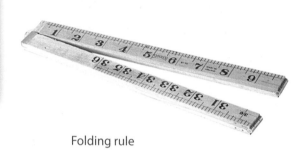

Folding rule

Retractable steel tape measures

Retractable steel tape measures, often referred to as spring tapes, are available in a variety of lengths. They are useful for setting out large areas or marking long lengths of timber and other materials. They have a hook at right angles at the start of the tape to hold over the edge of the material. On better tapes this should slide, so that it is out of the way when not measuring from an edge.

Retractable steel tape measure

Metal steel rules

Metal steel rules, often referred to as bar rules, are used for fine, accurate measurement work. They are generally 300 mm or 600 mm long and can also serve as a short straight edge for marking out. The rule can also be used on its edge for greater accuracy.

They may become discoloured over time. If so, give them a gentle rub with very fine emery paper and a light oil. If they become too rusty, replace them.

Pencils

Pencils are an important part of a tool kit. They can be used for marking out exact measurements, both across and along the grain. They must be sharpened regularly, normally to a chisel-shaped point, which can be kept sharp by rubbing on fine emery paper. A chisel edge will draw more accurately along a marking out tool, like a steel rule, than a rounded point.

Pencils are graded by the softness or hardness of the lead. B grades are soft, H grades hard, with HB as the medium grade. Increasing hardness is indicated by a number in front of the H. Harder leads give a finer line but are often more difficult to rub out. A good compromise for most carpentry work is 2H.

600 mm steel rule

A variety of pencils

Did you know?

The 'lead' in pencils is actually graphite, a naturally occurring form of compressed carbon. If graphite is pressed very much harder, it becomes diamond

Marking knife

Marking knives are used for marking across the grain and can be much more accurate than a pencil. They also provide a slight indentation for saw teeth to key into.

Marking knife

Tri-square

Tri-squares are used to mark and test angles at 90° and check that surfaces are at right angles to each other.

They should be regularly checked for accuracy. To do this, place the square against any straight-edged spare timber and mark a line at right angles. Turn the square over and draw another line from the same point. If the tool is accurate the two lines should be on top of each other.

Tri-square

Remember

Do not over-tighten thumbscrews on a sliding bevel as they may snap

Sliding bevel

The sliding bevel is an adjustable tri-square, used for marking and testing angles other than 90°. When in use, the blade is set at the required angle then locked by either a thumbscrew or set screw in the stock.

Sliding bevel

Mitre square

The blade of a mitre square is set into the stock at an angle of 45° and is used for marking out a mitre cut.

Mitre square

Combination square

A combination square does the job of a tri-square, mitre square and spirit level all in one. It is used for checking right angles, 45° angles and also that items are level.

Combination square

Remember

All squares should be checked for accuracy on a regular basis

Gauges

Gauges are instruments used to check that an item meets standard measurements. They are also used to mark critical dimensions, such as length and thickness.

Marking gauge

Marking gauge

A marking gauge is used for marking lines parallel to the edge or end of the wood. The parts of a marking gauge include stem, stock, spur (or point) and thumbscrew. A marking gauge has only one spur or point.

Mortise gauge

A mortise gauge is used for marking the double lines required when setting out mortise and tenon joints, hence the name. It has one fixed and one adjustable spur or point. Figure 6.1 shows setting of the adjustable point to match the width of a chisel.

Mortise gauge

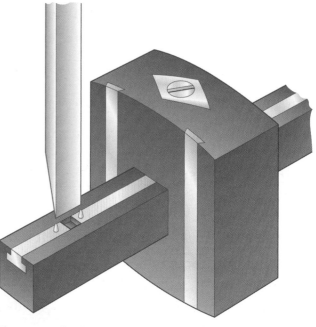

Figure 6.1 Setting mortise gauge to chisel blade width

Cutting gauge

The cutting gauge is very similar to the marking gauge but has a blade in place of the spur. This is used to cut deep lines in the timber, particularly across the grain, to give a clean, precise cut (e.g. for marking the shoulders of tenons).

Callipers and dividers

Callipers and dividers enable accurate checking of widths and gaps. They can have a simple friction joint or knurled rod and thread. The latter are more accurate for repetitive work, as the width setting can be maintained.

Callipers are designed for either internal and external gaps. Although some come with a graduated scale it is usually better to check measurements against a steel rule.

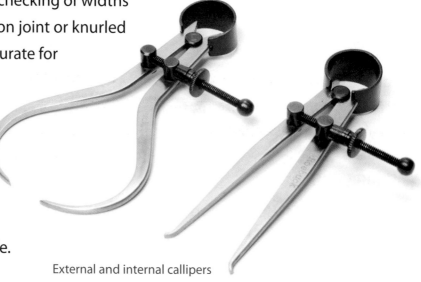

External and internal callipers

Sawing tools

There is a wide range of tools that cut using saw teeth. They can be classified as:

- hand saws, including rip saw, cross cut and panel saw

- back saws, so named because they have reinforcing metal along the back edge, including tenon, dovetail and bead saw

- saws for cutting circles or curves, including bow saw, coping saw, fret saw, pad, compass or keyhole saw.

They vary in the way they cut depending on the shape and size of the teeth, also on the angle the teeth are bent outwards from the line of the saw blade. This angle is called the set of the teeth. Cross cut teeth are designed to act like tiny knives that sever wood fibres while rip saw teeth are shaped to act like small chisels.

Saws are still commonly categorised by the number of 'teeth per inch' (TPI), but this is now taken to mean the number of teeth every 25 mm, as we have used below.

Many modern saws are designed to be used until blunt and then replaced. On older saws teeth need to be regularly maintained, which involves sharpening and setting. This is described in the section on tool maintenance later in this chapter.

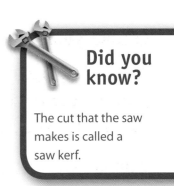

Did you know?

The cut that the saw makes is called a saw kerf.

Rip saw

Rip saws are usually used for cutting with the grain. Typically they are 650 mm – 700 mm long with 3–4 teeth per 25 mm. The teeth are filed at 90° across the blade, shaped like chisels and thus may be described as a gang of cutting chisels in a row. The saw should be at 60° to the work to cut most efficiently.

When starting to cut with a saw, make the first cut by drawing the saw backwards, as this avoids the saw jumping out from the mark, which can cause injury. Use your thumb as a guide as you start to cut.

Cross cut saw

Cross cut saws, as the name implies, are used for cutting across the grain, but can also be used for short rips on light timber.

Cross cut saw

Typically they are 650 mm long with 5–8 teeth per 25 mm. The teeth are bevelled (i.e. filed at an angle) across the saw to produce a knife-like edge on the forward and back edge of the tooth. The angle of this bevel is between 60° and 75°.

The cutting edge should ideally be at 45° to the work when sawing across the grain.

Panel saw

Panel saws are used for cutting plywood, large tenons and most fine work (e.g. on polished materials). They are obtainable up to 600 mm long. The teeth are practically the same as the cross cut saw, but usually there are 7–12 teeth per 25 mm.

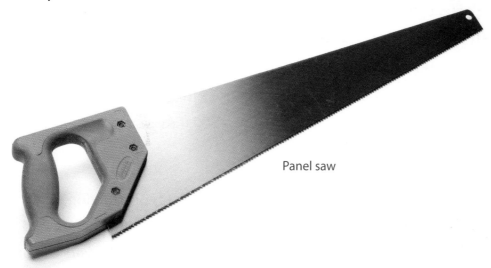

Panel saw

Tenon saw

The tenon saw has teeth in a similar pattern to a cross cut saw but with 12–14 teeth per 25 mm. It is used for cutting joints and general bench work. There is a reinforcing strip along the top of the blade made from steel or brass to keep the saw rigid. Tenon saws are typically 300 mm – 350 mm long.

There is no special virtue in brass or steel for the reinforcement, except that brass is kept clean more easily.

Tenon saw

Dovetail saw

The dovetail saw is a smaller edition of the tenon saw with the same tooth pattern, but the teeth are finer, 18–24 per 25 mm, and it has a thinner blade. It is used for dovetails and other fine work. Dovetail saws are obtainable up to 200 mm in length.

Bead saw

Even finer than the dovetail saw is the bead saw or 'gents saw' as it is sometimes known. They have 15–25 teeth per 25 mm and are designed for very delicate work. They are usually 150 mm – 200 mm long.

Bow saw

The bow saw, also known as a frame saw because of its construction, has a thin blade and is used for cutting circular or curved work. The blade is held in tension by a cord twisted tourniquet fashion, though modern versions are fitted with an adjustable steel rod. The teeth are of the cross cut saw pattern and blades are from 200 mm – 400 mm in length.

Bow saw

Coping saw

The coping saw has a very narrow blade held in tension by the springing of the frame and is also used for cutting curves, especially internal and external shapes. The teeth are of the rip saw pattern, typically 14 teeth per 25 mm and blades can be 150 mm long.

For internal shapes the blade can be released from the frame and reconnected and tensioned after pushing the blade through a hole drilled though part of the wood to be removed.

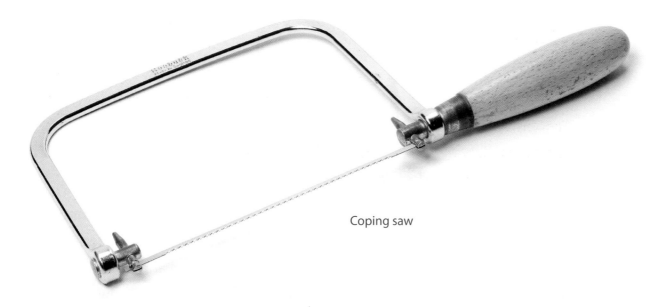

Coping saw

Fret Saw

Fret saws are very similar to coping saws but have a deep throat in the frame and smaller, finer blades, up to 32 teeth per 25 mm. They are used for cutting very tight curves and blades are generally no more than 125 mm long.

Fret saw

Pad, compass or key hole saws

Pad saws have no frame, so can be used where coping or fret saws cannot reach. They tend to have a single handle with interchangeable blades to carry out a range of tasks, especially for cutting key holes and large internal shaped work. The handle may be angled to the blade. Key hole saw handles are usually in line with the blade.

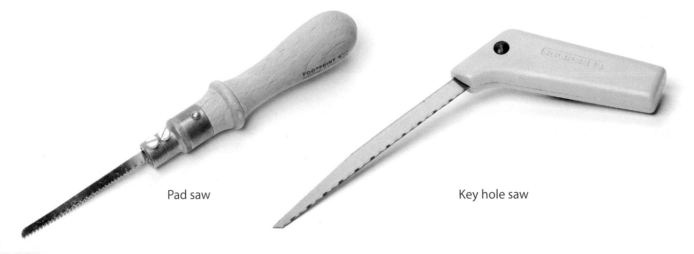

Pad saw

Key hole saw

Blades are tapered with a slot, which fits into the saw handle and is then secured with two screws. Blades for cutting wood may come in lengths from 125 mm – 375 mm and have teeth set in the rip saw or cross cut saw pattern. Other blades will cut plastic, metal, etc.

Hack saw

A hack saw is a framed saw that is used to cut metal components such as pipes. A hack saw can cut through copper, brass and steel.

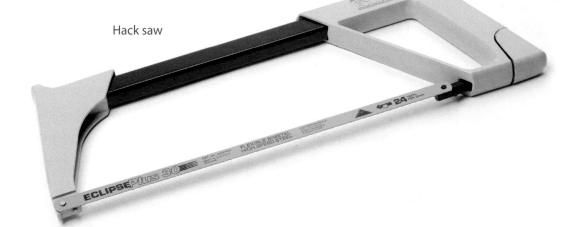

Hack saw

Flooring saw

Flooring saws are specially designed to cut through floorboards in situ. They have a curved blade, which means they can cut into a board without having to drill through first, and also cause less damage to neighbouring boards. There are also teeth on an angled front edge, which allow cutting into skirting boards.

Blades are short and stiff, generally no more than 320 mm, with 8 teeth per 25 mm.

Flooring saw

Cutting tools

There is a wide range of tools designed to cut material using a sharp blade rather than saw teeth, including knives, scissors, chisels, gouges and axes. Chisels, gouges and axes are covered in more detail below.

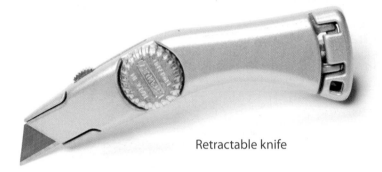

Retractable knife

Chisels

As with saws, chisels are available in a variety of shapes and sizes. The ones that you are most likely to use are described below. Like all edge tools, chisels work best when they are very sharp. This ensures less effort needed to cut, which enables greater accuracy.

Firmer chisel

A firmer chisel is the strongest type of chisel. It is used for general purpose wood cutting and designed to be used with a mallet, if required.

The blade is generally about 100 mm long when new, rectangular in cross-section and tapering slightly from the bolster to the cutting edge. Size is normally by blade width, which may range from 6 mm – 50 mm.

Safety tip

Never hit a chisel with your hand as this may cause injury

Selection of firmer chisels

Bevelled-edge chisel

Bevelled-edge chisels are variations on the standard firmer chisel and come in similar sizes. The two long edges are bevelled, which makes them lighter but not as strong. Hence, they should not be used with a mallet, except for very light taps.

They are used for short paring and other fine work. The bevelled edge also helps when cleaning out corners that are less than 90°.

Bevelled-edge chisels

Paring chisel

Paring chisels may be rectangular in cross-section or have bevelled edges. They are longer, normally around 175 mm, more slender than the firmer chisels and are, thus, a more delicate tool. Their main use is for cutting deep grooves and long housings. They should not be hit with a mallet.

Paring chisel

Mortise chisel

The mortise chisel is designed for heavy duty work, with a thick stiff blade and generally shorter than the firmer and paring chisel. It may also have a slight bevel on all edges to allow easy withdrawal from the work. Sizes are typically 6 mm – 50 mm.

The handle is longer than on other chisels, with a wide curved end designed to take blows from a mallet. It is sometimes encircled with a metal ring to give extra strength and a leather washer inserted between the shoulder of the blade and the handle to absorb mallet blows. The handles can either be held by a simple tang or in a socket.

Mortise chisel

Variants of the heavy duty mortise chisel are the sash mortise chisel for lighter work and the lock mortise chisel, with a swan neck, useful for removing waste from deep mortises.

Gouges

Gouges are a type of chisel with a curved cross-section to the blade. They come in two main types, similar to chisels, called firmer and paring.

Firmer gouge

Firmer gouges come with two blade types: out-cannel and in-cannel.

- Out-cannel gouges have the cutting edge ground on the outside, so that they can be used to make concave cuts (i.e. cuts into the surface).

- In-cannel gouges have the cutting edge ground on the inside, so that they can be used to make convex cuts (i.e. leaving a protruding bulge on the surface).

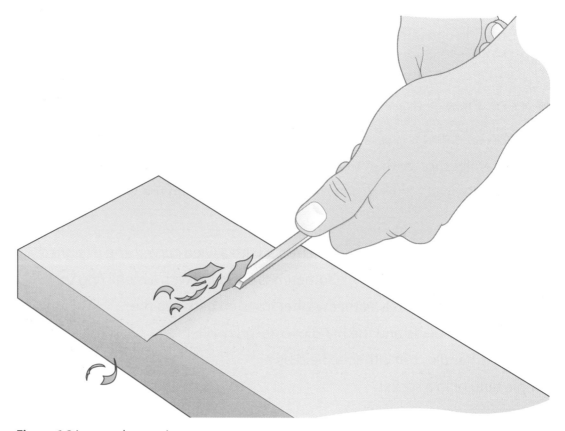

Figure 6.2 In-cannel gouge in use

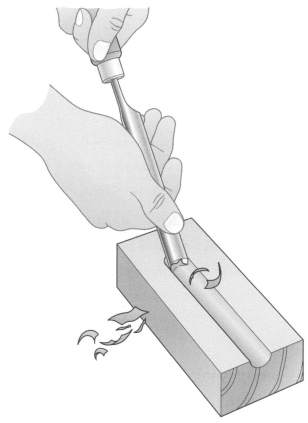

Figure 6.3 Out-cannel gouge in use

Blade length is about 100 mm when new and they are designed to be used with a mallet. Blade widths typically range from 6 mm – 25 mm, though larger ones are available. Both are usually ground square across, though the out-cannel blade is sometimes rounded for cutting deep hollows.

Figures 6.2 and 6.3 show the two gouges being used to make convex and concave cuts.

Paring gouge

Similar to paring chisels, and sometimes known as scribing gouges, paring gouges are longer and thinner than firmer gouges and used for finer work. They are only ground on the inside for in-cannel cuts. They are not designed to be used with a mallet and may have a double bend in the neck to keep the handle clear of the work surface.

Safety tip

When using any chisel, fix the timber securely and keep both hands behind the cutting edge. Also remember that blunt tools are more dangerous than sharp ones

Axes

When an axe is used correctly, it is highly effective at removing waste wood and cutting wedges. However, it must be kept sharp, and the edge protected when not in use.

Hand axe

Axes vary in the shape of the head and its weight. The head is fitted on to a wooden shaft, preferably hickory, and held by wedges in a similar manner to a hammer. Axes designed to be used with one hand are typically around 1 kg in weight. Felling axes, with longer handles and designed to be used with two hands, may be 2.75 kg or heavier.

Planing tools

Planing tools are used to cut thin layers of wood, leaving a flat surface. They come in many forms, each developed to carry out a specific function or job, from levelling a surface to cutting bevels, rebates or grooves. The most widely used are as follows:

- smoothing plane
- jack plane
- jointer or trying plane
- rebate plane
- plough plane
- shoulder plane
- bull nose plane
- block plane.

The first three are often referred to as bench planes. The different parts of a smoothing plane are labelled in the photo. See Table 6.1 for their names. Other planes have similar component parts.

A. Steel body	G. Cam
B. Toe	H. Cutting iron
C. Knob	I. Handle
D. Knob screw and nut	J. Heel
E. Cap iron screw	K. Adjusting nut
F. Cap iron	

Table 6.1 Parts of a smoothing plane

Smoothing plane

The smoothing plane is the shortest of the bench planes and is used for final finishing or cleaning up, bevelling and chamfering. It can be used to follow the grain and can even be used with one hand.

Did you know?

Chamfering is to bevel an edge or corner, usually cutting an equal amount from each face

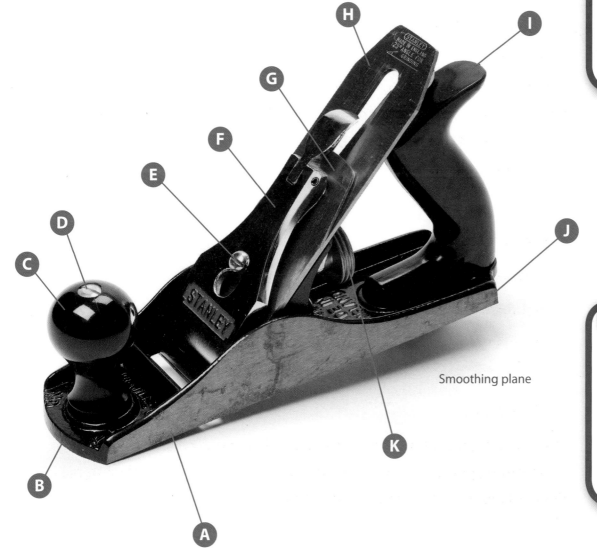

Smoothing plane

Remember

When bevelling or chamfering, mark with a pencil not a gauge because the gauge marks will still show when the chamfer or bevel is planed

Jack plane

The jack plane is a medium length bench plane, generally 350 mm – 380 mm with similar blade width to the smoothing plane. It is used for rapid and accurate removal of waste material, such as dressing doors for hanging.

Jack plane

Jointer or trying plane

The jointer, try or trying plane (sometimes also known as the long plane) is the longest bench plane, ranging from 450 mm – 600 mm. It is generally used for smoothing long edges of timber. The length helps to make the surface as level as possible. Typical blade width is 60 mm.

Jointer plane

The sequence of operations for squaring off a length of timber is:

1. One surface is planed square.

2. Then plane one edge to this dressed face.

3. The wood can then be dressed on all faces to the required width and thickness.

Rebate plane

Rebate planes, as the name suggests, are used for making and cleaning out rebates. The simplest is known as a bench rebate plane. It is similar to the other bench planes described above but has the cutting blade extending across the full width of the sole and at an angle of 55° – 60°. It is usually 37 mm wide and at right angles across the sole, but can be obtained with the blade set askew.

Rebate plane

More complex versions are called 'rebate and fillister planes', which have removable guide fences and depth gauges to assist in making accurate cuts. This avoids having to clamp a batten to the wood to act as a guide, which is advised with a standard bench rebate plane.

Plough plane or combination plane

Plough planes also have guide fences and depth gauges. They are usually used for cutting grooves along the grain of the timber, as well as rebates, typically from 3 mm – 12 mm wide. However, they come with a multiple choice of square and shaped cutters adapted for shaping **tongues**, bends, **beads**, **mouldings** etc. The combination plane is essentially the same but may have additional capabilities.

Plough plane

Definition

Tongues – the projecting pieces of timber that fit into a groove in a tongue and groove joint

Beads – the shaped pieces of timber added to the end of other pieces of timber to give a desired finish

Mouldings – decorative finishes around door openings and at floor and wall junctions

Shoulder plane

Shoulder planes are similar to rebate planes but, as the name implies, they are primarily for shaping the shoulders of tenons etc. They are often much narrower with blade widths down to 15 mm.

Shoulder plane

Bull nose plane

Bull nose planes are similar to shoulder planes but have the cutting edge very close to the front of the plane. Hence, they are particularly useful for cleaning out the corners of stopped housings or rebates. Some have a removable front end so that the plane can be worked right into the corners. They are obtainable with cutter widths from 10 mm – 28 mm.

Bull nose plane

Compass plane

Compass planes have a flexible sole to enable them to be used on concave or convex surfaces. There is screw adjustment to change the radius of the curve, within limits. Blade width is typically about 45 mm.

Block plane

Block planes come in a variety of designs but their key difference from other planes is the low angle at which the cutting blade is set, typically 20° but can be as low as 12°. This enables them to cut end grain.

Block plane

Shaping tools

Even though work on curved surfaces can be carried out with planes and chisels, the following tools are used for shaping curved surfaces and edges:

* spokeshaves

* rasps and files

* Surforms®.

Did you know?

Block planes are called this because they were used to cut butchers blocks, which traditionally used end grain timber

Spokeshave

Spokeshaves perform a similar role to a smoothing plane, except that they can do this on curved surfaces. They have a steel cutter set in either wood or metal handles and are designed to be used with two hands, pushing the tool along the wood to remove shavings.

There are two main types, a flat face for convex surfaces and round face for concave surfaces. Cutter widths are typically around 50 mm but they can be found up to 100 mm.

Round face spokeshave

Flat face spokeshave

Rasps and files

Rasps and files have a hard, rough surface of miniature teeth designed to smooth wood or metal by removing very small shavings. Rasps have teeth formed individually, whereas files have teeth formed by cutting grooves in the surface in patterns.

Files, in particular, come in a wide range of shapes and sizes, with rectangular, triangular, oval or circular cross-sections, and combinations of these. They are generally classified by the number of teeth per 25 mm and the pattern of cuts used to create them. These may range from 26 teeth per 25 mm on coarse files to 60 teeth on smooth ones, and the grade may differ between faces on the same file. Generally the longer the file the coarser it is.

Rasps are mainly flat, round or half round and the teeth coarse. They are mostly used for initial shaping of wood, able to remove a lot of material quickly but leaving a rough surface which then needs to be smoothed with a file or spokeshave.

Files

Rasp

Surforms®

Surforms® differ from rasps because the teeth are punched right through the metal, enabling timber shavings to pass through. Hence, the tool is less inclined to clog up. They can be flat or round, the latter being useful for enlarging holes and shaping cuts.

Surform®

Drilling or boring tools

There are countless reasons why holes may be required in timber, e.g. to insert screws, dowels or other fittings. Hand tools used for these tasks can be broken down into:

- bradawls
- hand drills
- carpenter's brace.

Many of these tasks, traditionally completed with hand tools, have been taken over by the power drill. In particular, the hand drill and carpenter's brace are much less used today. However, hand tools for making holes still play an important part in the workplace and the good carpenter and joiner should be able to use them all.

Did you know?

You can use a wire brush to clean rasps and files when they become clogged with shavings

Bradawl

The bradawl is used for making pilot holes for small screws or a centre mark for drilling. They come in various cross-sections, and with sharp points, tips like a sharpened screwdriver blade or even spiral cutters. The points work by pushing aside the wood fibres when pressure is applied, but this can cause the wood to split. A sharp screwdriver tip can reduce this risk by cutting the fibres initially, the hole then being further deepened by a point.

Bradawl

Hand drill or wheel brace

Hand drills, or wheel braces, are useful for boring screw holes up to 6 mm in diameter. A selection of twist bits is required, usually with a round shank as used with power drills.

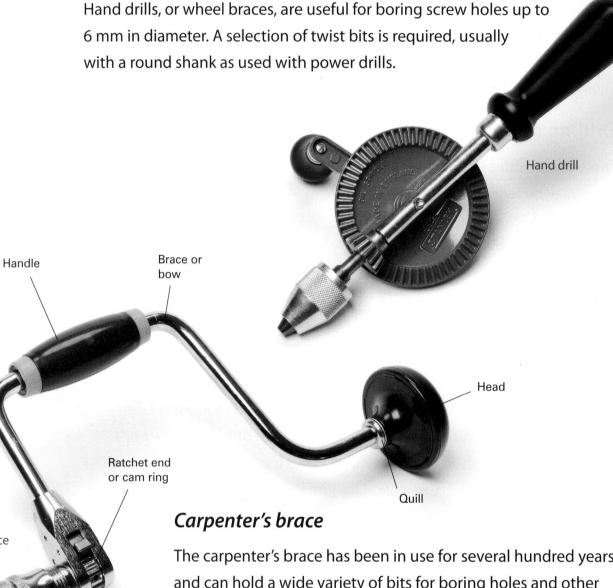

Hand drill

Handle

Brace or bow

Head

Ratchet end or cam ring

Quill

Carpenter's brace

Chuck or shell

Jaws

Carpenter's brace

The carpenter's brace has been in use for several hundred years and can hold a wide variety of bits for boring holes and other tasks. Most types of brace have a ratchet mechanism so that the tool can be used in restricted spaces.

The chuck of the brace is designed to grip bits with square shanks, called a tang. However some braces can accept rounded shanks that are designed for power tools. The main types of bits are described on the page opposite.

Centre bit

A centre bit is a short, fast cutting bit. It has a lead screw and a single cutting spur. It is used to bore accurate but shallow holes. To go right through the wood it is normal to drill into wood until the point comes through, then use this as the centre mark to drill from the other side.

Twist bit

Twist bits have a lead screw and two cutting spurs. The shank has a helical twist or spiral that clears the wood from the hole. Irwin bits have a single spiral, the Jennings a double spiral. Both are used for boring holes from 4 mm upwards. The Jennings bits are claimed to be more accurate and stronger because of the double spiral, so are favoured for longer bits, but, in practice, there is little to choose between them.

Irwin bit

Jennings bit

Forstner bit

Forstner bits are used for high quality, accurate work where a flat bottom to a hole is required. They have no threaded point and need a pilot hole made by other cutters to start and then steady pressure to make them cut. They can range in size from 10 mm – 50 mm.

Forstner bits

Expansion bit

Expansion bits are similar to centre bits but with an adjustable cutting spur. They are only designed to cut a shallow hole.

Expansion bit

Countersink bit

Countersink bits are used to form a recess for a screw head. They come with different cutter shapes. Snail countersinks are used in braces, rose countersinks in hand drills or power drills.

Safety tip

Never use an expansion bit in any power tool

Snail countersink

Rose countersink

Screwdriver bit

A carpenter's brace with a screwdriver bit can be very useful for removing stubborn and worn screws, as considerable pressure can be applied and the brace handle gives excellent leverage. They are often more controllable than a power drill and less likely to jump out, which can damage the screw further. They can also be used to insert screws.

Screwdriver bits

Percussion tools

Percussion tools can be grouped into:

- hammers
- mallets
- punches.

Hammers

Hammers are available in various types and sizes and are essential to the craftsman. The head has a protruding part, often called the bell, with a flat face for striking the work, an eye for fitting over the end of the shaft and a protruding part at the back, the pein, most often shaped as a claw, wedge or ball. Wooden shafts, made from a hardwood like ash or hickory, are still preferred for most work, as they absorb the shock. The head is secured to the shaft by driving a wedge or wedges into slots in the head of the shaft.

Claw hammer

The claw hammer is used to drive nails into timber, with the claw available to withdraw bent or unwanted nails. It should be of the best quality to perform safely and efficiently. They come in various weights up to about 570 g. Increasingly they have steel shafts and integral heads, as much more leverage can be applied when using the claw without danger of loosening the head.

Claw hammer

Safety tip

If hammer heads become loose they must be re-secured immediately and any damaged shafts replaced

Did you know?

Loose hammer heads can be temporarily tightened on a wooden shaft by steeping in water to cause the shaft to swell, but must be repaired or replaced as soon as possible

It is best to place a spare scrap of timber or hardboard under the claw as packing to protect the surface of the timber when using it. You can also get additional leverage and withdraw a nail straighter, thus causing less damage to the timber, by using thicker packing under the claw.

Cross pein hammer

The cross pein hammer has a wedge-shaped pein. The pein can have various patterns and the hammers come typically with head weights from 200 g – 570 g. The Warrington pattern with a tapered pein is favoured by bench joiners for lighter work.

Using a packer to add leverage

Cross pein hammer

Using a block to add leverage

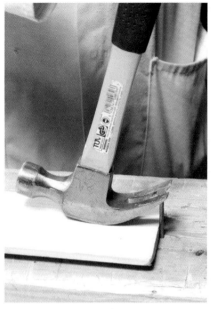
Mallet

Mallets

Carpenter's mallets have a much larger head than hammers, and are usually made from hardwood (beech is the commonest) with an ash or hickory shaft. The head can be rectangular in section or round.

They are primarily for use with chisels but also for a variety of 'persuading' purposes, such as knocking components or material into place without causing damage.

There are also soft-faced mallets with a either a rubber head or tightly rolled rawhide, glued and often loaded with lead. These are useful for material that wooden mallets may damage.

Punches

Punches come in a wide range of shapes and sizes with different shaped tips. The type most frequently employed by a carpenter and joiner is the nail punch.

Nail punches have a square head, a knurled gripping section and a tapered point with a hollow tip. They are used to punch nail heads below the surface of the wood. The punches are available in various sizes to suit the different diameters of nails available. Smaller ones are called pin punches. The hollow tip prevents the punch slipping off the nail.

Nail punch

Pin punch

Push pin nail drivers can be used with pins or small nails when a hammer would be impractical. They have a built-in spring mechanism to propel the nail into the wood and can be activated one handed.

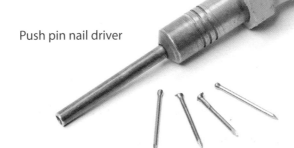

Push pin nail driver

> **Remember**
>
> Push pin nail drivers are not for use with large diameter nails

Screwdrivers

Screwdrivers are an important part of any tool kit. There are many types and styles but they all serve a similar purpose, i.e. inserting and withdrawing screws. Hence, they come with different tips to match the size and type of screws available, the most common of which for wood are:

- slotted head

- Phillips cross head

- Posidrive, similar to a Phillips head but with an additional square hole in the centre for added grip by the screwdriver.

Slotted screwdriver

Phillips screwdriver   Posidrive screwdriver

Screwdrivers also vary by the means used to drive screws. They can be grouped as:

- basic screwdrivers with no moving parts

- ratchet screwdrivers

- pump screwdrivers.

Basic screwdriver

Basic screwdrivers are available in various sizes from 50 mm – 400 mm. The handle is made of hardwood or unbreakable plastic. Traditional wooden handles are generally bulbous to give a good grip. Plastic ones are often moulded with flutes.

Screwdrivers to fit slotted screws may have tips that flare out, flared but then ground so that they are narrower towards the point, or parallel (i.e. the same width as the shank). Those made to fit other screw types are generally parallel.

Did you know?

The length of a screwdriver normally refers to the length of the blade only, not its overall length including handle

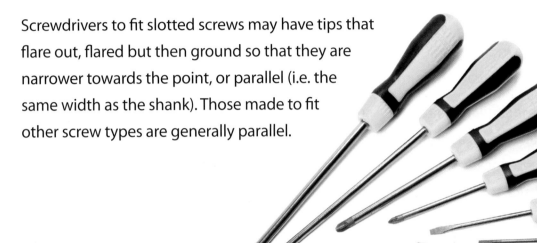

Various basic screwdrivers

Ratchet screwdriver

Ratchet screwdrivers have a ratchet mechanism built into the handle so that when turned one way the blade locks and acts like a basic screwdriver. When turned the other way the ratchet allows the handle to turn but leaves the blade in place.

There is a means to reverse the ratchet. Hence, screws can be driven in or withdrawn without changing grip on the handle. They often have interchangeable tips for different screw types, and can also be locked in one position so that they act like a basic screwdriver until the screw is sufficiently deep in the wood for the ratchet to work.

Ratchet type screwdriver

Pump action screwdrivers

Pump action screwdrivers have spiral grooves down the length of the screwdriver shank. There is then a cylinder as an extension of the handle, which can move over the grooves against an internal spring.

When pressure is applied to the handle it tries to follow the grooves and, if the handle is held still, the blade is forced to turn. When pressure is released the spring in the handle allows it to return to its starting point, leaving the blade in place and ready to pump the handle down again without changing grip.

This is similar to a ratchet screwdriver and, hence, these screwdrivers are often known as spiral ratchet screwdrivers. Like them, the mechanism can also be locked in place to operate like a basic screwdriver, and normally have a chuck to take different bits.

The pump action allows screws to be driven and removed quickly. Therefore they are useful in repetitive operations, though it is generally advisable to drill a pilot hole unless screwing into very soft wood.

Pump action screwdriver

Holding and clamping tools

Joiners frequently need to grip items and hold them steady while using tools, or while fixing them in position with nails, screws or glue. These include simple tools like pliers and pincers, as well as carpenters' vices attached to fixed or portable work benches, and a range of clamps (or cramps).

Pliers

Pliers are a universal gripping device used to grip small nuts and bolts. They can also be used to bend and cut, as well as to strip wire.

Pincers

Pincers are the simplest gripping tool and are an essential wood worker's tool. They are primarily used for removing nails but have many other uses. A good quality pair should give many years of service.

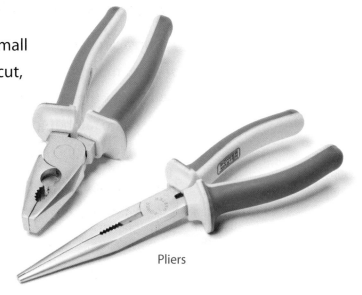

Pliers

Pincers

When using pincers for removing nails they should be operated similarly to a claw hammer. Scraps of wood should be used to avoid damage to the timber and thicker pieces used to get additional leverage. There is often a small claw on one handle, which is useful for removing tacks.

Clamps

Clamps, or cramps, have been developed to hold almost any shape of wood or other material in almost any position. Some are spring-operated, others have screw threads to pull jaws onto the material, others may use web straps that can be ratcheted tight, often around a frame. They may incorporate quick-release mechanisms.

The two you are likely to use most frequently are described below.

Sash clamp

Sash clamps are designed to hold large pieces of wood or frames together, usually while gluing.

A steel bar, either flat or T-section, has holes drilled along its length. An end shoe, flat to fit over the edge of the work to be clamped, is able to be moved a limited distance down the bar by using a screw mechanism driven by a tommy bar. A second shoe, the tail shoe, is designed to fit over the other edge of the work. It can be locked in place by a steel pin through any of the holes in the bar.

Sash clamp

With the end shoe withdrawn towards the end, the clamp is placed over the work and the tail shoe moved to give a loose fit. It is then locked in place with the pin. Pressure is then applied by screwing down the end shoe. The clamp must be square across the job to get even pressure.

G clamp

G clamps take their name from their shape, which resembles the letter 'G'. They come in various sizes and forms, and may include a quick-release mechanism but all have a fixed end and an adjustable end.

They are very versatile and particularly useful for clamping work pieces to the bench to allow operations to be carried out, such as routing or sawing. Again, pieces of scrap material can be used as packers to prevent damage to the work.

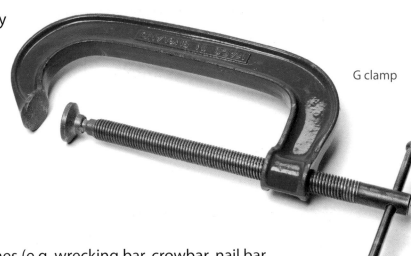

G clamp

Lever tools

Lever tools are known by various names (e.g. wrecking bar, crowbar, nail bar or tommy bar) and are designed for prising items apart, levering up heavy objects or pulling large nails.

Wrecking bar

Safety tip

Care must be taken when prising and removing large nails and the correct PPE worn

Tools for levelling

The most common levelling tool on site is the spirit level. It has a metal body into which are fitted one or more curved glass or plastic tubes known as 'vials'. These contain a liquid and a bubble of air. They work on the principle that a bubble of gas, enclosed in a glass tube containing a liquid, will always rise to the highest possible point within the tube. There are usually marks on the glass either side of the centre at the width of the bubble. When the bubble is positioned between them the tool is level.

Spirit level

Levels vary in length from 200 mm to 1 m or more and are used for marking and testing level surfaces or, in some cases, marking and testing vertical surfaces (plumbing). Good quality levels have adjustable tubes that can be reset should any inaccuracy develop.

Check for accuracy regularly by spanning something like a door frame and marking two level points, one at each end. Reverse the tool against the marks and see if the bubble is still level. If not, reset or replace the tool.

A range of electronic levels and plumb bobs are becoming available, based on lasers. They are often mounted on a stand and self-levelling.

Safety tip

Lasers can seriously damage eyesight, if not correctly used, so only use them if you are trained and have the appropriate PPE

Laser level

Jigs and guides

There are other items of equipment, on the bench and on site, which help in carrying out accurate work. Those designed to assist a specific task are generally referred to as **jigs**, some of which you can make yourself or they can be provided by the manufacturer (e.g. jigs to help fit kitchen units). Other items can provide more general support. Two of the commonest are guides to assist when sawing, described below.

Mitre boxes and blocks

Mitre boxes or blocks are used to guide the saw when cutting angles, particularly mitres. Usually they are made to suit the job and replaced when worn, though purpose-built versions can be purchased.

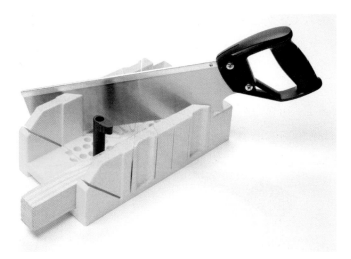

Mitre box

Mitre block

Bench hook

A bench hook is a very simple device for holding the timber on a bench when sawing.

Bench hook

Tool protection

When stored in a tool bag, tool box or cupboard all tools should be prevented from moving about, otherwise cutting edges and sharp points can be damaged. Some useful tips for protecting tools are given below.

- Planes should have blades retracted before being stored.

- Protective covers can be made or purchased for saw teeth.

- Most chisels are provided with plastic end covers when purchased and should be used. A strong, purpose-made chisel roll is also useful when storing in a tool bag or box.

- The sharp points on twist bits should always be protected as, unlike chisels, reshaping is difficult.

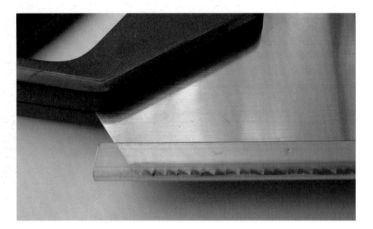

Saw teeth covered for protection

Chisel with plastic end cover

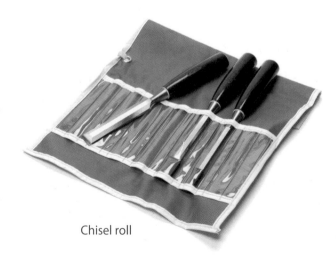

Chisel roll

Maintenance of hand tools

Good-quality hand tools will last a lifetime if well looked after. All metal tools need to be kept free of rust, which can be achieved by rubbing them over occasionally with an oily cloth to preserve a light film of oil.

Saw setting and sharpening

Most modern saws are of the hard-point type and cannot be re-sharpened. For these, replacement is the only option. Older saws do require periodic maintenance, the frequency depending on the amount of work they do.

There are four stages in returning a saw to tip-top condition:

1. topping
2. shaping
3. setting
4. sharpening.

For all four operations a pair of saw stocks is required to hold the saw blade tight with the teeth uppermost. These can be made by clamping two suitable lengths of softwood either side of the saw blade in a vice.

Saw blade held in saw stocks

There are then various saw files available, designed for the different tasks.

Topping or levelling the teeth is completed by running a flat saw file along the top of the teeth. A simple jig to help with this can be made of hardwood, with a slot cut in it to hold the file at right angles. The wood can then rub against the blade to ensure that the file remains flat on the teeth.

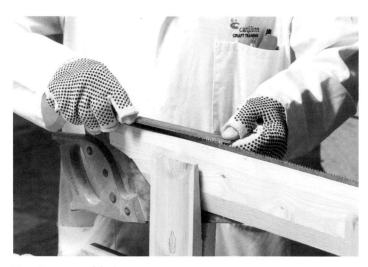

Topping a saw blade

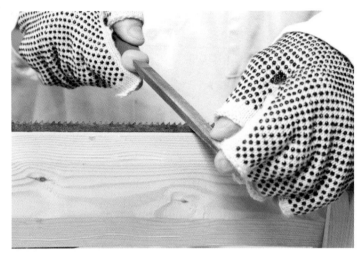

Shaping a saw blade

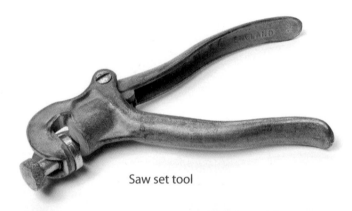

Saw set tool

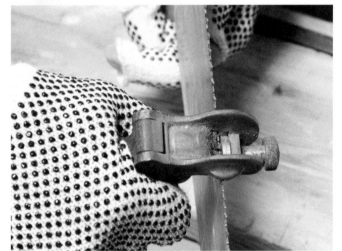

Setting saw teeth

Shaping is undertaken with a saw file designed for the task. This restores the teeth to their original shape and size. The aim is to have all teeth with the same angle, or pitch.

Teeth are then set individually to the required angle to give the saw blade clearance in its kerf. This is easiest with a tool called a saw set, which is used to bend the tips of the teeth to the correct angle.

The tool is operated by pre-selecting the required points per 25 mm for the saw blade being sharpened. Starting at one end, the tool is then positioned over a tooth and the handles squeezed. This will automatically set the angle of the tooth tip correctly. The procedure is repeated for each alternate tooth and then repeated from the opposite side for the teeth angled in the other direction.

Sharpening puts a cutting edge on the teeth. It is completed with a triangular file, holding the file at an angle to suit the type of saw blade and lightly filing each alternative 'V' between the teeth three times. When arriving at the end of the saw the blade is turned through 180° and the process repeated for the other teeth.

Rip saw teeth are filed at right angles across the blade to create a chisel effect. Cross cut saw teeth are normally filed with the file at approximately 70°, sharpening both the front of one tooth and the back of the next at the same time.

Planes and chisels

New plane or chisel blades will come with a bevel of 25° on the cutting edge. This has to be sharpened (honed) to an angle of 30° before use and regularly re-sharpened to this angle. See Figure 6.4.

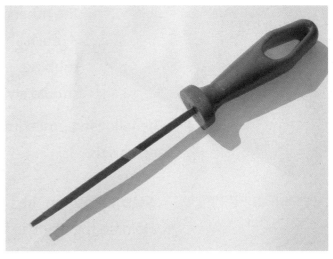

File used for sharpening saw teeth

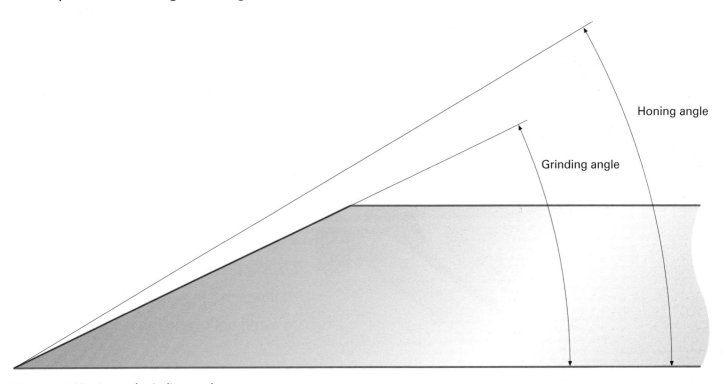

Figure 6.4 Honing and grinding angles

Sharpening is best done by hand using an oilstone. These come in coarse, medium or fine grades, often as a combination with two of them on opposite sides. Tool sharpening should always be completed on a fine grade, the others only used for reshaping. Stones can be cleaned with a brush and paraffin and should be re-levelled occasionally by rubbing on a sheet of glass with carborundum paste. The stone should always be kept oiled during sharpening.

The following procedures will enable you to sharpen the blades of planes and chisels.

Combination oilstone

Step 1 Position the blade. Holding the blade in both hands, position its grinding angle flat on the stone. This means the blade will be at an angle of 25°. Then raise the back end up a further 5°, so that the tool is now at the correct sharpened angle of 30°.

Step 2 Grind an initial burr. Slowly move the blade forwards and backwards until a small burr has formed at the cutting edge. Make sure that you use the entire oilstone surface, to avoid hollowing the stone.

Step 3 Form a wire edge. Remove the burr by holding the blade perfectly flat and drawing the blade towards you once or twice to form a wire edge on the end of the blade.

Step 4 Remove the wire edge. The wire edge can be removed by drawing the blade over a piece of waste timber. Now inspect the sharpened edge and, if you can still see a dull white line, then repeat Steps 2 to 4.

Two additional tips specifically for sharpening planes are:

1. Hold the blade at a slight angle to the line of the stone. This helps to ensure that the whole of the cutting edge makes contact with the stone.

2. To ensure that the cap iron fits neatly with the blade, also use the oilstone to flatten and straighten its edge.

Sharpening twist bits

The life of a twist bit is shortened every time it is sharpened, so only sharpen when necessary. Twist bits can come with or without spurs. See Figure 6.5 for a twist bit with spurs. The spurs are the first to become dull, followed by the cutters. If the screw point becomes blunt the twist bit must be replaced.

Tang

Shank

Spur

Cutting edge

Feed screw

Cutting edge

Twist

Spur

Figure 6.5 Parts of a twist bit

Twist bits can be sharpened with various shaped files, the shape depending on the type of twist bit.

Sharpening a twist bit with a triangular file

Sharpening a twist bit with a flat file

Power tools

By the end of this section you will have the basic knowledge to begin to use portable powered hand tools safely but, as with any tool, you will need practice to become competent in their use.

These tools are covered by legislation and you must fully comply with the following:

- *The Provision and Use of Working Equipment Regulations 1998*
- *The Abrasive Wheels Regulations 1974*
- *The Protection of Eye Regulations 1974*
- *The Health and Safety at Work Act 1974.*

Summary of power tool types

The following power tools are described in this section:

- power drills
- powered planer

Remember

You must receive training and obtain permission before using any power tool and an instructor must be present while you carry out the operation

- routers

- portable circular saws

- chop saws

- jig saws

- sanders

- cordless tools.

First we will cover:

- safety issues common to all power tools

- power supplies

- power tool maintenance.

Safety first

If used correctly, powered hand tools can save time, money and effort. Skill in using them comes only through training and experience – it cannot be picked up on site. All the safety precautions listed at the start of this chapter for hand tools apply but there are additional risks with power tools, especially portable ones.

Although each type of power tool has its own safe working procedures the following basic rules apply to ANY portable powered tools.

- Only use powered hand tools if you have been authorised to do so and have been taught how to use them correctly.

- Never use a power tool without permission.

- If you are unfamiliar with the equipment, read the instruction booklet and practise using the tool. Go ahead with the job only when you are sure you can do so safely and be certain of producing good results.

- Always select the correct tool for the work in hand. Check that it is in good condition and that any blade or cutter has been fitted correctly. IF IN DOUBT, ASK SOMEONE WITH EXPERIENCE.

Extension lead on drum

- Ensure that the tool and power supply are compatible. Do not mix voltages; i.e. 110 V tools must only be used on 110 V supplies.

- Ensure that plugs, wires, extension leads etc. are in good condition. If not, do not use the tool.

- Ensure that any extension leads are fully uncoiled before use, as they can easily overheat.

- Never carry any tool by its lead.

- Always use fitted safety guards correctly, as these have been designed with your safety in mind. Never use a tool without them.

- Do not let others touch tools or extension cords while in use and disconnect tools when finished with.

- Never put a tool down until all moving parts have stopped and, before making any adjustments, disconnect a tool from its power supply or switch off at source. Just switching off at the tool is not good enough.

- Should a tool not operate, do not tamper with it but report the matter immediately to your supervisor. Repairs should only be carried out by a competent person.

- Wear goggles when there is any danger of flying particles. A dust mask or respirator, ear protectors and safety helmet may also be necessary.

- Report any accident (or 'near miss') to your supervisor, whether or not it results in injury to yourself or others.

- If you are injured, even when it is a minor wound or scratch, get immediate first aid treatment.

- Guard against electric shock. Hence, never allow electrical equipment to become damp or wet and never use electrical equipment in damp or wet conditions.

Safety tip

Tools cannot be careless but you can, so do the job safely – it is quicker in the long run

Power supplies

For tools that need to be connected to a power supply this can be 240 V (normal domestic mains supply) or 110 V (as a reduced voltage via a transformer). The use of tools at 240 V is not recommended, as any electrical shock from the tool at this voltage can be fatal. Only tools using a supply of 110 V, reduced from 240 V through a transformer, can be used on construction sites.

All power tools are now made with double insulation and should be stamped with a double insulation sign and a kite mark. See Figures 6.6 and 6.7.

Transformer used to reduce voltage from 240 V to 110 V

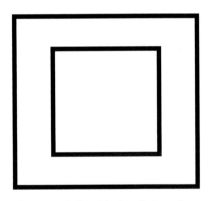

Figure 6.6 Double insulation sign

Figure 6.7 BS Kitemark

Safety tip

Just because safety information is displayed it does not mean there is no danger of electrical shock. Tools must be correct for purpose and used in accordance with manufacturers' guidance

Power tool maintenance

Most modern power tools are designed to operate over a long period of time with minimum maintenance. However, regular attention to powered hand tools improves safety and ensures that they work efficiently.

In particular they should be cleaned regularly (especially important with cutting and abrasive tools because the dust produced can easily damage the motor). This may mean a daily clean for tools in constant use.

Find out

What does double insulation mean?

Information for cleaning and maintenance of power tools can be found in the instruction manual for each machine. This will clearly state which actions should and can be undertaken by you and which must be undertaken by authorised repair agents. Not only are they trained, and have the necessary specialist tools to complete the work correctly, but unauthorised repairs will invalidate any guarantee.

Regular visual checks must be made to spot damage to the tool, leads and plugs. Make sure that the ventilation slots are clear. Any damaged parts should be replaced before use, but only attempt this if it is a user-authorised task and you have been trained to carry it out.

Power drills

Power drills are highly versatile and can be used with different bits, not just to drill holes in a range of materials but to drive or remove screws, cut circular holes with a saw cutter, or buff and polish. Various designs of chuck are available for rapid interchange of bits, the chuck size being matched to the power of the drill.

The simplest power drills just operate at a single speed. However, most drills today come with additional capabilities, which may include one or more of the following:

- dual speed, the slower speed for use when boring into brickwork or masonry using a tipped drill bit

- variable speed, controlled by trigger pressure

- reverse action, i.e. able to operate clockwise or anticlockwise and mainly used for driving or withdrawing screws

- percussion or hammer action, primarily for brickwork or masonry

- torque control, particularly useful to avoid over tightening screws, nuts or bolts.

Choosing the most suitable drill and drill bit for the job depends on:

- the type of material that needs to be drilled

- size of holes required or task to be completed

- how often the drill will be used.

Wood boring flat bits

Various twist drills for wood, masonry or metal

Some of the common types of power drill are described below.

Palm grip drill

The most common and versatile of the electric drills, palm grip drills can be used to carry out work on timber, steel, alloy and masonry. Dust should be cleaned from bore holes at regular intervals.

They are available with single or twin speeds but may have other options as listed on page 168.

Back handle drill

The back handle drill is a heavy-duty version of the palm grip drill. They have a larger chuck, allowing holes of greater diameter to be bored. They can also withstand long periods of heavy pressure but, as with the palm grip drill, dust should be cleaned from bore holes at regular intervals.

They are available in single-, two- and four-speed models but may also have other options as listed on page 168. A handle can be attached to give greater control during use.

Rotary percussion (hammer) drills

Hammer drills have a percussive hammer effect which enables them to bore into hard materials. This percussive action is optional and is brought into operation by means of a switch. It is particularly effective for drilling into masonry or concrete. A depth gauge can be fitted to the side handle to provide accuracy where required.

110 V hammer drill

Good practice when using drills

- Always tighten the chuck securely.

- Take advantage of speed selection. Start drilling into hard materials at slow speed and increase gradually.

- Slow down the rate of speed just prior to breaking through the surface, particularly metals, to avoid snatching and twisting.

- Keep drill vents clear to maintain adequate ventilation.

- Use sharp drill bits at all times.

- Apply as much pressure as possible, consistent with the size of the drill. This is more important than speed, as it is essential to keep the edge of the drill biting into the material rather than let it rub on the bottom of the hole.

- Especially when using larger drill sizes, make a pilot hole with a smaller drill. For example, for a 13 mm hole use a 10 mm or 12 mm drill and then open this out with a 13 mm drill.

- Check carbon brushes regularly. Excessive sparking indicates excessive wear or a possible short circuit. Report this to a supervisor.

- Make sure all plug connections are secure and correct.

- Keep all cables clear of the cutting area during use.

- Keep holes clear of dust. Drills should be withdrawn from holes at intervals, as an accumulation of dust not only causes overheating but also tends to blunt the drill bit.

Bad practice when using drills

- Never use a drill designed to operate with a 3-wire source (i.e. live, neutral and earth) on a 2-wire supply (i.e. live and neutral only). Always connect an earth.

- Do not use a drill bit with a bent spindle.

- Do not exceed the manufacturers' recommended maximum capacities for drill sizes on appropriate materials.

- Do not use high speed steel (HSS) bits without cooling or lubrication.

- Never use a hole saw cutter without the pilot cutter.

- Do not cool the hot point of a drill by dipping it in water, as this will crack the tip.

Powered planers

Powered planers are invaluable for removing large amounts of waste wood, especially on site. With large models it is possible to remove up to 3 mm in one pass. The machine has an adjustable depth gauge to allow the greater depths needed for rebating to be achieved.

Depth grip knob and depth of cut adjustment

Dust bag connection

Adjustable depth gauge

Fence securing screw

On/off button

110 V powered planer

The sequence of operations is similar to using a hand plane. One surface is planed square and then one edge is planed square to this dressed face. The wood can then be dressed to the required width and thickness.

Remember:

- Check that the cutters are sharp to prevent overloading the motor and producing a poor finish.

- Secure material to be planed in a vice or on a workbench against a stop.

- Make adjustments to the planer before connecting to the power supply.

- Do not put the machine down until the cutters have stopped rotating.

- Wear ear, eye and nose/mouth protection.

- All machines should be checked on a regular basis by a qualified electrical engineer but the operator should check the visual condition of the planer, voltage, power cable and plug.

Routers

The router is a very versatile machine. Like a power drill it has a chuck able to take different sizes of bit, the size depending on the power of the machine. However, the variety of bits and cutters that can be fitted is very wide and many different operations can be completed, including:

- cutting straight, curved and moulded grooves

- cutting slots and recesses

- rebating

- beading and moulding

- dovetailing

- laminate trimming.

Routers used by carpenters and joiners on site are most likely to be:

- heavy-duty routers

- heavy-duty plunge routers.

With the heavy-duty router the cutter projects from the base and great care must be taken to feed it gradually into the material to prevent it from snatching.

Most routers now are of the plunge type, where the cutter is brought downwards into contact with the material to be cut and then withdrawn out of the material when downward pressure is released. This is made possible by two spring-loaded plungers, which are fitted to each side of the machine.

Spring-loaded plunger

Cable

Grip handle

Depth setting gauge

Chuck with cutter

Adjustable fence

110 V heavy-duty plunge router

Both types are capable of producing excellent finishes, mainly due to the very high speed of the machine, but these speeds demand great control and concentration from the operator.

Router bits for grooving and trimming

Router bits for edging

For general work router bits and cutters are made of high-speed steel (HSS), but carbide-tipped bits and cutters offer a longer cutting life. Edging bits have a guide pin or roller which allows the cutter to follow an accurate path without biting into the material.

Routers come with various items as standard, including guides and fences, but some useful additional accessories are:

- trammel point and arm, used for cutting circles
- dovetail kit for producing dovetail joints
- bench or table stand that converts the router into a small spindle moulder
- trimming attachment to cut veneered edging.

Remember:

- Secure the work piece before commencing work.
- Make sure the cutter/bit is free to rotate.
- Allow the machine to reach its maximum speed before making the first trial cut (into waste material).
- Make any cut from left to right.
- Move the router quickly enough to make a continuous cut but never overload the motor (listen to the drone) by pushing too fast, which will blunt the cutter and burn the wood.
- At the end of each operation switch off the motor. The cutter/bit should be freed from the work and allowed to stop revolving before being left unattended.
- Goggles or safety glasses must always be worn as well as other appropriate items of PPE.
- All machines should be checked on a regular basis by a qualified electrical engineer but the operator should check the visual condition of the router, voltage, power cable and plug.

Portable circular saws

Portable circular saws are mainly used for cross cutting and ripping, but can also be used for bevel cuts, grooves and rebates. They can be used to cut a wide variety of materials:

- timber, including softwood and hardwood

- manufactured boards, including plywood, chipboard, blockboard, laminboard and fibre board

- plastic laminates.

We will refer mainly to timber below, but the same principles apply to all materials.

Before use the saw should be adjusted so that, when cutting normally, the blade will only just break through the underside of the timber. This is achieved by releasing a locking device, which controls the movement of the base plate in relation to the amount of blade exposed.

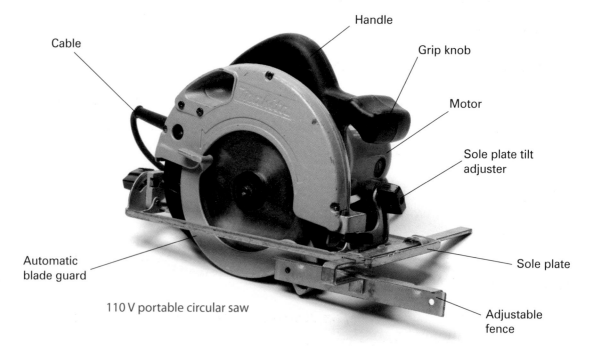

110 V portable circular saw

A detachable fence is supplied for ripping. For bevel cutting the base tilts up to 45° on a lockable quadrant arm. The telescopic saw guard, covering the exposed blade, will automatically spring back when the cut is complete.

Remember:

- Wear appropriate PPE.

- Any timber being cut should be securely held, clamped or fixed, making sure that fixings are clear of the saw cut.

- Ensure the power cable is clear of the cutting action.

- Always use both hands on the saw handles, as this reduces the risk of the free hand making contact with the cutting edge of the blade.

- The saw should be allowed to reach maximum speed before starting to cut, and should not be stopped or restarted in the timber.

- At the finish of the cut, keep the saw suspended away from the body until the blade stops revolving.

- Disconnect the machine before making any adjustments or when not in use. It is not sufficient just to switch off the machine.

- Do not overload the saw by forcing it into the material.

- Keep saw blades sharp.

- Always work in safe, dry conditions.

- All machines should be checked on a regular basis by a qualified electrical engineer but the operator should check the visual condition of the saw, voltage, power cable and plug.

Chop saws

Chop saws have a circular blade rotating in a housing and a fixed bed on to which items to be cut can be fixed. The blade can be pulled down on to the work to cut it.

They can be fitted with different blades, depending on the material to be cut and the task. These can then be set to cut:

- square at 90° in both directions

- mitres at any angle up to 45°

Remember

When cutting angles or bevels, the machine's effective cutting depth will be reduced

- bevels up to 45°

- compound bevels up to 45° (i.e. two angles in one cut, both face side and face edge of the material).

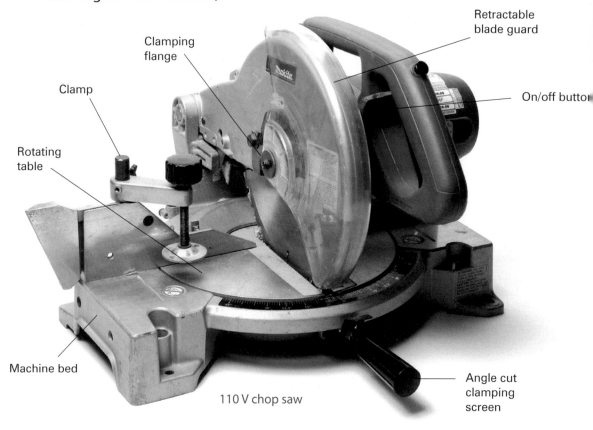

110 V chop saw

Chop saws are capable of causing serious injury and should be securely fixed to a workbench, or purpose-made stand, and at a height that is comfortable for the operator. The built-in bed tends to be short, so side extension tables or trestles must be used to support longer lengths of timber when cutting.

Remember:

- Because of the high risk of injury when using this type of machine, safety must be a priority. READ and understand the manufacturer's instructions before using the machine.

- Chop saws are available for 240 V or 110 V, so be sure to connect the machine to the correct voltage.

- Ensure that cables are clear of the machine's moving parts, and are not causing obstruction to the materials to be cut, or in a position that may cause a person to trip.

- Check the machine for damage, wear and operating functions before use.

- Complete all machine settings (blade changes, angles, stops, guards, fences etc.) when disconnected from the power supply. Blade changing must be carried out by a competent person and in conjunction with the manufacturer's instructions.

- Secure the work piece firmly to the machine bed. Hands should not be used to hold material in place while cutting.

- Concentrate on what you are doing. Keep an eye on the work being cut and NEVER allow your hands to be closer to the blade than 150mm.

- Do not force the machine to cut but allow it to cut at its own speed.

- Always use the recommended blade (blade size, tooth type, HSS, TCT etc.). Do not use blunt, wrongly set, or buckled blades.

- Wear protective clothing and equipment suitable for the type of work.

Jig saws

Powered jig saws have a reciprocating blade, which moves up and down at high speed to cut timber or other material. A range of interchangeable saw blades is available.

Jig saws are mainly used for cutting slots and curves but can also be used for straight cutting, usually with the aid of a guide attachment or fence to aid accuracy. Care must be taken to select the correct blade and speed setting, e.g. fast for wood, slow for metals.

Cutting can start at one edge of the material or, if cutting slots or holes, the saw blade can be inserted through a pre-drilled hole in the material to be removed.

On/off switch

Speed selector

Guard

Blade

Base plate

110 V jig saw

Remember:

- Always change or adjust the blades with the machine disconnected.

- Always allow the machine to run with ease, never force it around a curve.

- Select the correct blade for the task.

- Always position the machine before cutting; and avoid re-entry with an activated blade.

- Stop and allow the blade to become stationary before withdrawing it from the work piece.

- Use lubricants when cutting metals; oils for mild steel and paraffin for cutting aluminium.

- Never allow a cable to be in front of the cutter during use.

- All machines should be checked on a regular basis by a qualified electrical engineer but the operator should check the visual condition of the saw, voltage, power cable and plug.

Sanders

There are several types of powered sander available, designed for specific tasks. The two that you are most likely to use in carpentry and joinery work are the belt and orbital sander.

All sanders produce large quantities of dust, which can be harmful if breathed in. Always use any dust collection facility available with the machine and, if in doubt, wear a mask or respirator.

Belt sanders

Belt sanders are designed for fairly heavy-duty work and, using a coarse abrasive, can quickly remove large amounts of wood or other material like old paint. However, they can also be used to achieve a fine finish, depending on the abrasive belt used.

Dust bag connector

Handle

Grip knob

Cable

Front adjustable roller

Tracking switch

110 V belt sander

Grit size	Grade
20 grit and less	Very coarse
24 to 30 grit	Coarse
40 to 60 grit	Medium
80 to 150 grit	Fine
150 grit and over	Very fine

Table 6.2 Grades of abrasive belt

The fineness or coarseness of the grit used on the abrasive belt is graded according to size, as shown in Table 6.2.

Belt sanders tend to produce large amounts of dust. To compensate for this a dust bag is fitted, which collects the dust while at the same time allowing air to escape.

Orbital sanders

Orbital sanders use abrasive sheets, held to the base of the machine by spring clips situated at the front and rear of the sander. When the machine is switched on the base moves in 3 mm diameter orbits and, with care, a good quality finish can be produced.

A wide range of grit sizes is available but, unlike the belt sander, they should be used for finishing only and not used for removing waste material. They do not have any built-in dust collection facility, so a mask or respirator should be used.

Safety tip

Use only belts or sheets manufactured specifically for the machine, as using makeshift belts or sheets leads to accidents

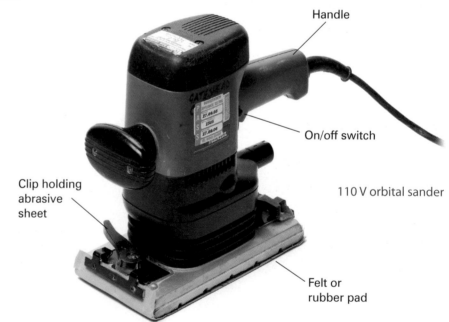

Handle

On/off switch

110 V orbital sander

Clip holding abrasive sheet

Felt or rubber pad

Cordless tools

An increasing range of battery operated (i.e. cordless) tools is becoming available, including drills, jig saws, sanders, screwdrivers etc. They are particularly convenient in situations where the mains power supply is not easily accessible, or even not available. There is no cable to cause problems when working some distance from a power point or hanging down when working at height.

Cordless tools usually have the same chuck options and can carry out all the functions of tools connected to mains power. However, the heavier the task the more rapidly batteries will discharge. Battery power is indicated by the voltage rating, e.g. 10 V, 12 V etc. – the higher voltage tools more suited for heavy-duty work.

Batteries are rechargeable and this generally only takes a couple of hours. However, it pays to carry a spare, which can be used while waiting for the spent one to recharge. Battery life is considerably shortened if this is not done correctly, so always use the charger purchased with the tool.

Cordless drill

Be careful, when the battery is not connected to either tool or charger, that nothing is allowed to touch the terminals, especially anything metal, as this will cause a short and probably destroy the battery.

Powered screwdrivers

Powered screwdrivers are really a specialised, simple powered drill, only available in a cordless form and specifically designed to drive or remove screws. They generally do not have removable batteries, so the whole tool is inserted into a purpose-built charger.

Cordless screwdriver

They are only designed to operate at slow speeds and should have variable torque control so that screws are not over-tightened. The chuck can take a full range of screwdriver bits.

Their shape enables them to be used in areas that would be difficult with a power drill.

FAQ

Can I use a 110 V tool with a 240 V power supply?

Yes and no. You cannot plug a 110 V tool into a 240 V socket simply because the plug and socket are different. If you use a transformer, you can use a 100 V power tool with a 240 V power supply as the transformer will 'knock down' the supply.

Do I always have to turn off a power tool to make an adjustment?

Yes, of course. Not only must you turn the machine off, you must also make sure it is removed from the power supply. If you don't, when you are making the adjustment the tool may be accidentally turned on and you could be very seriously injured.

Why do I have to fully unwind a reel-up extension cable when I use one with a power tool? Surely the unwound cable could cause an accident.

An extension cable left wound around the reel can overheat and cause a fire. Unwind the cable fully but, to prevent an accident, make sure the cable is not lying in the area where people will be walking.

On the job: Using power tools

Will is about to use a jig saw. What safety checks would you advise Will to carry out before he uses the jig saw? Can you think of any safety checks Will should carry out whilst he is using the jig saw? Finally, when Will has finished with the jig saw, is there anything you would recommend that he does?

Knowledge check

1. Name three types of rules which could be used by carpenters/ joiners. State the advantages of each.

2. What are the following used for: sliding bevel; tri-square; combination square?

3. State the uses of the following: smoothing plane; rebate plane; plough plane.

4. Name four types of bit that can be used with a ratchet brace.

5. Name and state the uses of five different types of saw.

6. Sketch the following: bevelled edge chisel; mortise chisel; paring chisel.

7. What do the kite mark and double square symbol indicate?

8. Name three portable power tools and state a task for which each can be used.

9. What type of work is a percussion drill best suited for?

10. What is the advantage of using a two-speed drill?

11. Why is it necessary to secure material being cut with a portable saw?

12. How are cordless tools powered?

13. What three things should always be checked by the operator before using a portable power tool?

14. Why is it important to maintain and clean power tools regularly?

15. State three points to remember when using a portable circular saw.

16. How are abrasive sanding belts graded?

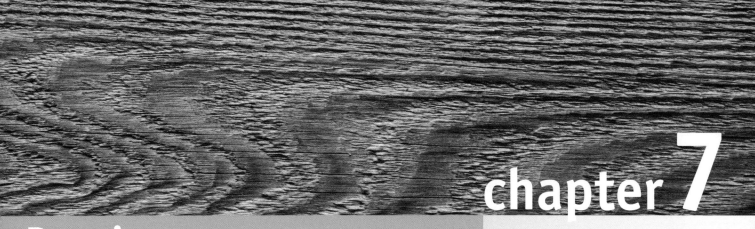

chapter 7

Drawings

OVERVIEW

Drawings are the best way of communicating detailed and often complex information from the designer to all those concerned with a job or project. They are therefore one of the main methods of communication used in the building industry.

Drawings are part of the legal contract between client and contractor and mistakes, either in design or interpretation of the design, can be costly. Details relating to drawings must follow guidelines by the British Standards Institute: *BS 1192 Construction Drawing Practice*. This standardises drawings and allows everyone to understand them.

This chapter will help you to understand the basic principles involved in producing, using and reading drawings correctly.

The following topics will be covered:

- Types of drawing
- Drawing equipment
- Scales, symbols and abbreviations
- Datum points
- Types of projection
- Specifications.

Types of drawing

Working drawings

Working drawings are scale drawings showing plans, elevations, sections, details and location of a proposed construction. They can be classified as:

- location drawings

- component range drawings

- assembly or detail drawings.

Location drawings

Location drawings include block plans and site plans.

Block plans identify the proposed site by giving a bird's eye view of the site in relation to the surrounding area. An example is shown in Figure 7.1.

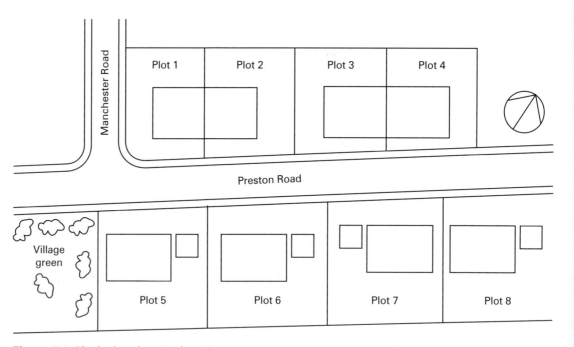

Figure 7.1 Block plan showing location

Site plans give the position of the proposed building and the general layout of the roads, services, drainage etc. on site. An example is shown in Figure 7.2.

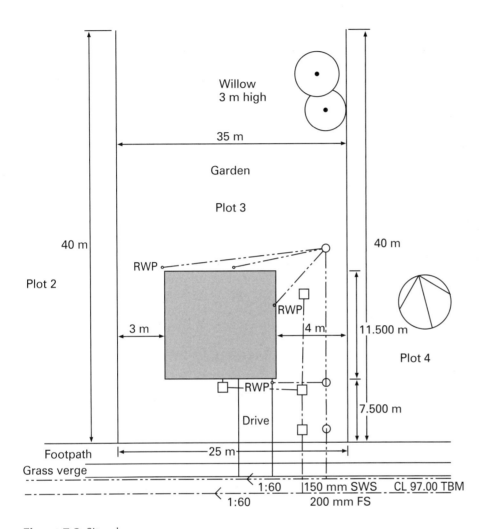

Figure 7.2 Site plan

Component range drawings

Component range drawings show the basic sizes and reference system of a standard range of components produced by a manufacturer. This helps in selecting components suitable for a task and available off-the-shelf. An example is shown in Figure 7.3.

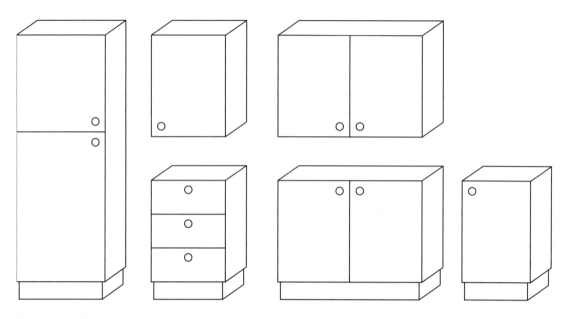

Figure 7.3 Component range drawing

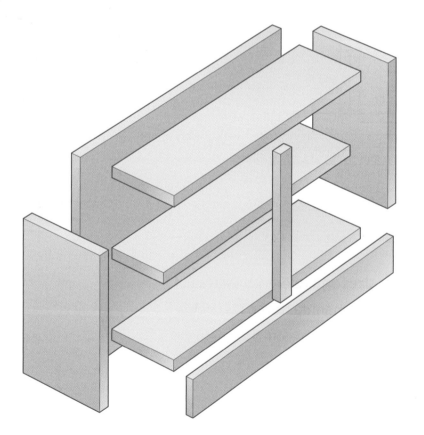

Figure 7.4 Assembly drawing

Assembly or detail drawings

Assembly or detail drawings give all the information required to manufacture a given component. They show how things are put together and what the finished item will look like. An example is shown in Figure 7.4.

Title panels

Every drawing must have a title panel, which is normally located in the bottom right-hand corner of each drawing sheet. See Figure 7.5 for an example. The information contained in the panel is relevant to that drawing only and contains such information as:

- drawing title
- scale used
- draughtsman's name
- drawing number/project number
- company name
- job/project title
- date of drawing
- revision notes
- projection type.

ARCHITECTS	CLIENT
Peterson, Thompson Associates 237 Cumberland Way Ipswich IP3 7FT Tel: 01234 567891 Fax: 09876 543210 Email: enquiries@pta.co.uk	Carillion Development
	JOB TITLE Appleford Drive Felixstowe 4 bed detached
DRAWING TITLE Plan – garage	**SCALE:** 1:50
	DRAWING NO: 2205-06
DATE: 27.08.2006	**DRAWN BY:** RW

Figure 7.5 Typical title panel

Remember

It is important to check the date of a drawing to make sure the most up-to-date version is being used, as revisions to drawings can be frequent

Drawing equipment

A good quality set of drawing equipment is required when producing drawings. It should include:

- set squares
- protractors
- compasses
- dividers
- scale rule
- pencils
- eraser
- drawing board
- tee square.

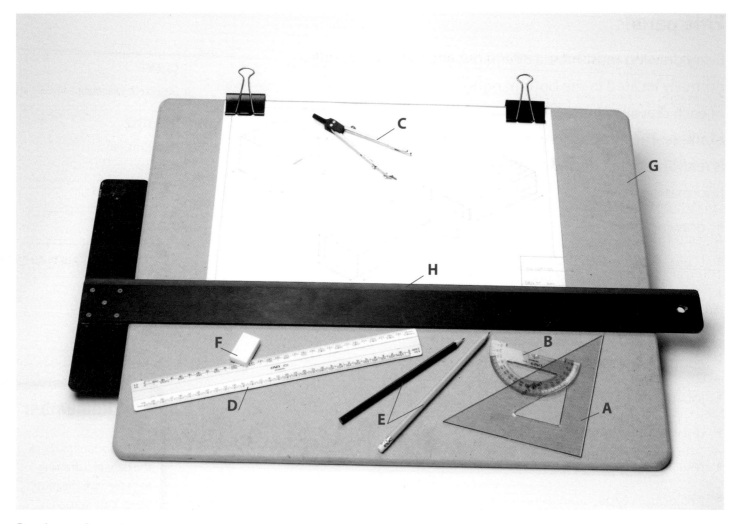

Drawing equipment

Set square

Two set squares are required, one a 45° set square and the other a 60° / 30° set square. These are used to draw vertical and inclined lines. A 45° set square (A) is shown in the photograph.

Protractor

Protractors (B) are used for setting out and measuring angles.

Compass and dividers

Compasses (C) are used to draw circles and arcs. Dividers (not shown) are used for transferring measurements and dividing lines.

Scale rules

A scale rule that contains the following scales is to be recommended:

1:5/1:50   1:10/1:100   1:20/1:200   1:250/1:2500

An example (D) is shown in the photo.

Pencils

Two pencils (E) are required:

- HB for printing and sketching
- 2H or 3H for drawing.

Eraser

A vinyl or rubber eraser (F) is required for alterations or corrections to pencil lines.

Drawing boards

Drawing boards (G) are made from a smooth flat surface material, with edges truly square and parallel.

T-square

The T-square (H) is used mainly for drawing horizontal lines.

Did you know?

Set squares, protractors and rules should be occasionally washed in warm soapy water

Scales, symbols and abbreviations

Scales in common use

In order to draw a building on a drawing sheet, the building must be reduced in size. This is called a scale drawing.

The preferred scales for use in building drawings are shown in Table 7.1.

Type of drawing	Scales
Block plans	1:2500, 1:1250
Site plans	1:500, 1:200
General location drawings	1: 200, 1:100, 1:50
Range drawings	1:100, 1:50, 1:20
Detail drawings	1:10, 1:5, 1:1
Assembly drawings	1:20, 1:10, 1:5

Table 7.1 Preferred scales for building drawings

These scales mean that, for example, on a block plan drawn to 1:2500, one millimetre on the plan would represent 2500 mm (or 2.5 m) on the actual building. Some other examples are:

- On a scale of 1:50, 10 mm represents 500 mm.

- On a scale of 1:100, 10 mm represents 1000 mm (1.0 m).

- On a scale of 1:200, 30 mm represents 6000 mm (6.0 m).

Why not try these for yourself?

- On a scale of 1:50, 40 mm represents:…………

- On a scale of 1:200, 70 mm represents:…………

- On a scale of 1:500, 40 mm represents:………….

The use of scales can be easily mastered with a little practice.

Remember

A scale is merely a convenient way of reducing a drawing in size

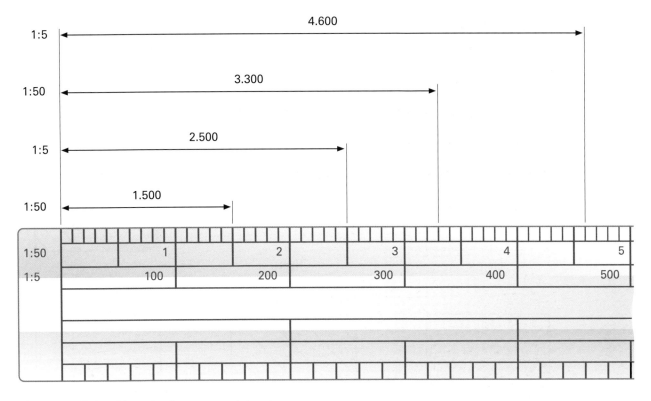

Figure 7.6 Rule with scales for maps and drawings

Variations caused through printing or copying will affect the accuracy of drawings. Hence, although measurements can be read from drawings using a rule with common scales marked, it is recommended that you work to written instructions and measurements wherever possible.

A rule marked with scales used in drawings or maps is illustrated in Figure 7.6.

Symbols and abbreviations

The use of symbols and abbreviations in the building industry enables the maximum amount of information to be included on a drawing sheet in a clear way. Figure 7.7 shows some recommended drawing symbols for a range of building materials.

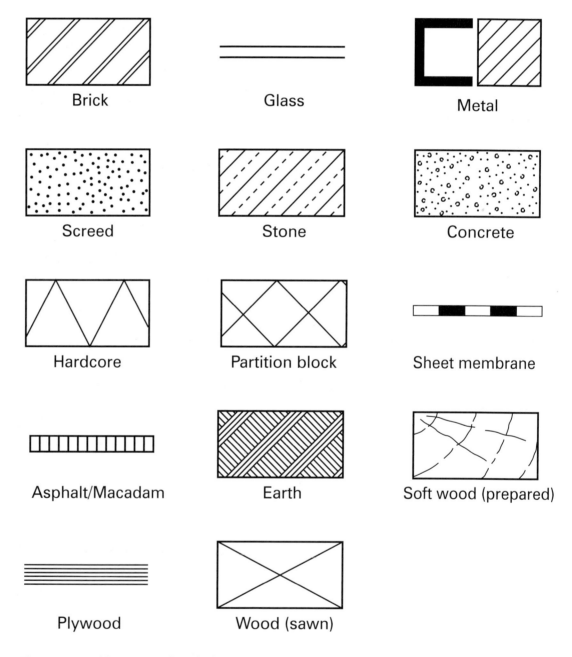

Figure 7.7 Building material symbols

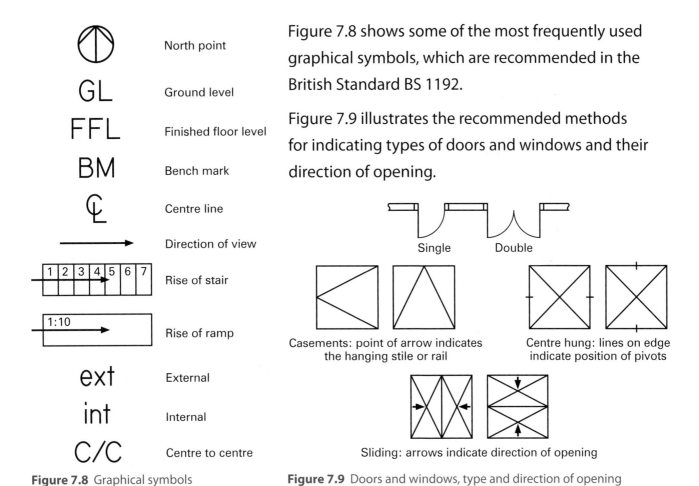

Figure 7.8 shows some of the most frequently used graphical symbols, which are recommended in the British Standard BS 1192.

Figure 7.9 illustrates the recommended methods for indicating types of doors and windows and their direction of opening.

North point

GL — Ground level

FFL — Finished floor level

BM — Bench mark

Centre line

Direction of view

Rise of stair

Rise of ramp

ext — External

int — Internal

C/C — Centre to centre

Figure 7.8 Graphical symbols

Single Double

Casements: point of arrow indicates the hanging stile or rail

Centre hung: lines on edge indicate position of pivots

Sliding: arrows indicate direction of opening

Figure 7.9 Doors and windows, type and direction of opening

Table 7.2 lists some standard abbreviations used on drawings.

Item	Abbreviation	Item	Abbreviation
Airbrick	AB	Cast iron	CI
Asbestos	abs	Cement	ct
Bitumen	bit	Column	col
Boarding	bdg	Concrete	conc
Brickwork	bwk	Cupboard	cpd
Building	bldg	Damp proof course	DPC

Table 7.2 Standard abbreviations used on drawings (*continued opposite*)

Item	Abbreviation	Item	Abbreviation
Damp proof membrane	DPM	Polyvinyl acetate	PVA
Drawing	dwg	Polyvinyl chloride	PVC
Foundation	fnd	Reinforced concrete	RC
Hardboard	hdbd	Satin chrome	SC
Hardcore	hc	Satin anodised aluminium	SAA
Hardwood	hwd	Softwood	swd
Insulation	insul	Stainless steel	SS
Joist	jst	Tongue and groove	T&G
Mild steel	MS	Wrought iron	WI
Plasterboard	pbd		

Table 7.2 Standard abbreviations used on drawings (cont'd)

FAQ

Why not just write the full words on a drawing?

This would take up too much space and clutter the drawing, making it difficult to read.

Datum points

The need to apply levels is required at the beginning of the construction process and continues right up to the completion of the building. The whole country is mapped in detail and the Ordnance Survey place datum points (bench marks) at suitable locations from which all other levels can be taken.

Ordnance bench mark (OBM)

OBMs are found cut into locations such as walls of churches or public buildings. The height of the OBM can be found on the relevant Ordnance Survey map or by contacting the local authority planning office. Figure 7.10 shows the normal symbol used, though it can appear as shown in Figure 7.11.

Figure 7.10 Ordnance Bench Mark

Site datum

It is necessary to have a reference point on site to which all levels can be related. This is known as the site datum. The site datum is usually positioned at a convenient height, such as finished floor level (FFL).

The site datum itself must be set in relation to some known point, preferably an OBM and must be positioned where it cannot be moved.

Figure 7.11 shows a site datum and OBM, illustrating the height relationship between them.

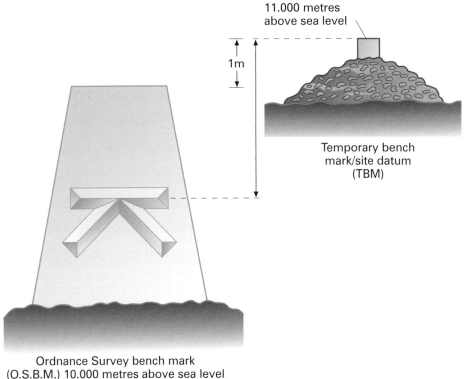

11.000 metres above sea level

1m

Temporary bench mark/site datum (TBM)

Ordnance Survey bench mark (O.S.B.M.) 10.000 metres above sea level

Figure 7.11 Site datum and OBM

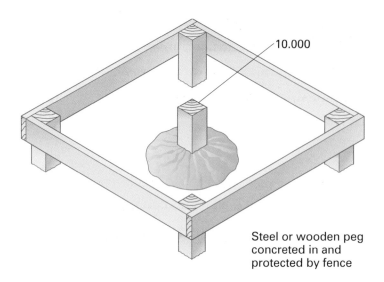

10.000

Steel or wooden peg concreted in and protected by fence

Figure 7.12 Datum peg suitably protected

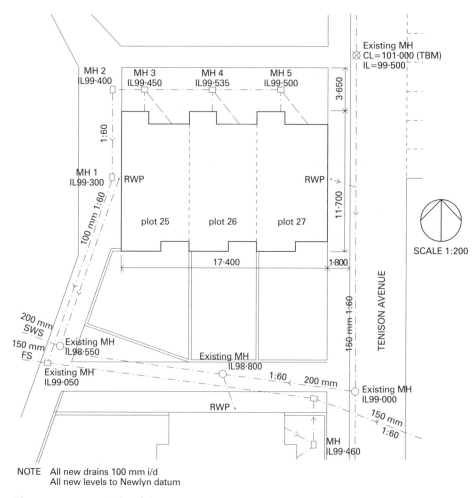

Figure 7.13 Example of datum points shown on a drawing

If no suitable position can be found a datum peg may be used, its accurate height transferred by surveyors from an OBM, as with the site datum. It is normally a piece of timber or steel rod positioned accurately to the required level and then set in concrete. However, it must be adequately protected and is generally surrounded by a small fence for protection, as shown in Figure 7.12.

Temporary bench mark (TBM)

When an OBM cannot be conveniently found near a site it is usual for a temporary bench mark (TBM) to be set up at a height suitable for the site. Its accurate height is transferred by surveyors from the nearest convenient OBM.

All other site datum points can now be set up from this TBM using datum points, which are shown on the site drawings. Figure 7.13 shows datum points on drawings.

Types of projection

Building, engineering and similar drawings aim to give as much information as possible in a way that is easy to understand. They frequently combine several views on a single drawing.

These may be elevations (the view we would see if we stood in front or to the side of the finished building) or plan (the view we would have if we were looking down on it). The view we see depends on where we are looking from. There are then different ways of 'projecting' what we would see onto the drawings.

The two main methods of projection, used on standard building drawings, are orthographic and isometric.

Orthographic projection

Orthographic projection works as if parallel lines were drawn from every point on a model of the building on to a sheet of paper held up behind it (an elevation view), or laid out underneath it (plan view).

There are then different ways that we can display the views on a drawing. The method most commonly used in the building industry, for detailed construction drawings, is called 'third angle projection'. In this the front elevation is roughly central. The plan view is drawn directly below the front elevation and all other elevations are drawn in line with the front elevation. An example is shown in Figure 7.14.

Figure 7.14 Orthographic projection

Front Elevation

Side Elevation

Isometric projection

In isometric views, the object is drawn at an angle where one corner of the object is closest to the viewer. Vertical lines remain vertical but horizontal lines are drawn at an angle of 30° to the horizontal. This can be seen in Figure 7.15, which shows a simple rectangular box.

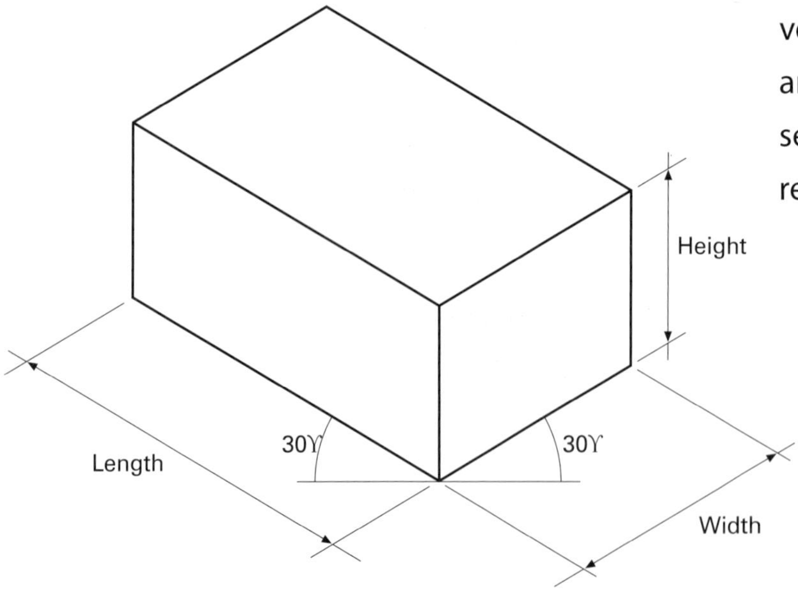

Figure 7.15 Isometric projection of rectangular box

Figures 7.16 and 7.17 show the method of drawing these using a T–square and set square.

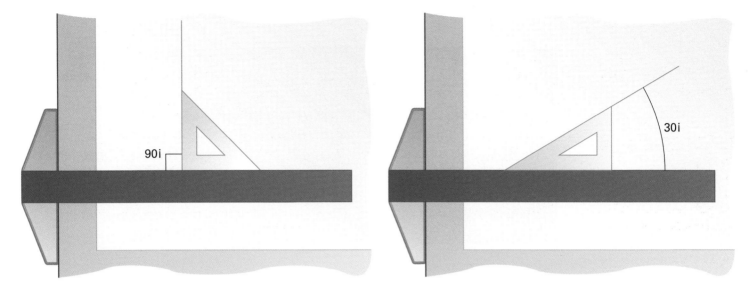

Figure 7.16 Drawing vertical lines   **Figure 7.17** Drawing horizontal lines

Specifications

Except in the case of very small building works, drawings cannot contain all of the information required by the contractor; in particular, the standard of materials to be used and quality of workmanship. For this purpose the architect will prepare a document called a specification to supplement the working drawings.

The specification is a precise description of all the essential information and job requirements that will affect the price of the work, but cannot be shown on drawings.

Typical items shown on the specification are:

- site description
- restrictions (limited access, working hours etc.)
- services and availability of services (waste, gas, electricity, telephone etc.)

- workmanship (quality, size tolerances, finishing requirements etc.)
- other information (nominated suppliers, sub-contractors, site clearance etc.).

On the job: Drawing plans

James is about to draw a kitchen plan. What should James consider when creating the drawing in terms of openings like doors and windows, and services such as water, electricity and gas supplies? Once James has created an outline of the kitchen, where should he start drawing? What sort of things should James have already discussed with the client (think about things like appliances, an extractor, electrical points, the client's budget etc.)?

Knowledge check

1. Briefly explain why drawings are used in the construction industry.

2. What do the following abbreviations stand for: DPC; hwd; fnd; DPM?

3. Sketch the graphical symbols which represent the following: brickwork; metal; sawn timber; hardcore.

4. Can you name the main types of projection that are used in building drawings?

5. What does a block plan show?

6. What are dividers used for?

7. What type of information could be found in a drawing's title panel?

8. Name two ways in which you can find out the height of a OBM?

9. In isometric projection, at what angle are horizontal lines drawn?

10. What type of information can be found in specifications?

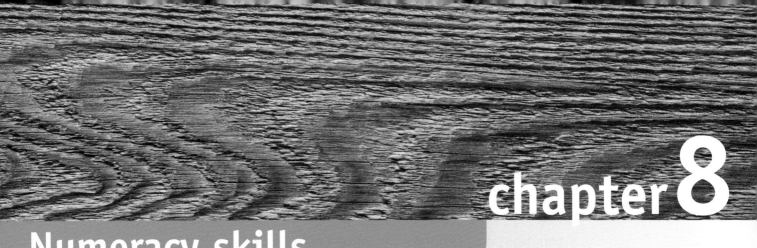

chapter 8

Numeracy skills

Overviews

Throughout your career in the construction industry you will have to make use of numbers and calculations in order to plan and carry out work. You will therefore need to make sure you are confident dealing with numbers, which may mean that you have to develop and improve your maths and **numeracy skills**.

Although you may often use a calculator to do calculations, you may find that a calculator is not always available and you may have to work something out on paper or in your head. This chapter will help you refresh and practise your skills in:

- Numbers
- Calculations
- Measures.

Numbers

Place value

0, 1, 2, 3, 4, 5, 6, 7, 8 and 9 are the ten digits we can work with. We can write any number you can think of, however huge, using any combination of these ten digits. In a number, the value of each digit depends upon its place value. Table 8.1 is a place value table and shows how the digit 2 has a different value, depending on its position.

Millions	Hundred	Ten thousands	Thousands	Hundreds	Tens	Units	Value
2	9	4	1	3	7	8	2 million
	2	5	3	1	0	7	2 hundred thousand
	7	2	5	6	6	4	2 × ten thousand = 20 thousand
		5	6	2	9	1	2 hundreds
			8	4	2	7	2 tens = 20
				1	6	2	2 units

Table 8.1 A place value table for the digit 2

Positive numbers

A positive number is a number that is greater than zero. If we make a number line, positive numbers are all the numbers to the right of zero.

0 1 2 3 4 5 6 7 8 9 10 11 12 13 …

Positive numbers

Negative numbers

A negative number is a number that is less than zero. If we make another number line, negative numbers are all the numbers to the left of zero.

… −13 −12 −11 −10 −9 −8 −7 −6 −5 −4 −3 −2 −1 0

← Negative numbers

Zero is neither positive nor negative.

Decimal numbers

Most of the time, the numbers we use are whole numbers. For example, we might buy 6 apples, or 2 loaves of bread or 1 car. However, sometimes we need to use numbers that are less than whole numbers, for example, we might eat 1 and a quarter sandwiches, 2 and a half cakes and three-quarters of a cup of tea. You can use decimals to show fractions or parts of quantities. Table 8.2 shows the value of the digits to the right of a decimal point.

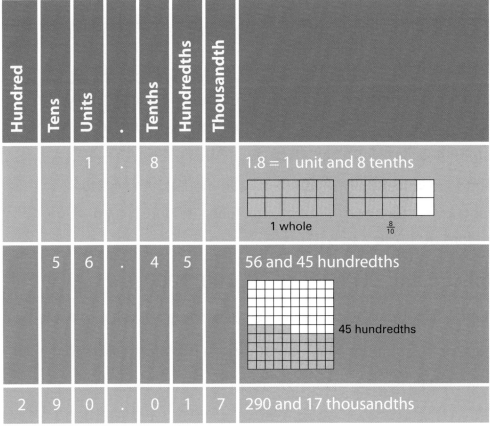

Hundred	Tens	Units	.	Tenths	Hundredths	Thousandth	
		1	.	8			1.8 = 1 unit and 8 tenths 1 whole $\frac{8}{10}$
	5	6	.	4	5		56 and 45 hundredths 45 hundredths
2	9	0	.	0	1	7	290 and 17 thousandths

Table 8.2 A place value table for digits to the right of a decimal point

Did you know?

Knowing about place value helps you to read numbers and to put numbers and quantities in order of size

Rounding to a number of decimal places

To round a number to a given number of decimal places, look at the digit in the place value position after the one you want.

- If it is 5 or more, round up.
- If it is less than 5 round down.

For example, say we wanted to round 4.634 to two decimal places, the digit in the third decimal place is 4, so we round down. Therefore, 4.634 rounded to 2 decimal places (d.p.) is 4.63.

If we look at the number 16.127, the digit in the third decimal place is 7, so we round up. Therefore, 16.127 round to 2 d.p. is 16.13.

Rounding to a number of significant figures

The most significant figure in a number is the digit with the highest place value. To round a number to a given number of significant figures, look at the digit in the place value position after the one you want.

- If it is 5 or more round up.
- If it is less than 5 round down.

For example, say we wanted to write 80 597 to one significant figure, the most significant figure is 8. The second significant figure is 0, so we round down. Therefore, 80 597 to 1 significant figure (s.f.) is 80 000.

If we wanted to write 80 597 to two significant figures, the first two significant figures are 8 and 0. The third significant figure is 5, so we round up. Therefore, 80 597 to 2 s.f. is 81 000.

Multiplying and dividing by 10, 100, 1000…

- To multiply a number by 10, move the digits one place value to the left.
- To multiply a by number 100, move the digits two place values to the left.
- To multiply a by number 1000, move the digits three place values to the left.

Remember

If a calculation results in an answer with a lot of decimal places, such as 34.568 923, you can round to 1 or 2 decimal places to make it simpler

For example:

	5		3.25
$5 \times 10 =$	50	$3.25 \times 10 =$	32.5
$5 \times 100 =$	500	$3.25 \times 100 =$	325
$5 \times 1000 =$	5000	$3.25 \times 1000 =$	3250

- To divide a number by 10, move the digits one place value to the right.

- To divide a number by 100, move the digits two place values to the right.

- To divide a number by 1000, move the digits three place values to the right.

For example:

$80\,000 \div 10 = 8000$		$473.6 \div 10 =$	47.36
$80\,000 \div 100 = 800$		$473.6 \div 100 =$	4.736
$80\,000 \div 1000 = 80$		$473.6 \div 1000 =$	0.4736

Converting decimals to fractions

You can use place value to convert a decimal to a fraction. For example:

0.3 is 3 tenths which is $\frac{3}{10}$

0.25 is 25 hundredths which is $\frac{25}{100}$

$\frac{25}{100}$ simplifies to $\frac{1}{4}$ (by dividing the top and bottom numbers by 25)

Table 8.3 shows some useful fraction/decimal equivalents.

See page 212 for more on simplifying fractions.

Decimal	0.1	0.25	0.333 333	0.5	0.75	0.01
Fraction	$\frac{1}{10}$	$\frac{1}{4}$	$\frac{1}{3}$	$\frac{1}{2}$	$\frac{3}{4}$	$\frac{1}{100}$

Table 8.3 Useful fraction/decimal equivalents

Did you know?

Knowing how to multiply and divide by 10, 100, 1 000 etc. is useful for converting metric units of measurement (see page 221) and finding percentages (see page 215)

Did you know?

Knowing how to convert between fractions and decimals helps with working out parts of quantities and calculating percentages (see page 215)

Multiples

Multiples are the numbers you get when you multiply any number by other numbers. For example:

- the multiples of 3 are 3, 6, 9, 12, 15, 18, 21, 24, 27, 30 and so on
- the multiples of 4 are 4, 8, 12, 16, 20, 24, 28, 32, 36, 40 and so on
- the multiples of 5 are 5, 10, 15, 20, 25, 30, 35, 40, 45, 50 and so on.

Common multiples

Here are the multiples of 3 and 5:

- Multiples of 3: 3, 6, 9, 12, 15, 18, 21, 24, 27, 30, 33, 36…
- Multiples of 5: 5, 10, 15, 20, 25, 30, 35…

3 and 5 have the multiples 15 and 30 in common. 15 and 30 are common multiples of 3 and 5. The lowest common multiple of 3 and 5 is 15.

Factors

The factors of a number are the whole numbers that divide into it exactly. For example:

- The factors of 18 are 1, 2, 3, 6, 9 and 18
- The factors of 30 are 1, 2, 3, 5, 6, 10, 15 and 30
- 5 is a factor of 5, 10, 15, 20…
- 7 is a factor of 7, 14, 21, 28…

Common factors

Here are the factors of 28 and 36:

- The factors of 28 are 1, 2, 4, 7, 14, 28
- The factors of 36 are 1, 2, 3, 4, 6, 9, 12, 18, 36

From these lists you can see that 28 and 36 have the factors 1, 2 and 4 in common. 1, 2 and 4 are the common factors of 28 and 36. 4 is the highest common factor of 28 and 36.

Fractions

Fractions describe parts of a whole, for example, a half of a pie, a third of a can of cola or a quarter of a cake.

In a fraction:

$\dfrac{3}{4}$ the top number is called the **numerator**

the bottom number is called the **denominator**

The denominator shows how many *equal parts* the whole is divided into. The numerator shows how many of those parts you have.

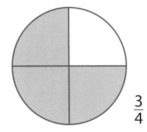

$\dfrac{3}{4}$

Finding a fraction of a quantity

To find a fraction of a quantity you divide by the denominator and multiply by the numerator. For example:

- to find $\dfrac{1}{2}$ of 500 m, divide by 2 (500 m ÷ 2 = 250 m)

- to find $\dfrac{2}{5}$ of £40, divide by 5 (£40 ÷ 5 = £8) and multiply by 2 (£8 × 2 = £16)

> **Did you know?**
>
> To find equivalent fractions you can:
>
> - multiply the numerator and denominator by the same number
>
> - divide the numerator and denominator by the same number.

Equivalent fractions

Two fractions are equivalent if they have the same value. For example:

$\dfrac{1}{2} = \dfrac{2}{4} = \dfrac{3}{6} = \dfrac{4}{8}$

 $\dfrac{1}{2}$ $\dfrac{2}{4}$ $\dfrac{3}{6}$ $\dfrac{4}{8}$

$\dfrac{2}{3} = \dfrac{4}{6} = \dfrac{6}{9} = \dfrac{8}{12}$

 $\dfrac{2}{3}$ $\dfrac{4}{6}$ $\dfrac{6}{9}$ $\dfrac{8}{12}$

Simplifying fractions

To simplify a fraction, write it as an equivalent fraction with smaller numbers in the numerator and denominator.

For example, $\frac{8}{12}$ simplifies to $\frac{2}{3}$.

When a fraction cannot be simplified any more, it is in its simplest form, or its lowest terms.

For example

$$\overset{\div 3}{\frac{12}{36}} = \overset{\div 4}{\frac{4}{12}} = \frac{1}{3}$$
$$\underset{\div 3}{} \qquad \underset{\div 4}{}$$

$\frac{12}{36} = \frac{1}{3}$ in its simplest form.

Multiplying fractions

To multiply a fraction by a whole number, multiply the numerator by the whole number.

For example,

$$\frac{2}{9} \times 4 = \frac{8}{9}$$

To multiply a fraction by another fraction, multiply the numerators and the denominators. For example,

$$\frac{2}{3} \times \frac{5}{8} = \frac{2 \times 5}{3 \times 8} = \frac{10}{24}$$

Give the answer in its simplest form:

$$\frac{10}{24} = \frac{5}{12} \qquad \text{(dividing numerator and denominator by 2)}$$

Dividing fractions

To divide one fraction by another, you invert (turn upside down) the fraction you are dividing by, and multiply.

For example

$$\frac{3}{4} \div \frac{2}{3} = \frac{3}{4} \times \frac{3}{2} = \frac{9}{8} = 1\frac{1}{8}$$

To divide a fraction by a whole number, or to divide a whole number by a fraction, write the whole number as a fraction with denominator 1, and use the same method.

$$\frac{4}{5} \div 3 = \frac{4}{5} \div \frac{3}{1} = \frac{4}{5} \times \frac{1}{3} = \frac{4}{15}$$

$$6 \div \frac{3}{4} = \frac{6}{1} \div \frac{3}{4} = \frac{6}{1} \times \frac{4}{3} = \frac{24}{3} = 8$$

Adding fractions

To add fractions with the same denominator, add the numerators.

For example,

$$\frac{1}{3} + \frac{1}{3} = \frac{2}{3}$$

$$\frac{1}{5} + \frac{3}{5} = \frac{4}{5}$$

To add fractions with different denominators, first write the fractions as equivalent fractions with the same denominator. Use the lowest common multiple of the two denominators. You can use any common multiple as the denominator, but using the lowest common multiple keeps the numbers smaller and the calculations simpler.

For example,

$$\frac{1}{2} + \frac{1}{3}$$

The denominators are not the same. The lowest common multiple of 2 and 3 is 6.

To write $\frac{1}{2}$ as an equivalent fraction with denominator 6, multiply numerator and denominator by 3, to give $\frac{3}{6}$.

To write $\frac{1}{3}$ as an equivalent fraction with denominator 6, multiply numerator and denominator by 2, to give $\frac{2}{6}$

The calculation is now $\frac{3}{6} + \frac{2}{6} = \frac{5}{6}$

A mixed number has a whole number and a fraction part, for example $3\frac{1}{4}$.

To add mixed numbers, add together the whole number parts and then the fractions.

For example, if we wanted to add together $1\frac{1}{2}$ and $2\frac{1}{3}$:

Add the whole numbers: $1 + 2 = 3$

Now add the fractions: $\frac{1}{2} + \frac{1}{3} = \frac{3}{6} + \frac{2}{6} = \frac{5}{6}$

Combine the two answers: $1\frac{1}{2} + 2\frac{1}{3} = 3\frac{5}{6}$

Subtracting fractions

To subtract fractions with the same denominator, subtract the numerators.

For example: $\frac{7}{8} - \frac{3}{8} = \frac{4}{8} = \frac{1}{2}$

$$\frac{7}{8} \qquad - \qquad \frac{3}{8} \qquad = \qquad \frac{4}{8}$$

To subtract mixed numbers, first write them as improper (top heavy) fractions with a common denominator

For example: $2\frac{1}{3} - \frac{1}{2} = \frac{7}{3} - \frac{1}{2} = \frac{14}{6} - \frac{3}{6} = 1\frac{5}{6}$

Percentages

Percentages are another way of showing parts of a quantity. Percentage means 'number of parts per hundred'. The symbol % means per cent. For example:

- 1% means 1 out of a hundred or $\frac{1}{100}$

- 10% means 10 out of a hundred or $\frac{10}{100}$

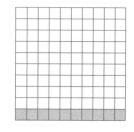

10%

- 84% means 84 out of a hundred or $\frac{84}{100}$

100% means the whole quantity.

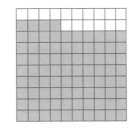

84%

Finding a percentage of a quantity

To find a percentage of a quantity, find 1% first, by dividing by 100, then multiply by the number you need. For example:

20% of £45

$$1\% \text{ of } £45 = \frac{£45}{100} = £45 \div 100 = £0.45$$

So   20% of £45 = 20 × £0.45 = £9

Percentage change

A number can be increased or decreased by a percentage. Wages are often increased by a percentage (e.g. a 4% rise in wages). Items are often reduced by a percentage in sales (e.g. 10% off, 20% reduction, etc.). For example:

A set of paintbrushes costs £12.99. In the sale there is 15% off.

(a) How much money do you save by buying the paintbrushes in the sale?

(b) What is the sale price of the paintbrushes?

(a) Work out 15% of £12.99

        1% of £12.99 = £0.1299

So   15% of £12.99 = 15 × £0.1299 = £1.9485 = £1.95 to the nearest penny

You save £1.95

(b) The sale price is

        £12.99 – £1.95 = £11.04

Did you know?

Percentages are also used for:

- paying deposits – a deposit is a percentage of the whole price (e.g. 20% deposit)
- paying interest – interest is a percentage of money. It is repaid on top of the money (e.g. a loan from a bank of £1000 at 15% interest)
- profit – when charging a client for work you have carried out, you will need to add on to your costs a percentage for your profit
- Value Added Tax (VAT) – VAT is a government tax added to many items or goods that we buy (the standard VAT rate is 17.5%)

Ratio

A **ratio** describes a relationship between quantities. You can read a ratio as a 'for every' statement. For example:

- Green paint is made by mixing blue and yellow in the ratio 1:2. This means, *for every* 1 litre of blue paint you need 2 litres of yellow paint.

- A labourer and a bricklayer agree to share their bonus in the ratio 2:5. The bonus is £42. The ratio 2:5 means that for every 2 parts the labourer receives, the bricklayer receives 5 parts. So the bonus needs to be split into 2 + 5 = 7 parts. One part can be calculated: £42 ÷ 7 = £6. Therefore, the labourer receives two parts = 2 × £6 = £12 and the bricklayer receives five parts = 5 × £6 = £30.

Calculations

Addition

When adding numbers using a written method, write digits with the same place value in the same column. For example, to work out 26 + 896 + 1213 write the calculation:

Add up the digits in columns, starting with the units column.

```
      2 6
      8 9 6
    1 2 1 3
    ───────
    2 1 3 5
    1 1 1
```

(4) 1 + 1 = 2

(1) 6 + 6 + 3 = 15
Write 5 in the digits column and carry 1 ten to the tens column.

(3) 8 + 2 = 10
Add the carried 1 from the tens column 10 + 1 = 11. Write 1 and carry 1 to the thousands column.

(2) 2 + 9 + 1 = 12
Add the carried 1 from the digits column 12 + 1 = 13. Write 3 in the tens column and carry the 1 hundred to the hundreds column.

To add decimals, write the numbers with the decimal points in line:

$$
\begin{array}{r}
4.56 \\
10.2 \\
\underline{0.32} \\
\underline{15.08}
\end{array}
$$

In a problem, these words mean you need to add:

- What is the *total* of 43 and 2457?   (43 + 2457)

- What is the *sum* of 56 and 345?   (56 + 345)

- *Increase* 3467 by 521.   (3467 + 521)

Subtraction

When subtracting numbers using a written method, write digits with the same place value in the same column.

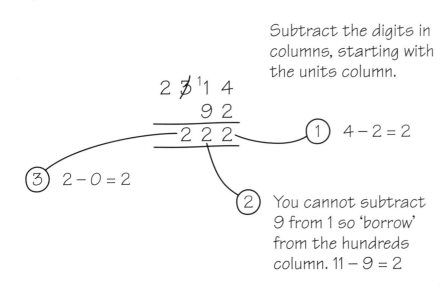

Subtract the digits in columns, starting with the units column.

① 4 − 2 = 2

③ 2 − 0 = 2

② You cannot subtract 9 from 1 so 'borrow' from the hundreds column. 11 − 9 = 2

In a problem, these words mean you need to subtract:

- *Find the difference* between 200 and 45.   (200 − 45)

- *Decrease* 64 by 9.   (64 − 9)

- *How much greater than* 98 is 110?   (110 − 98)

Multiplication

Knowing the multiplication tables up to 10×10 helps with multiplying single digit numbers. You can use multiplication facts you know to work out other multiplication calculations. For example:

$$20 \times 12$$

You know that $20 = 2 \times 10$

So

$$20 \times 12 = 2 \times 10 \times 12$$

$$= 2 \times 12 \times 10$$

$$= 24 \times 10 = 240$$

To multiply larger numbers you can write the calculation in columns or use the grid method. Both methods work by splitting the calculation into smaller ones.

In columns

```
      2 5
  ×   3 6
  ─────────
    1 5 0        6 × 25 ⎫  Add these to
    7 5 0       30 × 25 ⎬  find 36 × 25
  ─────────             ⎭
    9 0 0
```

The grid method

$36 \times 25 =$

×	20	5
30	600	150
6	120	30

$30 \times 20 = 600$
$30 \times 5 = 150$
$6 \times 20 = 120$
$6 \times 5 = 30$
$\overline{900}$

Division

Division is the opposite of multiplication. Knowing the multiplication tables up to 10×10 helps with division. Each multiplication fact gives two related division facts. For example:

$$4 \times 6 = 24 \qquad 24 \div 6 = 4 \qquad 24 \div 4 = 6$$

To divide by a single digit number, use short division.

$$161 \sqrt{7} =$$

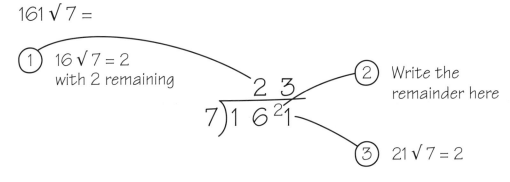

① $16 \sqrt{7} = 2$
with 2 remaining

$$7\overline{)1\ 6\ ^{2}1}$$

② Write the remainder here

③ $21 \sqrt{7} = 2$

To divide by 10 or more, use long division.

$$12\overline{)2952}$$

with quotient 246

$$
\begin{array}{r}
2\ 4\ 6 \\
12\overline{)2\ 9\ 5\ 2} \\
2\ 4 \\
\overline{5\ 5} \\
4\ 8 \\
\overline{7\ 2} \\
7\ 2 \\
\overline{0}
\end{array}
$$

$2 \times 12 = 24$

$29 - 24 = \quad 5$. Bring down the next 5

$12 \times 4 = 48$

$55 - 48 = \quad 7$. Bring down the 2

$12 \times 6 = 72$

Did you know?

You can use values rounded to 1 s.f. to estimate approximate areas and prices

Estimating

Sometimes an accurate answer to a calculation is not required. You can estimate an approximate answer by rounding all the values in the calculation to 1 significant figure (see page 208). For example:

Estimate the answer to the calculation 4.9×3.1

4.9 rounds to 5 to 1 s.f.

3.1 rounds to 3 to 1 s.f.

A sensible estimate is $5 \times 3 = 15$

Measures

Units of measurement

The metric units of measurement are shown in Table 8.4.

Length	millimetres (mm), centimetres (cm), metres (m), kilometres (km)
Mass (weight)	grams (g), kilograms (kg), tonnes (t)
Capacity (the amount a container holds)	millilitres (ml), centilitres (cl), litres (l)

Table 8.4 Units of measurement

Metric units are all based on 10, 100, 1000 which makes it easy to convert between units.

milli means one thousandth $1 \text{ mm} = \frac{1}{1000} \text{ m}$ $1 \text{ ml} = \frac{1}{1000} \text{ litre}$

centi means one hundredth $1 \text{ cm} = \frac{1}{100} \text{ m}$ $1 \text{ cl} = \frac{1}{100} \text{ litre}$

kilo means one thousand $1 \text{ kg} = 1000 \text{ g}$ $1 \text{ km} = 1000 \text{ m}$

Table 8.5 shows some useful metric conversions.

Length	Mass	Capacity
1 cm = 10 mm 1 m = 100 cm = 1000 mm 1 km = 1000 m	1 kg = 1000 g 1 tonne = 1000 kg	1 l = 100 cl = 1000 ml

Table 8.5 Useful metric conversions

Remember

To convert from a smaller unit to a larger one, divide; to convert from a larger unit to a smaller one, multiply

To convert 2657 mm to metres: $2657 \div 1000 = 2.657$ m

To convert 0.75 tonnes to kg: $0.75 \times 1000 = 750$ kg

For calculations involving measurements, you need to convert all the measurements into the same unit. For example, a plasterer measures the lengths of cornice required for a room. He writes down the measurements as 175 cm, 2 metres, 225 cm, 1.5 m. In order to work out the total length of cornice needed, we first need to write all the lengths in the same units:

175 cm   2 metres = $2 \times 100 = 200$ cm   1.5 m = $1.5 \times 100 = 150$ cm   225 cm

So the total length is:

$$175 + 200 + 225 + 150 = 750 \text{ cm}$$

Imperial units

In the UK we still use some imperial units of measurement (see Table 8.5).

Length	inches, feet, yards, miles
Mass (weight)	ounces, pounds, stones
Capacity (the amount a container holds)	pints, gallons

Table 8.5 Some imperial units of measurement

To convert from imperial to metric units, use the approximate conversions shown in Table 8.6.

Length	Mass	Capacity
1 inch = 2.5 cm 1 foot = 30 cm 5 miles = 8 km	2.2 pounds = 1 kg 1 ounce = 25 g	1.75 pints = 1 litre 1 gallon = 4.5 litres

Table 8.6 Converting imperial measurements to metric

For example, if a wall is 32 feet long, what is its approximate length in metres?

1 foot = 30 cm

So   32 feet = 32 × 30 cm = 960 cm = 9.6 m.

Scale drawings

Building plans are drawn to scale. Each length on the plan is in proportion to the real length. On a drawing to a scale of 1 cm represents 10 m:

- a length of 5 cm represents an actual length of 5 × 10 = 50 m

- a length of 12 cm represents an actual length of 12 × 10 = 120 m

- an actual length of 34 m is represented by a line 34 ÷ 10 = 3.4 cm long.

Scales are often given as ratios. For example:

- a scale of 1 : 100 means that 1 cm on the drawing represents an actual length of 100 cm (or 1 metre)

- a scale of 1 : 20 000 means that 1 cm on the drawing represents an actual length of 20 000 cm = 20 m.

Table 8.7 shows some common scales used in the construction industry.

1 : 5	1 cm represents 5 cm	5 times smaller than actual size
1 : 10	1 cm represents 10 cm	10 times smaller than actual size
1 : 20	1 cm represents 20 cm	20 times smaller than actual size
1 : 50	1 cm represents 50 cm	50 times smaller than actual size
1 : 100	1 cm represents 100 cm = 1m	100 times smaller than actual size
1 : 1250	1 cm represents 1250 cm = 1.25 m	1250 times smaller than actual size

Table 8.7 Common scales used in the construction industry

Let's look at the following examples:

(a) A plan is drawn to a scale of 1 : 20. On the plan, a wall is 4.5 cm long. How long is the actual wall?

  1 cm on the plan = actual length 20 cm

So 4.5 cm on the plan = actual length 4.5 × 20 = 490 cm or 4.9 m

(b) A window is 3 m tall. How tall is it on the plan?

  3 m = 300 cm

  an actual length of 20 cm is 1 cm on the plan

  an actual length of 5 × 20 = 100 cm is 5 × 1 cm on the plan

  an actual length of 3 × 100 cm is 3 × 5 cm on the plan.

The window is 15 cm tall on the plan.

To make scale drawings, architects use a scale rule. The different scales on the ruler give the equivalent actual length measurements for different lengths in cm, for each scale.

Perimeter of shapes with straight sides

The perimeter of a shape is the distance all around the outside of the shape. To find the perimeter of a shape, measure all the sides and then add the lengths together. For example:

The perimeter of this room is

4.5 m

3.2 m   3.2 m

4.5 m

4.5 + 3.2 + 4.5 + 3.2 = 15.4 m

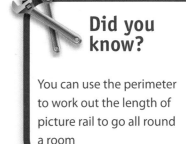

Did you know?

You can use the perimeter to work out the length of picture rail to go all round a room

Area of shapes with straight sides

The area of a 2-D (flat) shape is the amount of space it covers. Area is measured in square units, such as square centimetres (cm^2) and square metres (m^2).

This rectangle is drawn on squared paper. Each square has an area 1 cm^2.

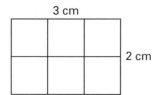

You can find the area by counting the squares. Area = 6 squares = 6 cm^2

You can also calculate the area by multiplying the number of squares in a row by the number of rows: $3 \times 2 = 6$

The area of a rectangle with length l and width w is

$$A = l \times w$$

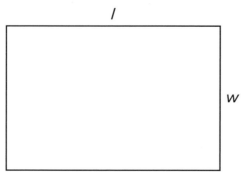

For example, if the length of a rectangular room is 3.6 metres and the width is 2.7 metres, the area is

$$A = 3.6 \times 2.7 = 9.72 \text{ m}^2$$

Area of a triangle

The area of a triangle is given by the formula:

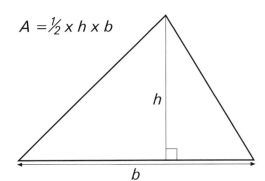

$A = \frac{1}{2} \times h \times b$ where h is the **perpendicular** height and b is the length of the base. The perpendicular height is drawn to meet the base at right angles (90°).

For example, say we wanted to find (a) the area and (b) the perimeter of this triangle

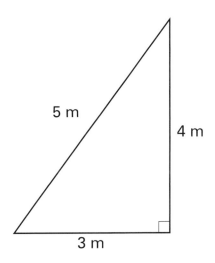

(a) Perpendicular height = 4 m, base = 3 m

$$A = \frac{1}{2} \times h \times b = \frac{1}{2} \times 4 \times 3 = 6 \text{ m}^2$$

(b) Perimeter = 5 + 4 + 3 = 12 m

Pythagoras' theorem

You can use Pythagoras' theorem to find unknown lengths in right-angled triangles. In a right-angled triangle:

• one angle is 90° (a right angle)

• the longest side is opposite the right angle and is called the **hypotenuse**.

Pythagoras' theorem says that for any right-angled triangle with sides a and b and hypotenuse c,

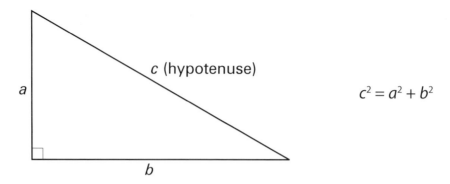

$$c^2 = a^2 + b^2$$

For example, if we wanted to find the length of the hypotenuse of this triangle

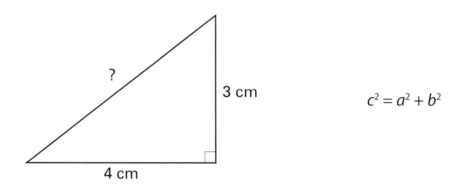

$$c^2 = a^2 + b^2$$

$1^2 = 1 \times 1 = 1$	$\sqrt{1} = 1$
$2^2 = 2 \times 2 = 4$	$\sqrt{4} = 2$
$3^2 = 3 \times 3 = 9$	$\sqrt{9} = 3$
$4^2 = 4 \times 4 = 16$	$\sqrt{16} = 4$
$5^2 = 5 \times 5 = 25$	$\sqrt{25} = 5$
$6^2 = 6 \times 6 = 36$	$\sqrt{36} = 6$
$7^2 = 7 \times 7 = 49$	$\sqrt{49} = 7$
$8^2 = 8 \times 8 = 64$	$\sqrt{64} = 8$
$9^2 = 9 \times 9 = 81$	$\sqrt{81} = 9$
$10^2 = 10 \times 10 = 100$	$\sqrt{100} = 10$

Table 8.8 Useful square roots

In the theorem, c is the hypotenuse.

$$c^2 = 3^2 + 4^2$$
$$= 9 + 16$$
$$= 25$$
$$c = \sqrt{25} = 5$$

The hypotenuse is 5 cm long.

a^2 is 'a squared' and is equal to $a \times a$. 3^2 is '3 squared' and is equal to 3×3. The opposite or inverse of squaring is finding the square root. $\sqrt{25}$ means 'the square root of 25': $5 \times 5 = 25$, so $\sqrt{25} = 5$

Learning these squares and square roots will help with Pythagoras' theorem calculations. Table 8.8 shows some square roots you will often find useful.

Using Pythagoras' theorem to find the shorter side of a triangle

You can rearrange Pythagoras' theorem like this:

$$c^2 = a^2 + b^2$$

$$a^2 = c^2 - b^2$$

For example, say we wanted to find the length of side a in this right-angled triangle

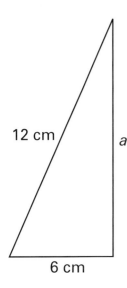

$$a^2 = c^2 - b^2$$

$$= 12^2 - 6^2$$

$$= 144 - 36 = 108$$

$$a = \sqrt{108} = 10.3923\ldots \qquad \text{Using the } \sqrt{} \text{ key on a calculator}$$

$$= 10.4 \text{ cm (to 1 decimal place)}$$

You can also use Pythagoras' theorem to find the perpendicular height of a triangle. For example, if we wanted to find the area of this triangle we would need to find the perpendicular height

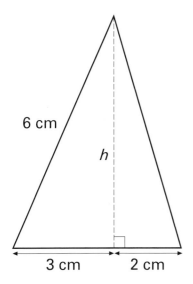

Using Pythagoras $\quad h^2 = 6^2 - 3^2$

$$= 36 - 9 = 27$$

$$h = \sqrt{27} = 5.196\ldots = 5.2 \text{ cm (to 1 d.p.)}$$

Area $\quad = \dfrac{1}{2} \times b \times h$

$$= \dfrac{1}{2} \times 5 \times 5.2 \qquad \text{Base length} = 3 + 2 \text{ cm}$$

$$= 13 \text{ cm}^2$$

Areas of composite shapes

Composite shapes are made up of simple shapes such as rectangles and squares. To find the area, divide up the shape and find the area of each part separately. For example, to work out the area of this L-shaped room

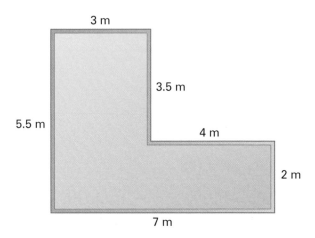

First divide it into two rectangles, A and B

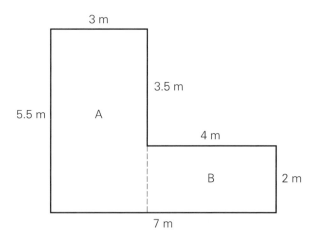

Area of rectangle A = 3 × 5.5 = 16.5 m²

Area of rectangle B = 4 × 2 = 8 m²

Total area of room = 16.5 + 8 = 24.5 m²

You could divide the rectangle in the example above into two different rectangles, C and D, like this (see page 229)

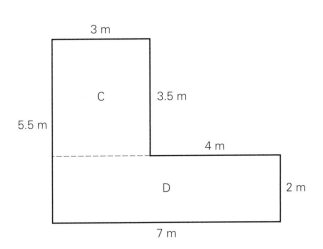

Check that you get the same total area.

Some shapes can be divided into rectangles and triangles. For example, to find the area of this wooden floor:

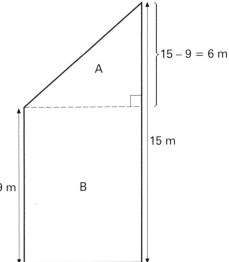

Divide the floor into a right-angled triangle A and a rectangle B

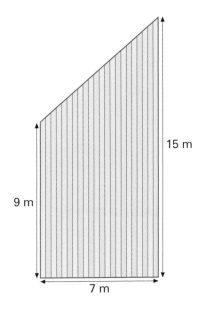

Triangle A has vertical height 6 m and base 7 m

$$\text{Area triangle A} = \frac{1}{2} \times b \times h$$

$$= \frac{1}{2} \times 7 \times 6 = 21 \text{ m}^2$$

Area rectangle B = $9 \times 7 = 63$ m²

Total area = $21 + 63 = 84$ m².

Circumference of a circle

The circumference of a circle is its perimeter – the distance all the way around the outside. The formula for the circumference of a circle of radius r is

$$C = 2\pi r$$

The radius is the distance from the centre of a circle to its outside edge. The diameter is the distance across the circle through the centre (diameter = 2 × radius).

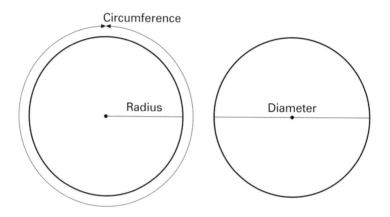

$\pi = 3.141\,592\,654\ldots$

To estimate the circumference of a circle, use $\pi = 3$. For more accurate calculations use $\pi = 3.14$, or the π key on a calculator.

For example, to estimate the circumference of this circular pond, with radius 2 m

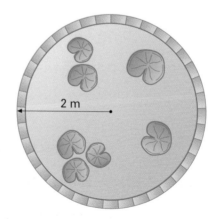

For an estimate, use $\pi = 3$

$\qquad$ Circumference $= 2\,\pi\,r = 2 \times \pi \times r = 2 \times 3 \times 2 = 12$ m

Calculate the circumference of a circular patio with radius 3.5 m.

$\qquad$ Circumference $= 2\,\pi\,r = 2 \times \pi \times r = 2 \times 3.14 \times 3.5$

$$= 21.98 \text{ m}$$

$$= 22 \text{ m to the nearest metre}$$

Area of a circle

The formula for the area of a circle of radius r is

$\qquad$ Area $= \pi r^2$

We can calculate the area of a circle with radius 3.25 m

$\qquad$ Area $= \pi r^2$

$$= \pi \times r^2 = 3.14 \times 3.25 \times 3.25 = 33.166\,25$$

$$= 33 \text{ m}^2 \text{ to the nearest metre.}$$

Did you know?

If you are given the diameter of the circle, you halve the diameter to find the radius

Part circles and composite shapes

You can use the formulae for circumference and area of a circle to calculate perimeters and areas of parts of circles, and shapes made from parts of circles. For example, we can work out the perimeter and area of this semicircular window

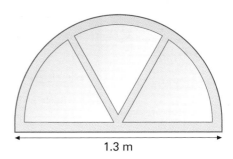

1.3 m

The diameter of the semi circle is 1.3 m, so the radius is $1.3 \div 2 = 0.65$ m. The length of the curved side is half the circumference of the circle with radius 0.65 m.

$\qquad$ Length of curved side $= \frac{1}{2} \times 2\,\pi r = \frac{1}{2} \times 2 \times \pi \times r$

$$= \frac{1}{2} \times 2 \times 3.14 \times 0.65 = 2.041 \text{ m}$$

$\qquad$ Circumference of the semi circle $=$ curved side $+$ straight side

$$= 2.041 + 1.3 = 3.341 \text{m}$$

$$= 3.34 \text{ m (to the nearest cm)}$$

Area of semicircle = half the area of the circle with radius 0.65m

$$= \frac{1}{2} \times \pi r^2 = \frac{1}{2} \times \pi \times r^2$$

$$= \frac{1}{2} \times 3.14 \times 0.65 \times 0.65 = 0.663\,325 \text{ m}^2$$

$$= 0.66 \text{ m}^2 \text{ (to 2 d.p.)}$$

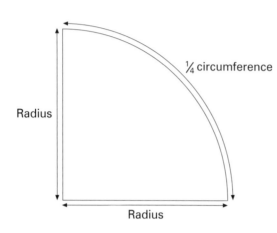

Radius

¼ circumference

Radius

To find the area of a quarter circle, use $\frac{1}{4}\pi r^2$. To find the perimeter of a quarter circle, work out $\frac{1}{4}$ circumference + 2 × radius.

To find the area of a composite shape including parts of circles, divide it into circles and simple shapes and find the areas separately.

Units of area

Area is measured in **square units** such as mm², cm², m².

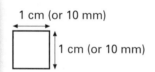

1 cm (or 10 mm)

1 cm (or 10 mm)

The area of this square is 1 cm² or 10 × 10 = 100 mm²

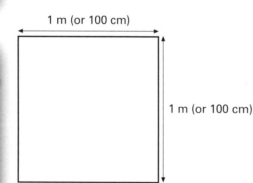

1 m (or 100 cm)

1 m (or 100 cm)

The area of this square is 1 m² or 100 × 100 = 10 000 cm²

We can work out the area of this rectangle

(a) in cm^2

(b) in m^2

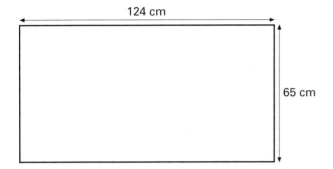

124 cm

65 cm

(a) $A = l \times w = 124 \times 65 = 8060$ cm^2

(b) $8060 \div 10\,000 = 0.806$ m^2

Volume

Volume is the amount of space taken up by a 3-D or solid shape. Volume is measured in cube units, such as cubic centimetres (cm^3) and cubic metres (m^3).

A cuboid is a 3-D shape whose faces are all rectangles.

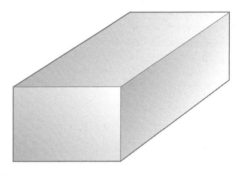

A cube is a 3-D shape whose faces are all squares.

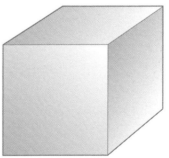

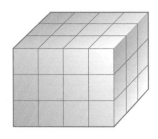

This cuboid is made of 1cm³ cubes

You can find the volume by counting the cubes.

Volume = number of cubes = 36 cm³.

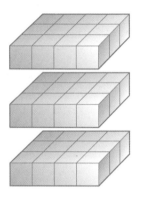

You can also calculate the volume by splitting the solid into equal rectangular layers.

Each layer has 4 × 3 cubes.

There are three layers, so the total number of cubes is 3 × 4 × 3 = 36 cm³.

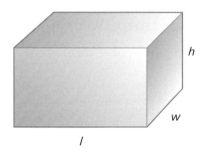

The volume of a cuboid with length l, width w and height h is

$$V = l \times w \times h$$

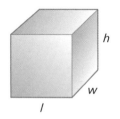

For a cube, length = width = height, so the volume of a cube with side l is

$$V = l^3$$

You can find the volume of concrete needed for a rectangular floor by measuring the length and width of the floor, and the depth of the concrete required and using the formula for volume of a cuboid. For example, we can work out the volume of concrete needed for the floor of a rectangular room with length 3.7 m and width 2.9 m, if the depth of the concrete is to be 0.15 m.

Visualise the floor as a cuboid, like this

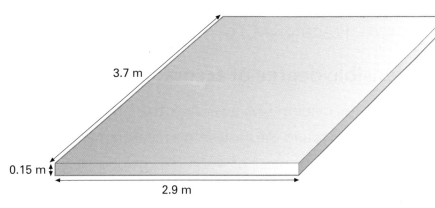

The depth of the concrete (0.15 m) is the height of the cuboid.

$$V = l \times w \times h$$

$$= 3.7 \times 2.9 \times 0.15$$

$$= 1.6095 \text{ m}^3$$

$$= 1.61 \text{ m}^3 \text{ (to 2 d.p.)}$$

Units of volume

Volume is measured in **cube units** such as mm^3, cm^3, m^3. The volume of this cube is 1 cm^3 or $10 \times 10 \times 10 = 1000$ mm^3

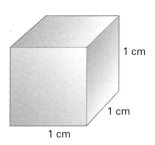

The volume of this cube is 1 m^3 or $100 \times 100 \times 100 = 1\,000\,000$ cm^3

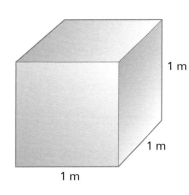

A cuboid is a 3-D shape with rectangular faces (like a box). The formula for the volume of a cuboid is $V = l \times w \times h$. For example, we can calculate the volume of this cuboid:

(a) in cm^3

(b) in m^3

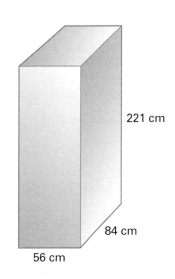

Remember

1 cm^3 = 1000 mm^3

1 m^3 = 1 000 000 cm^3

(a) $V = l \times w \times h = 56 \times 84 \times 221 = 1\,039\,584$ cm³

(b) $1\,039\,584 \div 1\,000\,000 = 1.039584$ m² $= 1.04$ m³ (to 2 d.p.)

Rounding to a sensible degree of accuracy

Remember

In some situations it is most sensible to round up

Sometimes measurement calculations give an answer to a large number of decimal places. It is sensible to round the answer to a measurement that is practical. For example, Ahmed has a piece of wood 190 cm long. He wants to cut it into 7 equal lengths.

He works out $190 \div 7 = 14.28578142$ cm

You cannot measure 0.28578142 of a centimetre!

It is sensible to round to 14.3 cm (to 1 d.p.), which is 14 cm and 3 mm and can be measured.

For more on rounding to a number of decimal places, see page 208.

Let's look at another example:

A plasterer calculates the total area of walls in a room as 36 m².

Plasterboard sheets have area 2.88 m².

The number of plasterboard sheets needed is $36 \div 2.88 = 12.5$

If the plasterer buys 12 sheets he will not have enough.

If he buys 13 sheets he will have half a sheet left over.

In this case it is sensible to round up, and buy 13 sheets.

You may find there are times when you need to round down.

In some situations it is most sensible to round down. How many 2 metre lengths can be cut from 7 metres of pipe?

$7 \div 2 = 3.5$

You can cut three 2 metre lengths. The rest (0.5 of a 2 metre length) is wasted.

So in this case it is sensible to round down: you can only cut three 2 metre lengths.

chapter 9

First fixing

Carpenters and joiners will undertake many different types of work on site. One of the main areas, and probably the most important, is called 'first fixing'.

This is work carried out before plastering takes place and includes the following, all of which will be covered in this chapter:

- Roofs – traditional, trussed and flat
- Suspended timber floors
- Windows
- Stairs
- Timber studwork
- Door frames and linings
- Ground lats
- Sills.

Roofs – traditional, trussed and flat

Roofing carpenters need a sound knowledge of traditional and modern roof construction. They must also understand the methods used to construct them, including finding the lengths and angles of roofing members and the use of geometry, roofing square, templates and a 'roofing ready reckoner'. Pitched roofs offer the biggest challenge and this section will mainly address these, although other types will also be covered.

Over the next few pages we will look at the following practical issues involved in roof construction:

- basic structure of roofs

- pitched roof types, including single, double, gable-end and hipped

- roofing terminology, including the main elements and components

- setting out

- sequence of operations

- flat roofs

- lean-to roof.

Basic structure of roofs

Timber is used to form the skeleton structure of the roof. This gives support to the actual roof covering, such as tiles or slates, which protects the building from the elements (i.e. sun, rain, snow and wind).

Roofing structures vary according to their design but will be either:

- pitched roof

- flat roof

- lean to.

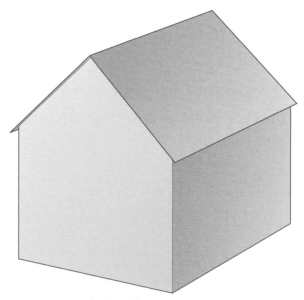

Figure 9.1 Pitched roof

Figure 9.2 Flat roof

It is the roof covering that determines the pitch or slope of the roof, which is one of the most important factors in roof design. Other factors that might affect this are:

- size of building

- its purpose

- architect's preference

- client's requirements

- local planning requirements

- exposure that the building will have to the elements.

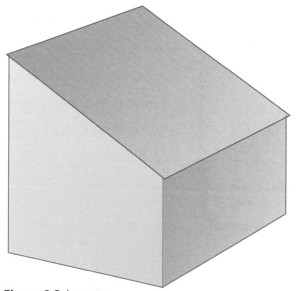

Figure 9.3 Lean-to

Traditional roofing consists of a series of rafters, which are pitched up to a ridge board. These rafters are supported by **purlins** and **struts**, which work together to transfer the load to binders and ceiling joists, and on to a load-bearing wall.

Modern roofing uses trussed rafters, which usually only need to be supported at the ends, without the need for purlins and ridge boards. These are pre-fabricated in a factory and delivered to site ready for fixing – much simpler than traditional roofing carried out entirely on site.

Pitched roof types

Pitched roofs are the most complex with varying designs. They may be single or double, depending on their span, and be gable-ended or hipped. They are described briefly below but their components are covered in more detail later.

Single roofs

The rafters of single roofs have no immediate support. They are therefore not used for spans over 5.5 m as they would require very large sectioned timber, making them uneconomical. A central binder may be hung from the ridge to prevent any sagging when ceiling joists are used (**close couple**).

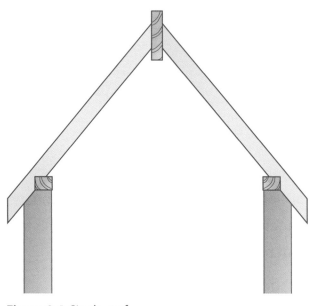

Figure 9.4 Single roof

Double roofs

The rafters of double roofs require extra support due to their length. This is provided by purlins to give support in mid-span.

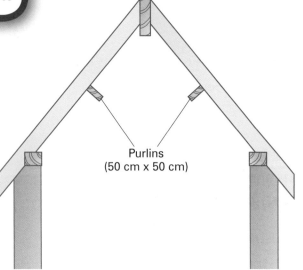

Purlins
(50 cm x 50 cm)

Figure 9.5 Double roof

Gable-end roof

Gable-end roofs are very common in modern roofing due to their simplicity and relatively low cost. The triangular ends of the roof are known as **gable-ends** and are formed by building up the outer walls.

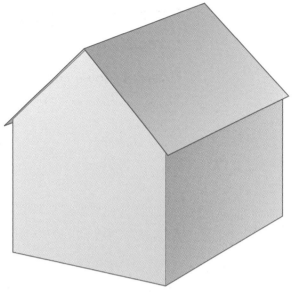

Figure 9.6 Gable-end roof

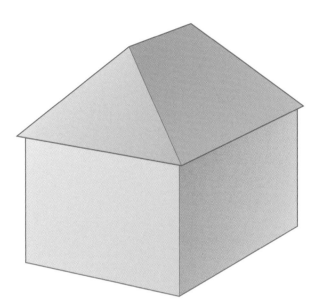

Figure 9.7 Hipped roof

Hipped roof

Also used in modern roofing but not as common as the gable roof, the hipped ends are normally the same pitch as the main roof.

Roofing terminology

Roofs are made up of a number of different parts called 'elements'. These, in turn, are made up of 'members' or 'components'.

Elements

The main elements are defined below and shown in Figure 9.8.

- **ridge** – acts as a spine at the apex of the structure, running horizontally and against which the uppermost ends of the rafters are fixed

- **gable** – the triangular part of the end walls

- **hip** – part of the roof where two external sloping surfaces meet

- **valley** – part of the roof where two sloping surfaces meet

- **verge** – where the roof overhangs at the gable

- **eaves** – lowest part of the roof surface where it meets the outside walls.

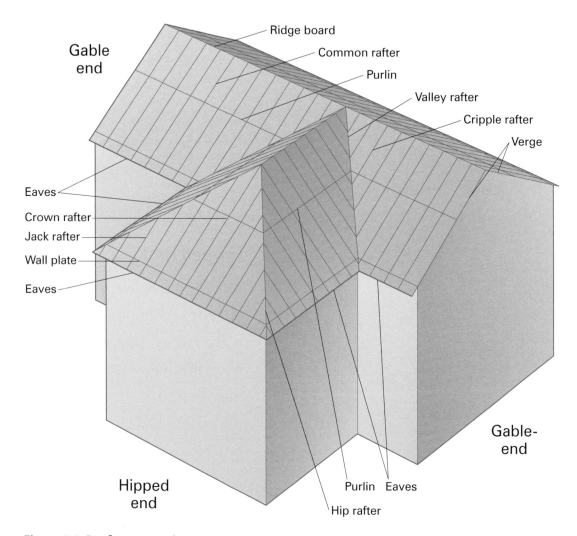

Figure 9.8 Roofing terminology

Members or components

The main members or components are described below and shown in Figures 9.9 and 9.10. They are not arranged in alphabetical order but logically how they can be found when looking at a roof construction.

- **wall plates** – timber plates laid flat and bedded on mortar, running along the wall to carry the feet of all rafters and ceiling joists; anchored down with restraint straps to prevent movement

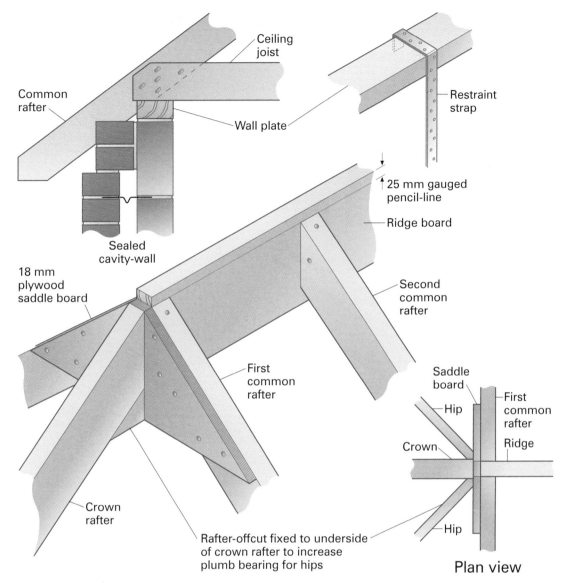

Figure 9.9 Roof components

- **common rafters** – load-bearing ribs that pitch up opposite each other from the wall plate on each side of the roof span, and fixed to the ridge board

- **hip rafters** – pitched up from the wall plate corners of a hipped end to the saddle board at the ridge; acting as a spine for the heads of the jack rafters

- **saddle board** – a timber board that is fixed to the common rafter and used as a bearing for the crown and hip rafters to fix to

- **jack rafters** – fixed in pairs on each side of the hip rafter, diminishing in size from ridge to wall plate

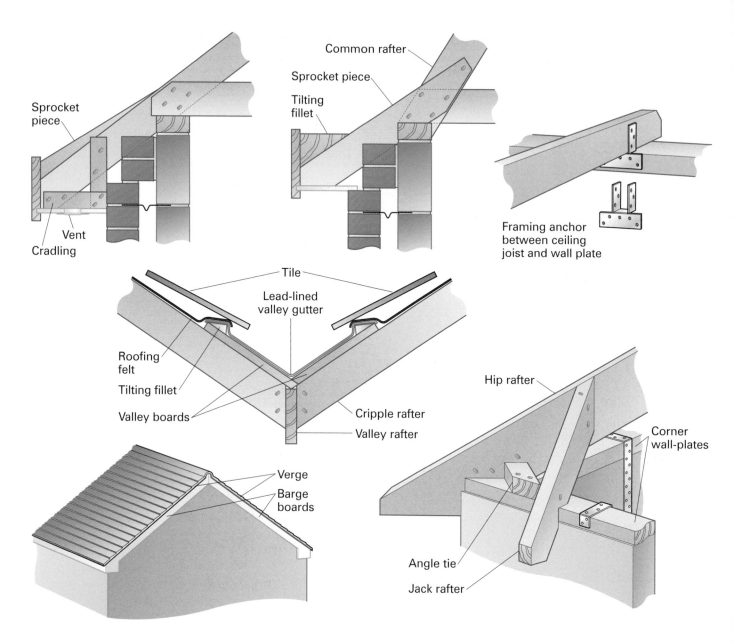

Figure 9.10 Further roof components

- **valley rafters** – like hip rafters but forming an internal angle, acting as a spine for fixing cripple rafters

- **cripple rafters** – pairs of rafters similar to jacks, spanning from the ridge to the valley rafter

- **purlins** – horizontal beams that support the rafters mid-way between the ridge and the wall plate when the rafters are longer than 2.5 m

- **struts** – timbers that support purlins at every fourth or fifth pair of rafters, used to transfer roof load to ceiling joists and onto a load-bearing wall or partition

- **straining pieces** – sole plates fixed to the ceiling joists, between the base of struts

- **collars** – sawn timber ties, sometimes used to give extra strength to prevent roof spreading out at purlin level

- **binders** – timbers fixed on edge in the roof space, at right angles to ceiling joists, to give support if the span is greater than 2.5 m

- **fascia board** – board of about 175 mm x 20 mm p.a.r. (planed all round timber) fixed to the plumb (i.e. vertical) cuts of the rafters at the eaves to provide a finish and a fixing board for guttering

- **soffit board** – board, similar to a fascia, fixed to the underside of the cradling in closed-eaves design

- **cradling** – L-shaped brackets used to provide fixing for the soffit

- **sprocket pieces** – long, wedge-shaped pieces of rafter material fixed on top of each rafter at the eaves to create an upward tilt; thus reducing the slope on a steep roof to ease flow of rainwater into guttering

- **tilting fillet** – triangular-shaped timber fixed behind a raised fascia to give it support

- **valley boards** – used to form a gutter in the valley

- **barge boards** – fascia boards inclined like a pair of rafters and fixed to the face of the verge on a gable–ended roof; sometimes with soffit boards added if the barge boards project from the wall

- **tile or slate battens** – sawn battens fixed at regular intervals on top of the lapped roofing felt; usually fixed by a slater and tiler, not the carpenter.

Setting out

Setting out covers all the actions necessary before commencing construction. To do this properly the roofer must be able to work out the basic geometry of the roof structure and use a roofing square, template and 'roofing ready reckoner'.

Basic terms

There are several terms with which the roofer must be familiar before attempting to set out a roof. Figure 9.13 on page 250 illustrates the basic terms described below.

Figure 9.13 on page 250

- **setting out,** or **pattern, rafter** – rafter selected as the basic rafter from which all setting out is done

- **span** – the distance measured in the direction of ceiling joists, from the outside of one wall plate to the other; known as the overall (O/A) span

- **run** – equal to half of the span, it is used to reduce the roof shape to a right-angled triangle

- **rise** – distance measured from the outside of the wall plates at wall plate level to the apex of the pitch lines, which run at two-thirds of the depth of the rafters

- **pitch or pitch angle** – the rise and run gives the pitch angle or, knowing the pitch angle and the run, we can calculate the rise and basic rafter length

- **pitch line** – plumb line marked at the base of the setting out rafter, marked down two-thirds of its depth to the top of the birdsmouth cut, which acts as a reference or datum point for the rafter's length

Did you know?

Clear span is the distance between joist supports; **effective span** is the distance between centres of joist bearings

- **birdsmouth** – notch cut out of the rafter to form a seating on the outside edge of the wall plate

- **plumb cut** – the vertical cut at the top of the rafter where it meets the ridge

- **side cut** – the angled cut at each end of the purlin where it meets the hip

- **edge cut** – the angled cut on top of the jack rafter where it meets the hip

Calculating the pitch

The pitch is expressed either in degrees (generally 45°, 30° or 20°) or as a fraction of the rise divided by the span. See Figure 9.11.

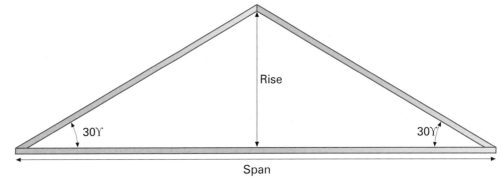

Figure 9.11 Rise and span

Example 1:

If a roof has a span of 4 m and a rise of 2 m, then:

$$\text{Pitch} = \frac{\text{rise}}{\text{span}} = \frac{2}{4} = \frac{1}{2}$$

or 45 degrees (half a right angle of 90 degrees)

Example 2:

If a roof has a span of 9 m and a rise of 3 m, then:

$$\text{Pitch} = \frac{\text{rise}}{\text{span}} = \frac{3}{9} = \frac{1}{3}$$

or 30 degrees (third of a right angle of 90 degrees)

Setting out a rafter

There are a series of steps to be followed when setting out a rafter.

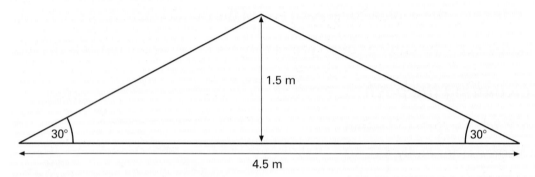

Figure 9.12 Step 1 Scale drawing of roof elevation

Step 1 Produce a scale drawing to find the true lengths and angles for cuts to the rafters. A simple drawing, as shown in Figure 9.12, will be sufficient for this purpose.

Step 2 Mark the pitch line

Step 3 Mark a plumb cut

Step 2 Mark the pitch line on the rafter.

Step 3 Set an adjustable bevel to mark a plumb cut.

Step 4 Mark true length of the pitch line

Step 5 Mark a birdsmouth

Step 4 Mark the true length of the pitch line on the rafter.

Step 5 Mark a birdsmouth. This is formed by two lines taken from the plumb cut and the **seat cut**.

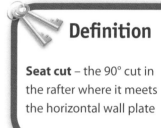

Definition

Seat cut – the 90° cut in the rafter where it meets the horizontal wall plate

Step 6 Re-mark the plumb cut allowing half the thickness of the ridge board. This rafter becomes the 'pattern rafter'.

Remember

The pitch line extends to the centre of the ridge

Step 6 Re-mark the plumb cut

Geometrical setting out of a hipped roof

Refer to Figure 9.13 for all the following steps.

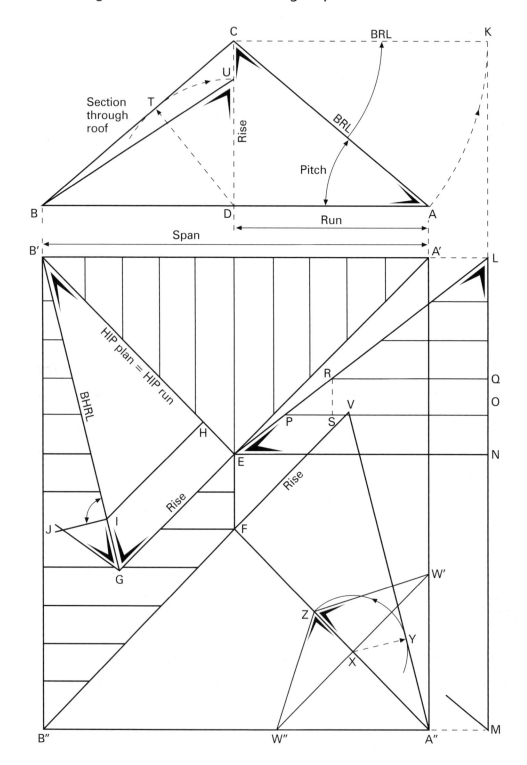

Figure 9.13 Geometry for a hipped roof

Step 1 Draw bevels and length of a common rafter by drawing triangle ABC (section through roof); where AB = the span, AD = the run (half the span), CD = the rise, angle DAC = the seat cut, angle ACD = the plumb cut and line AC or CB = basic rafter length (BRL).

Step 2 Draw bevels and length of hip rafter.

Step 3 Draw plan of the roof, showing two hipped ends (always drawn at angles of 45 degrees in equal pitched roofs), shown as A'E, B'E, and A'F, B'F. At right angles to B'E, draw line EG, equal in length to rise at CD. Join G to B'. Angle FB'G is the seat cut. Angle B'GE is the plumb cut. Line B'G = basic hip rafter length (BHRL).

Step 4 Draw hip edge cut (for square-edged hips) by drawing line HI, parallel to EG at any distance from E; then draw line IJ, equal to distance EH and at right angles to B'I. Draw line JG. Angle JGI is the edge cut.

Step 5 Draw jack and cripple rafter bevels and lengths by using the radius CA to describe an arc from A to K, equal to the basic rafter length. Project K down to form LM. Join L to E to give the elevated, true shape of the roof side. Draw single lines to represent rafters at 400 mm (scaled) centres. Angle LEN is the jack/cripple edge cut. (Jack/cripple side cut is the same as common rafter plumb cut). Line OP is the basic length of the first jack rafter; QR is the second.

Step 6 The perpendicular, SP, of the triangle RSP, is equal to the constant diminish of the jack rafters.

Step 7 Draw purlin bevels. Angle QLR is the purlin edge cut. With compass at D and CB as a tangent as T, describe an arc to cut CD at U. Join U to B. Angle DUB is the purlin side cut.

Step 8 Draw dihedral angle or backing bevel (for top edge of hips, if required). Establish triangle A"VF, as at B'GE. Draw a 45 degree line at any point, marked W'W". With compass at X and A"V as a tangent as Y, describe an arc to cut A"F at Z. Join Z to W' and W". Angle W'ZX or XZW" is the required backing bevel.

Using a 'Roofing ready reckoner'

The simplest alternative to using geometry for finding the bevels and lengths in roofing is to use a booklet called a 'Roofing ready reckoner'. The booklet consists of a series of reference tables, which are very easy to follow once a few basic principles have been understood.

The tables cover a wide variety of roof pitches and the various bevels required for pitches up to 75 degrees. Basic rafter lengths (BRL) and basic hip rafter lengths (BHRL) can be worked out from the tables.

To use this method, the span of the roof must first be measured from the bedded wall plates and halved to give the run. The pitch must also be known or taken from the elevation drawing using a protractor.

Example:

Take a hipped roof of 36° pitch, with a span of 7.460 m. Halve this to give a run of 3.730 m. Referring to the tables, we can work out the lengths of the common and hip rafters as follows:

Length of common rafter for:

```
1.0 m run    =  1.236
3.0 m run    =  3.708
0.7 m run    =  0.865
0.03 m run   =  0.0371
             ---------
3.730 m run  =  4.6101
             ---------
Hence BRL    =  4.610
```

The results would then be shown as on Figure 9.14.

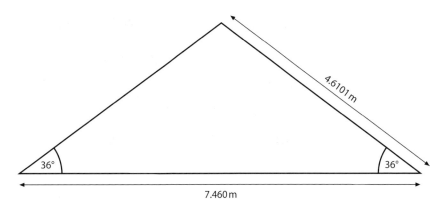

Figure 9.14 Length of common rafter

The same steps are followed to find the length of the hip rafter as shown in Figure 9.15.

Using a metric rafter square

This is the modern version of the steel roofing square and is another method of finding bevels and lengths.

The square comes with an explanatory booklet, which is illustrated and clearly explains how to use the square.

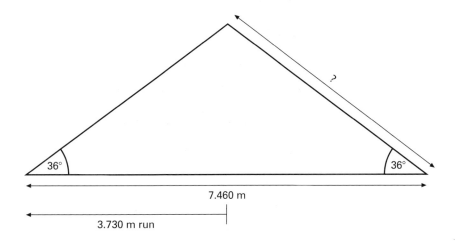

Figure 9.15 Length of hip rafter

Using templates

As the bevels are determined they are usually marked on the face of a spare piece of dressed timber for easy reference. The various bevels are identified with abbreviations such as hip plumb cut (hip p/c). From this they can be very easily transferred to the sliding bevel.

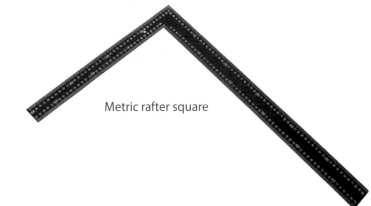

Metric rafter square

As an alternative, small templates can be made to the required bevels.

Sequence of operations

Bedding wall plates

The initial operation for adding any roof is bedding the wall plates. This is usually done as a joint effort by the bricklayer and the carpenter. The bricklayer spreads the mortar, beds and levels the plates and the carpenter checks that they are square and parallel to each other across the span.

To check that they are square the carpenter uses the '3:4:5' rule for creating a right angle. The 3:4:5 rule is a very simple method used in trigonometry (the part of mathematics concerned with triangles and angles). The rule states that if you take a line 3 cm long, another line 4 cm long and another line 5 cm long and make them into a triangle, the angle opposite the longest line will always be a perfect right angle.

If the plates are all square to each other, they should also be parallel. However, it is sensible to check to see that plates are the same distance apart on each side of the rectangle.

The sequence of operations now varies between types of roof, so each is described in turn.

Gable roof

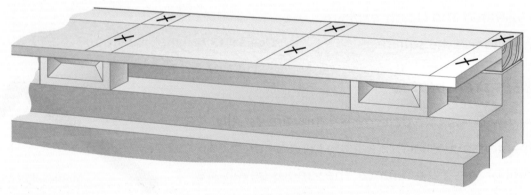

Figure 9.16 Step 1 Mark rafter positions on plate and ridge

Step 1 Once the wall plates have set, the ridge board can be laid against the wall plate and the positions of the common rafters marked across both members.

Step 2 Fix the restraint straps over the wall plates and the ceiling joists next to the rafter marks. They are either screwed, nailed or fixed with framing anchors.

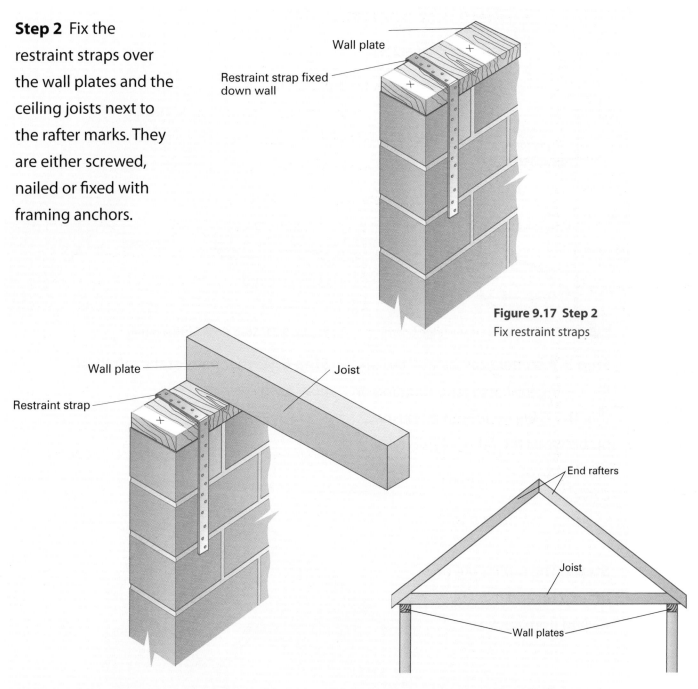

Wall plate

Restraint strap fixed down wall

Figure 9.17 Step 2 Fix restraint straps

Wall plate

Joist

Restraint strap

Figure 9.18 Step 3 Fix joists to cross walls

End rafters

Joist

Wall plates

Figure 9.19 Step 4 Fix end rafters

Step 3 The joists should also be fixed to any internal cross walls. The joists can be boarded with scaffold boards to provide a work area.

Step 4 At each end of the roof a pair of rafters is pitched and fixed to the wall plates and the joists. They will root against each other at their plumb cuts.

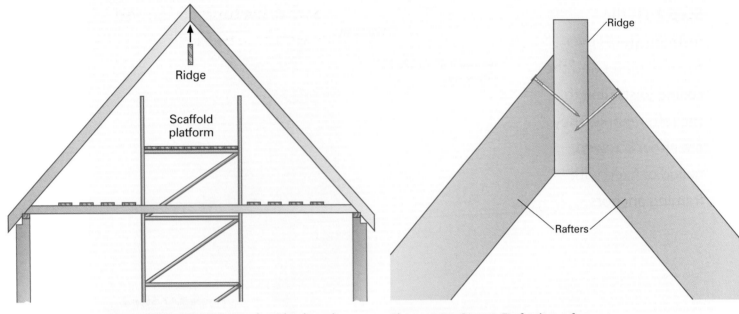

Figure 9.20 Step 5 Insert the ridge board

Figure 9.21 Step 6 Fix further rafters

Step 5 A scaffold can be erected on the ceiling joist area and, standing on this, the ridge board can be pushed up between the rafter plumb cuts and fixed.

Step 6 Further pairs of the rafters are now fixed.

Step 7 The purlins are now offered up and fixed by screw nailing from above.

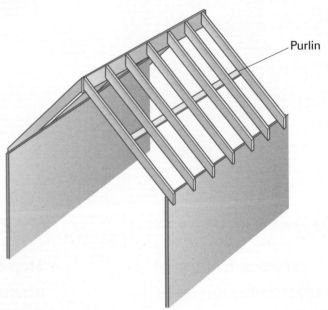

Figure 9.22 Step 7 Fix purlins

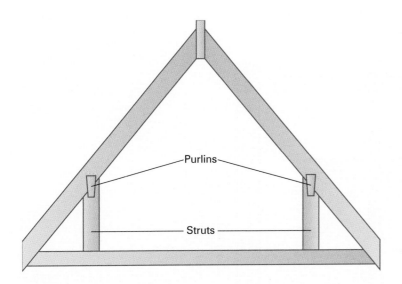

Step 8 The struts are the next members to be fixed.

Figure 9.23 Step 8 Fix struts

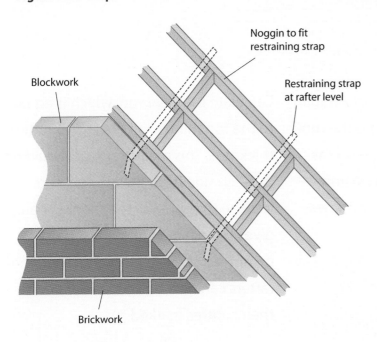

Figure 9.24 Step 9 Fix horizontal restraint straps

Step 9 Finally, horizontal restraint straps are fixed across the rafters (maximum 2.0 m centre to centre) on to the inner leaf of the gable walls.

Hipped roof

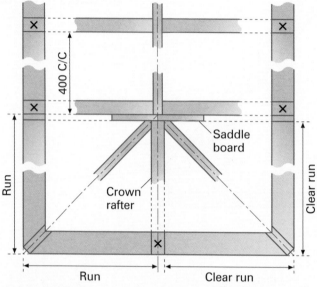

Figure 9.25 Step 1 Mark out a hipped end and mark rafter positions

Step 1 First check the actual span and divide by two to find the run. Mark this as a centre line on the wall plate at each hip end and mark the **crown rafter** thickness.

Calculate the clear run, which is equal to the run minus half the crown rafter thickness. This measurement is marked up each side from the hip end and, less the thickness of the saddle board, gives the position of the first pair of common rafters at each end. The other rafters can now be spaced out and their centres marked.

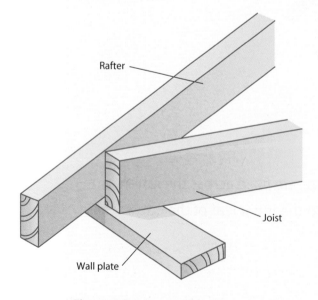

Figure 9.26 Step 2 Fix ceiling joists

Step 2 Now the ceiling joists can be fixed to the common rafters, but not those that are fixed to the jack rafters at each end.

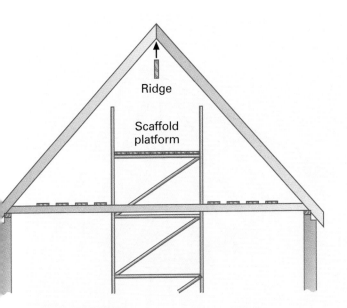

Figure 9.27 Step 3 Insert the ridge board

Step 3 The ridge board is inserted and fixed.

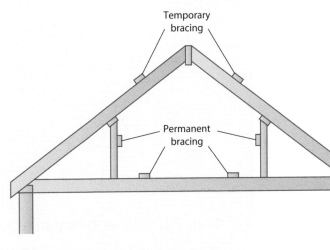

Figure 9.28 Step 4 Brace the rafters

Step 4 The rafters are now braced temporarily.

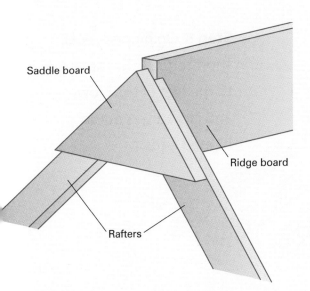

Figure 9.29 Step 5 Fix the saddle board

Step 5 The saddle board is now fixed in place.

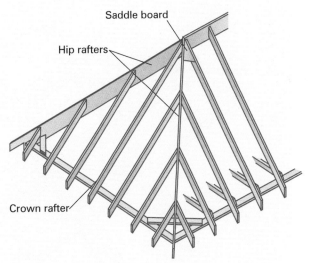

Figure 9.30 Step 6 Fix the crown rafters and hips

Step 6 The crown rafters and hips are now fixed. Next, the jack rafters, remaining joists, binders and struts are fixed to complete the roof structure.

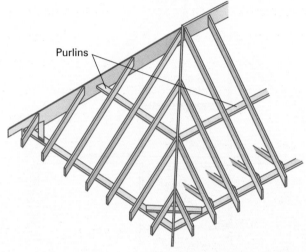

Purlins

Step 7 It is usual to fix purlins next. This will save struggling against a full set of rafters and provides a ledge to rest the rafters against on their way to the ridge.

Figure 9.31 Step 7 Fix purlins

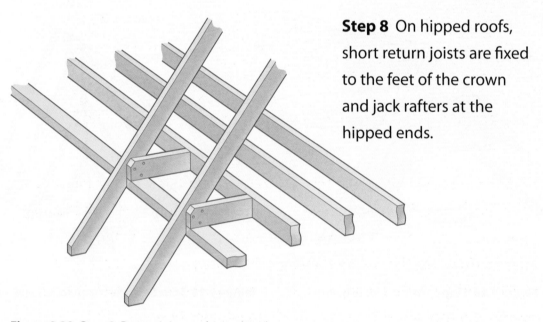

Step 8 On hipped roofs, short return joists are fixed to the feet of the crown and jack rafters at the hipped ends.

Figure 9.32 Step 8 Return joists on hipped end

Trussed rafters

Most roofing on domestic dwellings now comprises factory-made trussed rafters. These are made of stress graded, **p.a.r.** timber to a wide variety of designs, depending on requirements. All joints are butt jointed and held together with fixing plates, face fixed on either side. These plates are usually made of galvanised steel and either nailed or factory pressed. They may also be **gang-nailed** gusset plates made of 12 mm resin bonded plywood.

Definition

p.a.r. – a term used for timber that has been 'planed all round'

Definition

Gang-nailed – galvanised plate with spikes used to secure butt joints

Standard trussed rafters

One of the main advantages of this type of roof is the clear span achieved, as there is no need for intermediate, load-bearing partition walls. Standard trusses are strong enough to resist the eventual load of the roofing materials. However, they are not able to withstand pressures applied by lateral bending. Hence, damage is most likely to occur during delivery, movement across site, site storage or lifting into position.

Wall plates are bedded as described above. Following this, the positions of the trusses can be marked at a maximum of 600 mm between centres along each wall plate. The sequence of operations then varies between gable and hipped roofs.

Remember

Never alter a trussed rafter without the structural designer's approval

Gable roofs

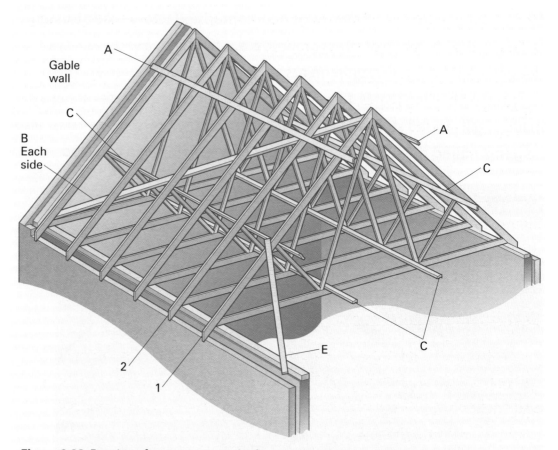

Figure 9.33 Erection of common trussed rafters

Step 1 Fix first truss using framing anchors 1.

Step 2 Stabilise and plumb first truss with temporary braces E.

Step 3 Fix temporary battens on each side of ridge A.

Step 4 Position next truss 2.

Step 5 Fix the wall plate and temporary battens A. Continue until last truss is positioned.

Step 6 Fix braces B.

Step 7 Fix braces C.

Step 8 Fix horizontal restraint straps at max 2.0 m centres across trusses on to the inner leaf of the gable walls.

Flat roof

The term 'flat roof' refers to any roof which has its upper surface inclined at an angle (also known as the slope or fall) not exceeding 10 degrees.

The amount of fall should be sufficient to clear water away to the outlet pipe(s) as quickly as possible across the whole roof surface. This may involve several directional changes of fall.

Failure to dispose of surface water effectively could result in ponding (i.e. forming pools of water), which may also increase the load on the roof and also provide a catchment area for enough silt to encourage plant life. This could have a harmful effect on the roof covering and become powerful enough to break open water seals.

Setting out requirements

Find the size of the timbers being used. Next, determine the spacing between the joists (400 mm or 600 mm). Lay the joints from wall to wall and anchor down the wall at 2 m intervals. Fix the noggings around the perimeter 50 mm from the wall.

Basic construction

Flat roofs are similar in construction to upper floors (discussed later) but unless accessible are not so heavily loaded. Joists are, therefore, of a smaller dimension.

The joists may be laid to a fall to carry off rainwater, in which case the ceiling below will slope.

More usually timber **firring** is used on the upper edges of the joists to provide a suitable fall.

The openings, known as trimmings, for roof lights or access traps are constructed in the same way as for floors, discussed in a later section.

Safety tip

Roof erection is a two-handed job

Definition

Firring – a long wedge, tapered where joists are parallel to the fall, or of variable depth for joists at right angles

If joists are fixed, level firrings are fixed to the top edge to form a fall for the drainage of rainwater.

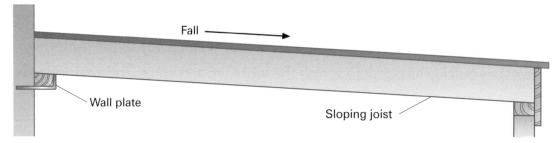

Figure 9.34 Joists laid to a fall

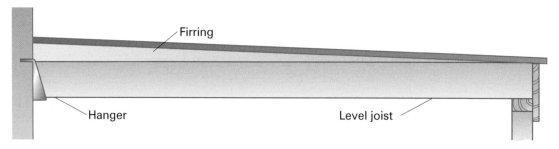

Figure 9.35 Joists with firrings to provide fall

Figures 9.36 and 9.37 show the alternative methods of fixing a flat roof.

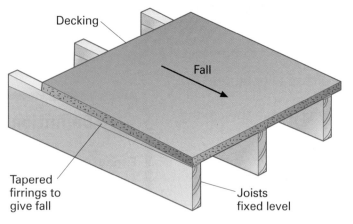

Figure 9.36 Joists fixed parallel to the fall

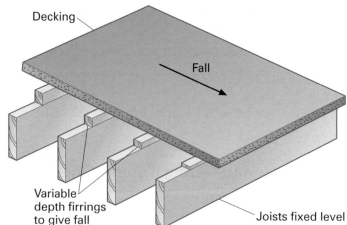

Figure 9.37 Joists fixed at a right angle to the fall

Materials used

The material for the roof decking must be capable of supporting the chosen roof system. Any of the following may be used as decking:

- **Tongued and grooved board**. Rarely used these days as a decking material. If used, then boards should be laid either with, or diagonal to, the fall of the roof. Cupping of the boards laid across the fall could cause the roof covering to form hollows of sufficient depth to partially hold back the flow of water off the roof and leave pools.

- **Plywood**. Only roofing grades must be used. Plywood is classified according to its veneer bond performance, as discussed in Chapter 4 Timber technology (see page 79). Weather and Boil Proof (WBP) should be used. Boards should be supported on all edges, leaving a joint gap of 1 mm per metre run of board, be it along its length or width. This allowance is made in case of any moisture movement.

- **Chipboard**. Only types with the required water resistance, and which have been classified for this purpose, must be used. Boards are available which have a covering of bituminous felt bonded to one surface, which gives the board temporary protection against wet weather. Once it has been laid the edges and joints can be sealed.

- **Oriented strand board (OSB)**. Generally more stable than chipboard, but again only roofing grades are suitable. Provision for moisture movement should be made as with chipboard.

- **Cement bonded chipboard**. Strong and durable, with high density (much heavier and greater moisture resistance than standard chipboard). Moisture movement provision should be as for chipboard.

- **Metal decking**. Profiled sheets of aluminium or galvanised steel with a variety of factory-applied colour coatings and co-ordinated fixings are available. More usually associated with large steel sub-structures and fixed by specialist installers. May be used on small roof spans to some effect. Sheets can be rolled to different profiles and cut to any reasonable length to suit individual requirements.

- **Translucent sheeting**. Can be corrugated or flat (e.g. polycarbonate twin-wall etc.). It must be installed following manufacturer's instructions.

Edge support, laying and fixing are similar to floors (covered later). Moisture movement will be greater than plywood, therefore a 2 mm provision per metre run should be allowed with at least a 10 mm gap around the roof edges. Tongued and grooved boards should be laid as per the manufacturer's instructions.

Cut and fix verges

At edges other than drainage, water must be prevented from spilling over onto the wall. The upstand of the verge has a triangular internal fillet to give an easy bend and support to the felt.

Sharp arises should be removed on the fascia board to avoid cracking the felt.

Cut and fix eaves

At the eaves of a flat roof a drip fillet is fixed to carry the roof covering into the gutter. Where joists are at right angles to the fall short blocks are fixed to the final joist to support the fascia and soffit.

Roof decking

Roof decking can be made of timber sheeting or boards and is fixed to the joints prior to weatherproofing.

Lean-to roof

Commonly used on outer buildings such as garages, rafters are fixed to a wall plate that has been fixed to the existing building.

Suspended timber floors

There are several types of floor construction used in buildings. However, the only one covered in the NVQ syllabus and of interest to the carpenter is a suspended timber floor. These could be fitted to upper or lower floors. The latter is also called the ground floor.

Over the next few pages we will look at:

- basic structure
- joists
- floor coverings.

Basic structure of floors

Suspended timber floors are constructed with timbers known as joists, which are spaced parallel to each other across the floor. In a single floor the joists rest on their edges at each end and in a double floor they are given intermediate support. Various types of floor covering are then laid on top.

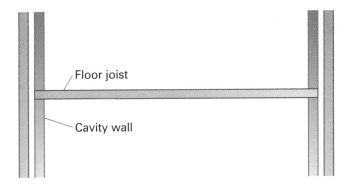

Figure 9.38 Single floor

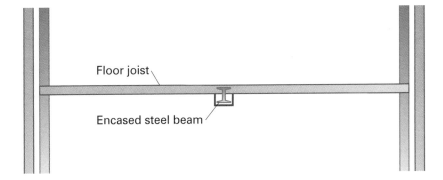

Figure 9.39 Double floor

Floors must be constructed to conform to the *Building Regulations*, in particular Part C which is concerned with dampness. A damp proof course (DPC) is inserted by the builder at not less than 150 mm above ground level, to prevent moisture moving from the ground to the upper side of the floor. No timbers are allowed to be used below the DPC.

Damp proof course (DPC)

Air bricks, which are built into the external walls of the building, allow air to flow continually through the under-floor area. This ventilation prevents conditions that can lead to an attack of dry rot.

Joists

In domestic dwellings, suspended upper floors are usually single floors, with the joist supported at each end by the structural walls. These joists are called bridging joists, but any joists that are affected by an opening in the floor such as a stairwell are called **trimmer**, **trimming** and **trimmed joists**.

Joists

Bridging joists are usually sawn timber 50 mm thick. The trimmer that carries the trimmed joists and transfers this load to the trimming joist must be made thicker by 12.5 mm – 25 mm. The depth of the joists will have been calculated by the architectural team during design of the building.

A method of checking the depth of joists is to divide the span by 20 and add 20. This will give the joist depth.

Example:

Span = 4000 mm

$$\text{Depth} = \frac{4000}{20} + 20$$

$$= 220 \text{ mm}$$

Thus the joist depth is 220 mm or 22 cm. The nearest commercial size timber would be 225 mm × 50 mm.

Figures 9.40 and 9.41 show the alternative methods of constructing a floor.

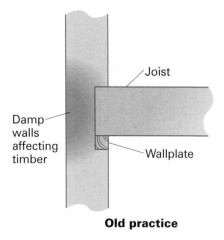
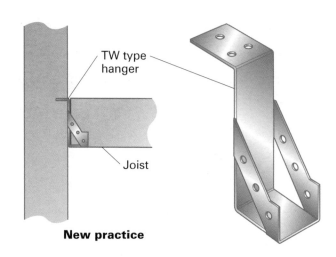

Old practice **New practice**

Figure 9.40 Solid floor bearings

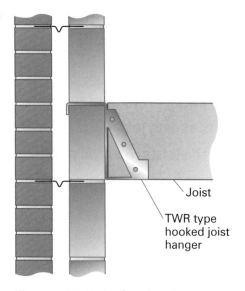
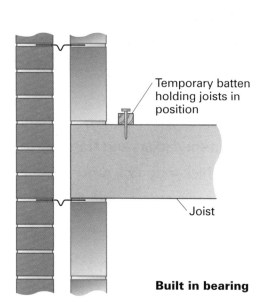

Built in bearing

Figure 9.41 Cavity floor bearings

Traditional tusk tenon joint

Framing joints between trimming joist and trimmer

Traditionally, a tusk tenon joint was used (and is sometimes preferred), between the trimming joist and the trimmer. If the joint is formed correctly it is extremely strong.

Metal timber connectors are now used in place of traditional joints. These take the form of metal framing anchors and timber-to-timber joist hangers. The saving of labour hours is a great advantage over traditional methods.

Fitting joists for floors

Before the carpenter can begin constructing the floor, the bricklayer needs to build the honeycomb sleeper walls. This type of walling has gaps in each course to allow the free flow of air through the under floor area. It is on these sleeper walls that the carpenter will lay the timber wall plate, which will provide a fixing for the floor joists. The following pages describe the steps in fitting floor joists.

Timber-to-timber joist hangers

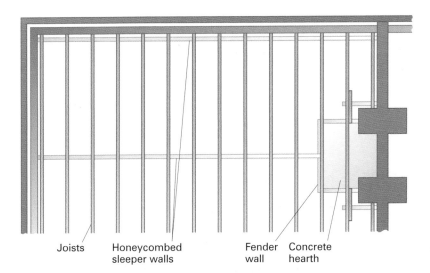
Figure 9.42 Part plan view of exposed floor

Joists   Honeycombed sleeper walls   Fender wall   Concrete hearth

Figure 9.43 Sequence of fixing joists

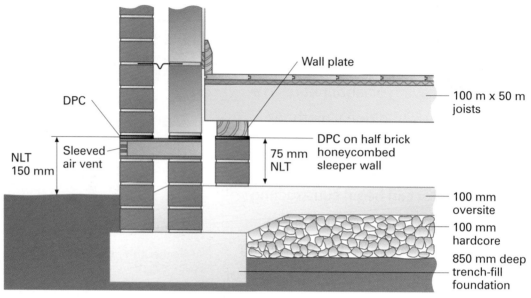

DPC

Wall plate

100 m x 50 m joists

NLT 150 mm

Sleeved air vent

DPC on half brick honeycombed sleeper wall

75 mm NLT

100 mm oversite

100 mm hardcore

850 mm deep trench-fill foundation

Figure 9.44 Section view through floor and wall

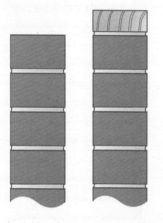

Figure 9.45 Step 1 Bed in the wall plate

400 or 600 mm

Figure 9.46 Step 2 Space out joists

Step 1 The wall plate is bedded and levelled on a bed of sand and cement mortar.

Step 2 When the wall plates are set the joists can be cut to length and the ends sealed with preservative. Space the joists out and fix temporary battens near each end to hold the joists in position. Ends should be kept away from the walls by approximately 12 mm. It is important that cambered edges are turned upwards.

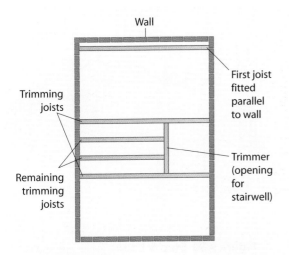

Figure 9.47 Step 3 Fit first joist and trimmers

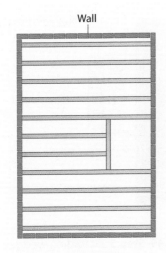

Figure 9.48 Step 4 Fit remaining joists

Step 3 Fix the first joist parallel to the wall with a gap of 50 mm. Usually trimming joists and trimmer are positioned next, to allow any intended opening, such as a stairwell, to be formed correctly.

Step 4 Fix subsequent joists at required spacings until the opposite wall is reached. Spacing depends on the thickness of the floor boards, or sheets, to be used but 400 mm centre to centre is normal in domestic dwellings. When using chipboard flooring panels the spacing is more critical, as the cross-joints in the length of the panel must bear centrally on a joist. On upper floors joist spacing must also allow for the plasterboard sheets that will form the ceiling below.

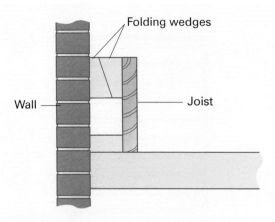

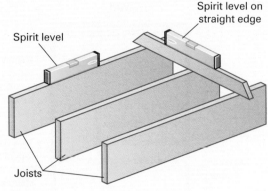

Figure 9.49 Step 5 Fit folding wedges

Figure 9.50 Step 6 Ensure joists are level

Step 5 Fit folding wedges to keep end joists parallel to the wall. Over tightening is to be avoided in case the wall is strained.

Step 6 Check that joists are level with a straight edge or line and, if necessary, pack with off-cuts of DPC or lower them by packing the joist-bearing area.

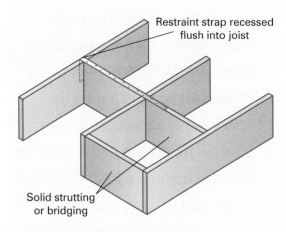

Step 7 Fit restraint straps and, if the joists span more than 3.5 m, fit struts and bridges. These are described separately below.

Figure 9.51 Step 7 Fit restraint straps, struts and bridges

Remember

Once completed, it is very important to clean the under-floor area before fitting flooring, as timber cuttings or sawdust are likely to attract moisture.

Strutting and bridging

When a joist spans more than 3.5 m, a row of struts must be fixed midway between each joist. The strutting or bridging stiffens the floor and prevents movement and twisting, hence holding it in place while flooring and ceilings are fixed. There are various methods in use but the main ones are covered on pages 275–277.

Solid bridging

For solid bridging, timber struts the same depth as the joist are cut to fit tightly between each joist and skew-nailed to hold them in place. A disadvantage of solid bridging is that it tends to loosen when the joist shrinks.

Solid bridging

Herring-bone strutting

With herring-bone strutting, timber battens (usually 50 mm × 32 mm) are cut to fit diagonally between the joists. A small saw cut is put into the ends of the battens before fixing to prevent splitting. It will remain tight even after joist shrinkage. The following steps describe the fitting of timber herring-bone strutting.

Step 1 Space joists

Step 2 Mark joist depths

Step 1 Nail a temporary batten near the line of strutting to keep the joists spaced at correct centres.

Step 2 Mark the depth of a joist across the edge of the two joists.

Step 3 Lay strut across two joists as a diagonal

Step 4 Cut to the mark

Step 3 Lay strut across two joists as a diagonal to the lines drawn in step 2.

Step 4 Draw pencil line underneath as shown in step 3 and cut to the mark. This procedure will provide the correct angle for nailing.

Step 5 Fixing the strut

Step 5 Fix the strut between the two joists.

Steel strutting

There are two types of galvanised steel herringbone struts available. The first type has angled lugs for fixing with minimum 38 mm round head wire nails.

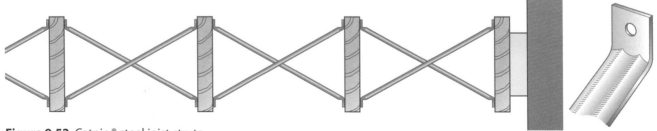

Figure 9.52 Catnic ® steel joist struts

The second type has pointed ends which bed themselves into joists when forced in at the bottom and pulled down at the top. Unlike the other types of strutting this type is fixed from below.

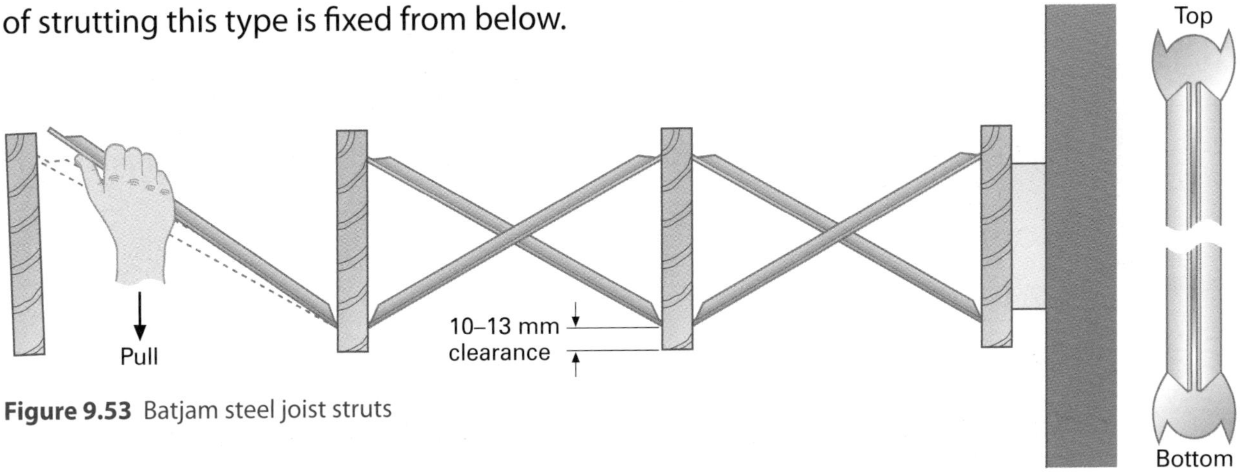

Top

10–13 mm
clearance

Pull

Figure 9.53 Batjam steel joist struts

Bottom

The disadvantage with steel strutting, which is made to suit joist centres of 400, 450 and 600 mm, is that there will always be places in any floor that will require reduced size struts.

Restraint straps

Anchoring straps, normally referred to as restraint straps, are needed to restrict any possible movement of the floor and walls due to wind pressure. They are made from galvanised steel, 5 mm thick for horizontal restraint and 2.5 mm for vertical restraint, 30 mm wide and up to 1.2 m in length. Holes are punched along the length to provide fixing points.

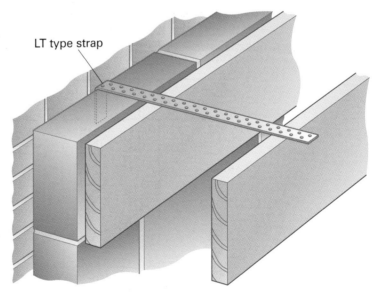

LT type strap

Figure 9.54 Restraint straps for joists parallel or at right angles to a wall

When the joists run parallel to the wall, the straps will require notching-in, whereby a notch is created to house the strap to make it level with the top of the joist.

The anchors should be fixed at a maximum of 2 m centre to centre.

Further information can be found in Schedule 7 of the *Building Regulations*.

Floor coverings
Softwood flooring

Softwood flooring can be used either at ground or upper floor levels. It usually consists of 25 mm × 150 mm tongued and grooved (T & G) boards. The tongue is slightly off-centre to provide extra wear on the surface that will be walked upon.

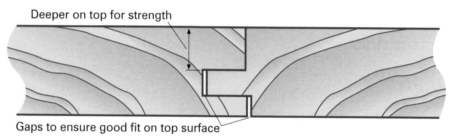

Deeper on top for strength

Gaps to ensure good fit on top surface

Figure 9.55 Section through softwood covering

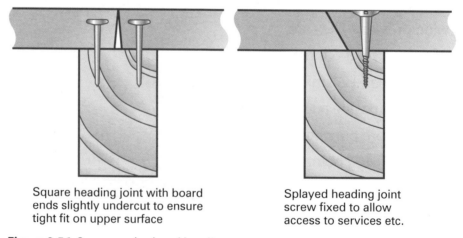

Square heading joint with board ends slightly undercut to ensure tight fit on upper surface

Splayed heading joint screw fixed to allow access to services etc.

Figure 9.56 Square and splayed heading

When boards are joined together, the joints should be staggered evenly throughout the floor to give it strength. They should never be placed next to each other, as this prevents the joists from being tied together properly. The boards are fixed with either floor brads nailed through the surface and punched in, or secret-nailed with lost-head nails through the tongue. The nails used should be 2½ times the thickness of the floorboard in length.

Splayed heading will prevent softwood board from splitting (see Figure 9.56).

The first board is nailed down about 12 mm from the wall. The remaining boards can be fixed four to six boards at a time, leaving 12 mm around the perimeter. This gap is to allow for expansion and will eventually be covered by the skirting board. There are two methods of cramping the boards before fixing which are shown in Figure 9.57.

Did you know?

Secret-nailing means that no nails are visible once the job is completed

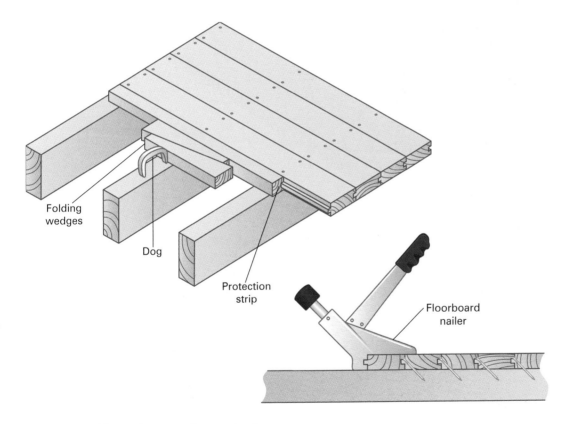

Folding wedges

Dog

Protection strip

Floorboard nailer

Figure 9.57 Alternative cramping methods

Chipboard flooring

Flooring-grade chipboard is now being increasingly used for domestic floors. It is available in sheet sizes of 2440 mm × 600 mm × 18 mm and can be square edged or tongued and grooved on all edges. The latter is much to be preferred.

If square edged is used, it must be supported on all edges.

Tongued and grooved boards are laid end to end, at right angles to the joist. Cross-joints should be staggered and, as with softwood flooring, expansion gaps of 12 mm left around the perimeter. The ends must be supported.

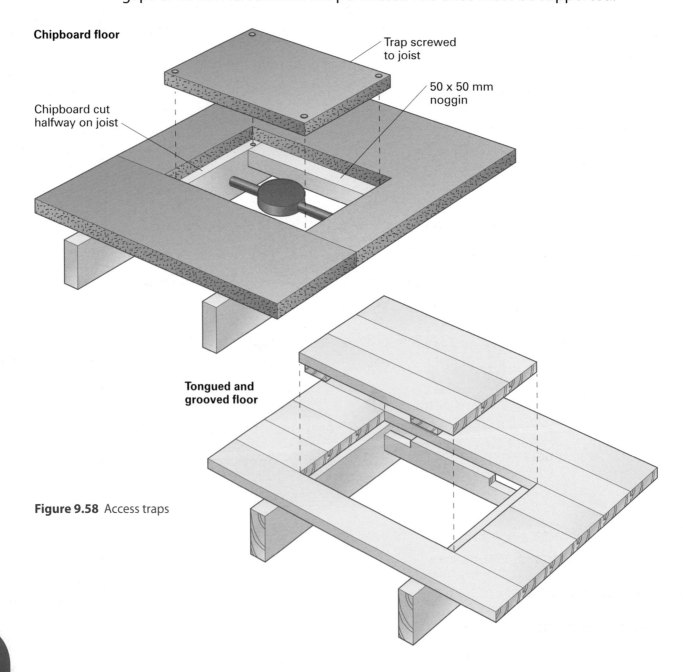

Chipboard floor

Trap screwed to joist

50 x 50 mm noggin

Chipboard cut halfway on joist

Tongued and grooved floor

Figure 9.58 Access traps

Hence, when setting out the floor joists the spacing should be set to avoid unnecessary wastage. The board should be fixed with 50 mm or 65 mm annular-ring shank nails.

Access traps must be created in flooring in order to allow access to services such as gas and water. See Figure 9.58.

Windows

Windows are generally designed to allow daylight and air into a room and give people an outside view, but they must also conserve heat and be able to withstand the weather.

There are many forms and designs, the most common being:

- traditional casement windows
- stormproof windows
- bay windows.

They are traditionally made from timber, softwood and hardwood but, with new materials and improved manufacturing methods, they are also available in metal, aluminium and pvc (sold under a variety of names including PVC, PVCu, uPVC, PVC-Upvc and others).

As windows are subjected to extreme weather conditions they must be constructed in such a way as to give maximum protection against the worst possible weather conditions.

A window should also be secure, durable, with easy opening operation and provide, where necessary, good sound and thermal insulation.

This section will look at:

- main window types
- assembly of frames and sashes
- installing windows
- window boards.

Did you know?

pvc stands for polyvinyl chloride, a tough, white solid plastic that is easy to colour and is strongly resistant to fire, chemicals and weather

Did you know?

In 1696 houses were taxed on the number of windows per household – this was called 'Window Tax' and it is the reason some very old houses don't have many windows!

Main window types
Traditional casement windows

Casement windows comprise a solid outer frame with one or more smaller and lighter frames within it, called sashes or casements.

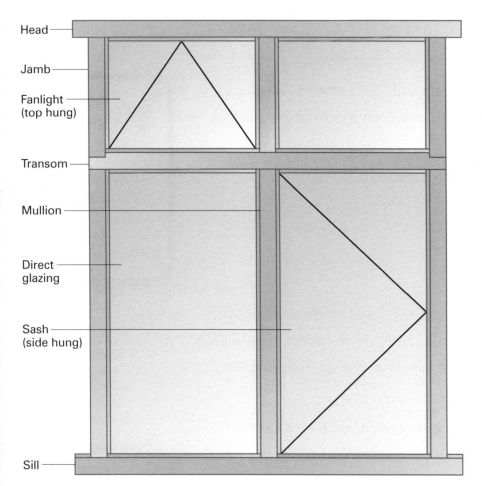

Figure 9.59 Traditional casement window

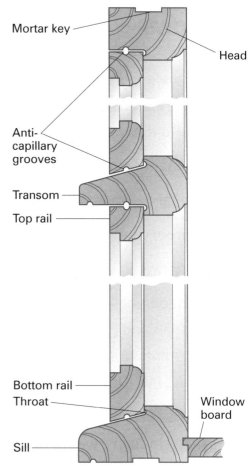

Figure 9.60 Section through traditional window incorporating top and side hung sashes

The main components are:

- **Frame.** The main frame consists of a head, sill and two vertical jambs. Intermediate members are incorporated to form openings for sashes or to alter the design. The vertical sections are known as mullions and horizontal members are transoms.

- **Opening casement.** Consists of top and bottom rails with two stiles. If a casement is divided up, these members are known as glazing bars. When glass is fixed into the main frame itself this is known as direct glazing. Opening casements above a transom are called fanlights.

- **Joints.** All joints used on a traditional casement frame are mortise and tenon, the mortises being formed in the head and sill, while the jambs are tenoned. Casements are haunched mortise and tenons and both are held together using wedges or draw pins and star dowels; draw pins being more suitable when the **horns** are to be cut off later. Joints are covered in more detail in Chapter 12 Marking and setting out joinery products.

- **Weather proofing.** During manufacture a groove is formed around the outside edges of the head, sill and jambs to provide a mortar key. Grooves, known as anti-capillary grooves, are also incorporated along the inside of the rebates in order to prevent water passing into the building; while the transom and sill have a 'throat' to stop water penetrating and are sloped to allow rainwater to run off .

Definition

Horns – these are extensions to the frame that protect it during storage or transport, cut off before installation

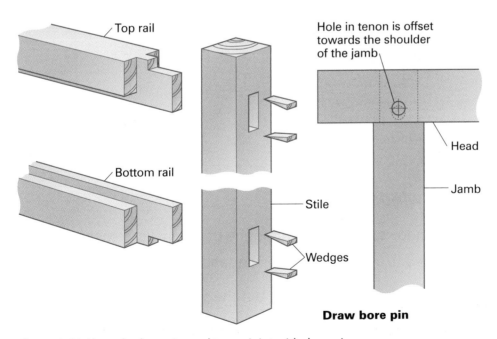

Figure 9.61 Haunched mortise and tenon joint with draw pin

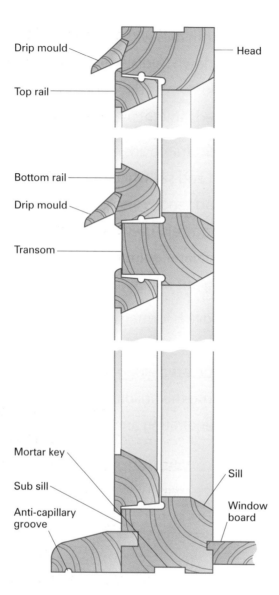

Figure 9.62 Section through typical stormproof window

Stormproof windows

Stormproof windows are a variation on the traditional casement windows and are designed to increase their performance against bad weather.

The outer frame is basically the same but the sashes are rebated to cover the gap between sash and frame. This reduces the possibility of driving rain entering the building.

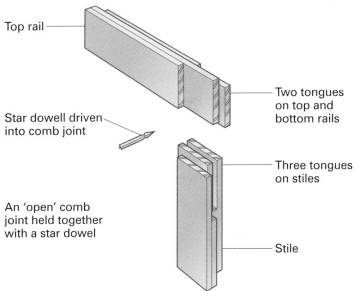

Top rail

Star dowell driven into comb joint

An 'open' comb joint held together with a star dowel

Two tongues on top and bottom rails

Three tongues on stiles

Stile

Figure 9.63 Joining of main frame

The main frame is joined together using mortise and tenon joints, but the sashes are held together using a comb joint and star dowels, although mortise and tenon can be used.

During manufacture anti-capillary grooves are incorporated along the inside of the rebates to prevent water passing into a building.

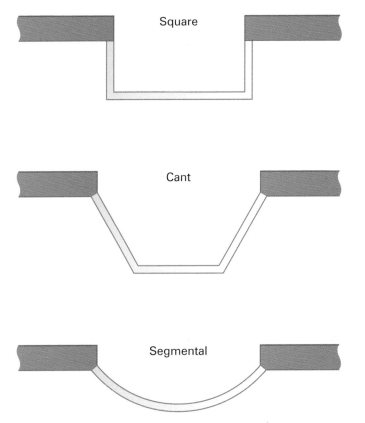

Square

Cant

Segmental

Figure 9.64 Common types of bay window

Bay windows

A window projecting from the face of a building is called a bay. There are various types, which take their name from the shape they form when seen in plan view.

The majority of bay windows are constructed in a similar way to the outer frame of a casement window. With the segmental type angle posts are added to the corners to form its shape.

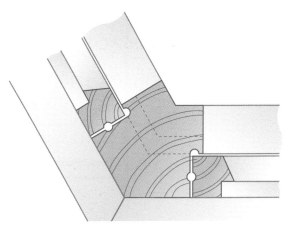

Figure 9.65 Detail of solid angle post

The heads, sills and transoms are all mitred at the intersection and held together by dowelling or by using a handrail bolt.

The mullions or angle posts can be built up from two pieces or made out of solid timber. These are tenoned into the sill and head as with the jambs.

Assembly of frames and sashes

Windows may be delivered fully constructed. However, if they have to be assembled, the procedure below shows how this should be done:

Step 1 Prior to gluing, frames and sashes should be assembled dry to check the joints, sizes and that they are square.

Step 2 Lay a **squaring rod** across the diagonals to check that each one measures the same. The length of a diagonal should be marked on the rod, then do the same for the other diagonal. If the pencil mark is in the same place the frame is square. New joints may have to be made if the frame is distorted.

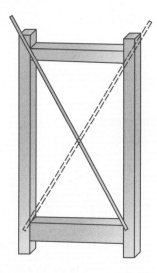

Figure 9.66 Step 2 Check diagonals with a squaring rod

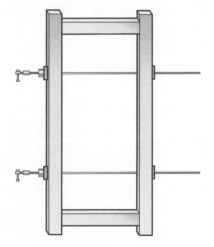

Figure 9.67 Step 3 Glue together and cramp

Step 3 Once a sash or frame has been assembled dry and checked, a waterproof adhesive can be applied to the faces of the tenons and shoulders and the items glued and cramped together to dry.

Step 4 Check again that the sash is square and not in wind, as well as ensuring the overall size is correct. Then wedges should be lightly tapped into each tenon joint and, if everything is correct, they can be driven in fully, outside wedges first, and star dowels inserted if required.

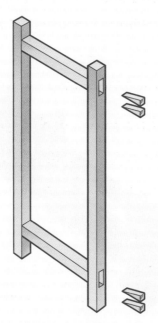

Figure 9.68 Step 4 Secure with wedges

Installing windows

As brickwork rises

Casement windows made of wood are usually built in as the brickwork proceeds. They are secured with separate fixing devices, traditionally referred to as frame clamps (see photograph on page 288).

Essentially, according to the type used, they are either screwed or hammered into the wooden side-jambs as the brickwork rises, where they will be bedded into the mortar between the bricks. Two or three per side is usual, like built-in door frames covered later.

Initially the windows are put in position, checked that they are plumb and then supported at the head with one or two weighted scaffold boards.

If the windows have a separate sill of stone or pre-cast concrete these must be bedded first and protected with temporary boards on their outer face, sides and edges.

Frame clamp

Projecting sills, formed with sloping **brick-on-edge**, are usually built at a later stage, the windows having been packed up with spare timber to leave space for these to be inserted.

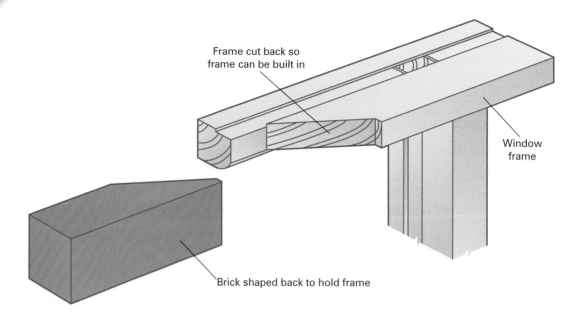

Frame cut back so frame can be built in

Window frame

Brick shaped back to hold frame

Figure 9.69 Built-in window frame

Temporary profile frames

Sometimes it is not possible to build the windows
in as the brickwork rises. If this is the case a
temporary profile frame may be made on site or
in the workshop to match the window size and
put in place during building. It can be replaced
by the window as soon as the brickwork is dry
and stable, using suitable fixings.

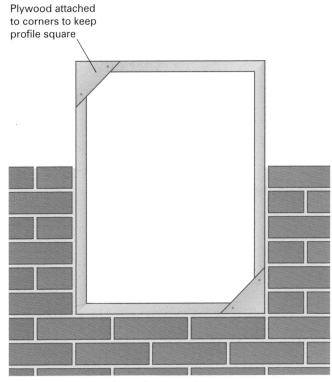

Plywood attached
to corners to keep
profile square

Figure 9.70 Temporary profile frame

Fixing components

There is a range of commercially available fixing components. Common ones
are described below:

- **Galvanised steel frame cramps.** These provide good fixings and, because
  they are screwed to the frame, any cramps (or ties) already fixed and bedded in
  mortar are not disturbed by hammering. Also, by resting on the last laid bricks,
  the next brick above the tie is easily bedded. The disadvantages are their small
  screws, requiring a screwdriver and bradawl. If there is no groove in the frame,
  the upturned end of the cramp inhibits the next brick from touching the frame.
  There will be problems later, if rust-proofed screws are not used.

- **Zinc-plated screw ties.** These also provide good fixings and are screwed to
  the frame, avoiding vibration from hammering. They do not require screws,
  bradawl or screwdriver and can be offset or skewed to avoid the cavities
  in hollow blocks. On the negative side, the brickwork has to be stopped
  one course below the required fixing to allow rotation of the loop when

screwing in, then the brick or block beneath the tie is bedded – with some difficulty and loss of normal bedding adhesion.

Definition

Still green – mortar that is unset and not at full strength

- **Sherardised holdfast.** Holdfasts are fixed quickly and are easily driven in by hammer. The spiked ends spread outwards when driven into the wood, forming a fishtail with good holding power. The main disadvantage is that the hammering disturbs the frame and permanently loosens any holdfasts already positioned in the **still green** mortar.

Figure 9.71 Galvanized steel frame cramp

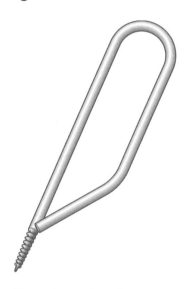

Figure 9.72 Zinc-plated screw tie

Window boards

The window board forms the finish or trim to the top of the inner leaf of the cavity wall, where it finishes at the window opening. Window boards can be formed from solid timber, blockboard, MDF, plywood or plastic. They are used to give a neat finish on the inside of the window sill. They are usually fixed before plastering and, thus, are part of the first fix.

The window board shown in Figure 9.73 has been fixed to wooden plugs (similar to fixing a door lining, which is covered later). The back edge of the window board is fitted into a groove in the sill to allow for any movement in the timber. This will prevent a gap showing should shrinkage occur, which can often happen as radiators are usually situated below the windows.

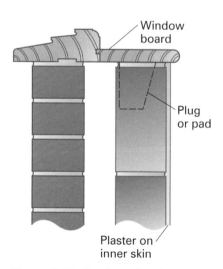

Window board
Plug or pad
Plaster on inner skin

Figure 9.73 Fixed window board

The front end of the window board is usually nosed or rounded and the ends cut to run past the brick jambs.

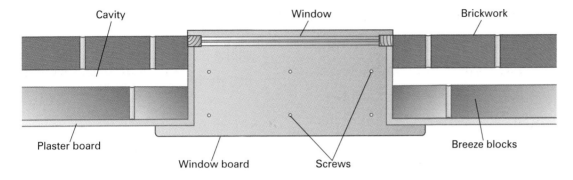

Figure 9.74 Plan view of window board fixed in position

The sequence for fixing window boards is as follows:

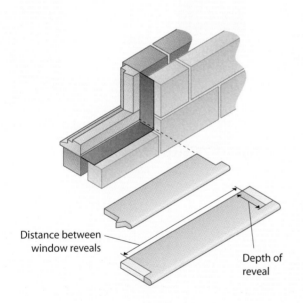

Step 1 Check the board for length. Then mark and cut to length as necessary.

Figure 9.75 **Step 1** Mark length of window board

Definition

Packing – any material, generally waste wood, used to fill a gap

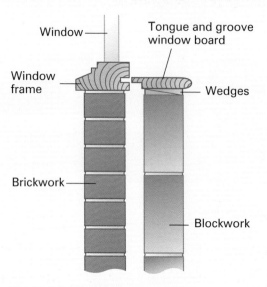

Figure 9.76 Step 2 Fit into position

Step 2 Check for height and level, ensuring engagement of tongue and groove, then make and fix **packings** until height and level are achieved.

Step 3 Fix board with nails through packings, if this can be done into material suitable to receive nails; otherwise use plugs.

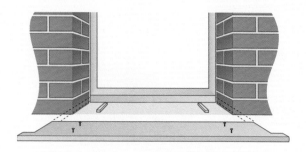

Figure 9.77 Step 3 Fix window board with nails

Did you know?

The back edge of a window board can be rebated to form a tongue to fit into a groove on the inside sill of a window

Stairs

Stairs are a means of providing access from one floor to another. They are made up of a number of steps and each continuous set of steps running in one direction is called a flight. Hence, a staircase may have several flights. They are often the cause of accidents in buildings and are governed very strictly by *Building Regulations*.

Stairs in this section will be looked at under the headings of:

- terminology

- *Building Regulations*

- setting and marking out

- how to cut and construct stairs

- how to install them.

Terminology

There are a number of terms and definitions associated with construction of stairs, which you will need to know and understand. The main ones are listed on pages 294–295 and shown in Figure 9.78.

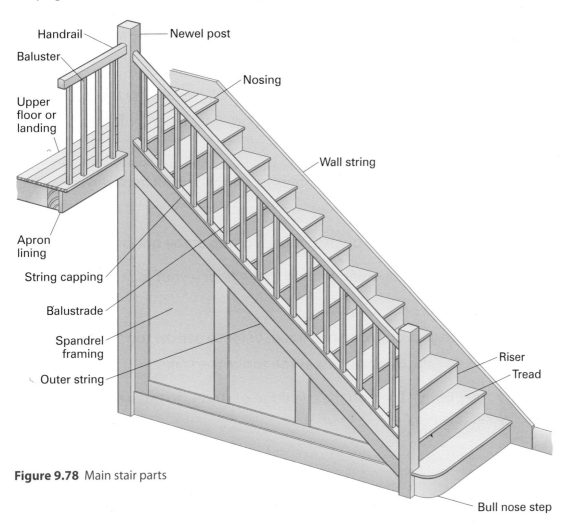

Figure 9.78 Main stair parts

landings – between floor levels to break up the overall length of a flight and can be used to change the direction of a flight of stairs

string – main board to which treads and risers are fixed, including: wall string, outer string, close string and cut string

tread – flat, horizontal part of the step

Straight flight stairs

riser – vertical part of the step

rising – the height of the step (the measurement from the top of one step to the top of another)

step – combination of one tread and one riser

going – the depth of the step (the measurement from a step's riser to the edge of the step)

newel – heavy vertical member at each end of the stair to which the handrail is fixed

balustrade – unit comprising handrail, newels and the infill between it and the string, which provides a barrier for the open side of the stair

balusters – vertical members forming the infill between the string and the handrails

bull nose step – quarter-rounded step at the bottom of a stair

stair well – opening formed in the floor layout to accommodate a stair

nosing – front edge of a tread, or loose narrow top tread which sits on the trimmer joist at the top of the stairs

capping – fixed on the top edge of strings to take the fixing of a balustrade

Stair detail at bottom newel post

cap – shaped top of a newel post, which can be fixed on or turned on the solid newel

spandrel framing – where the triangular area is formed under the stairs, which can be framed to form a cupboard.

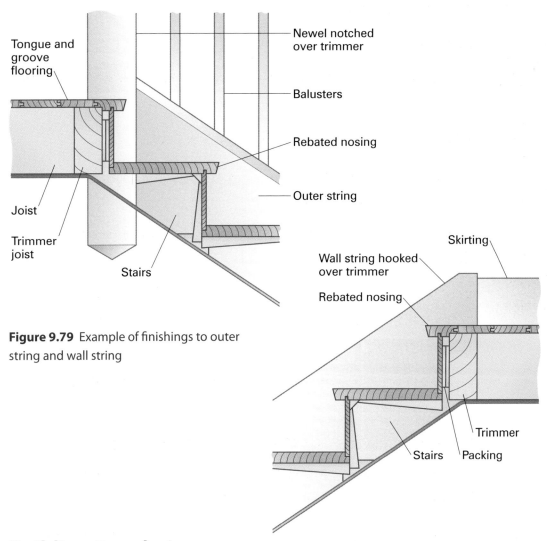

Figure 9.79 Example of finishings to outer string and wall string

Building Regulations

The construction and design of a stair is controlled under *Building Regulations 1985: Part K*. These specify the requirements for different types of stairs depending on the type of building and what it is to be used for.

Tables 9.1 to 9.3 and Figures 9.80–9.82 detail some of the requirements in the regulations.

Description of stair (to meet)	Max rise (mm)	Min going (mm)	Range (to meet pitch limitation) (mm)
Private stair	220	220	155–220 rise with 245–260 going or 165–200 rise with 220–350 going
Common stair	190	350	155–190 rise with 240–320 going
Stairway in institutional building (except stairs only used by staff)	180	280	
Stairway in assembly area (except areas under 100 m square)	180	250	
Any other stairway	190	250	

Table 9.1 Regulations for rise and going

Description of stair	Minimum balustrade height (mm)	
	Flight	Landing
Private stair	840	900
Common stairway	900	1000
Other stairway	900	1100

Table 9.2 Regulations for minimum balustrade heights

Description of stair	Minimum width (mm)
Private stair giving access to one room only (except kitchens and living room)	600
Other private stair	800
Common stair	900
Stairway in institutional building (except stairs used only by staff)	1000
Stairway in assembly area (except areas under 100 m square)	1000
Other stairway serving an area that can be used by more than 50 people	1000
Any other stairway	800

Table 9.3 Regulations for width of stairs

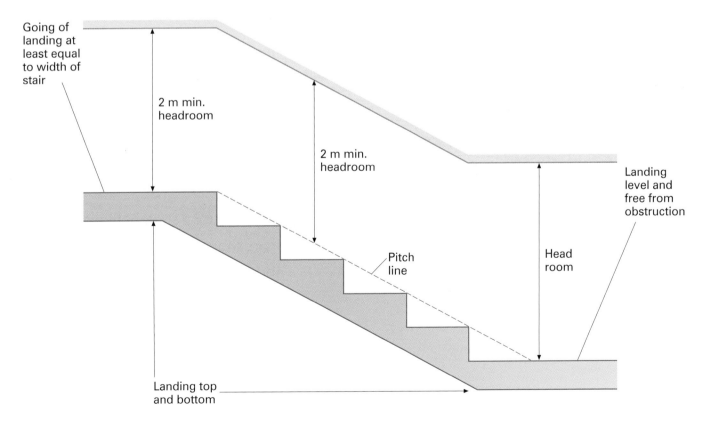

Figure 9.80 Regulations for minimum headroom height and landing requirements

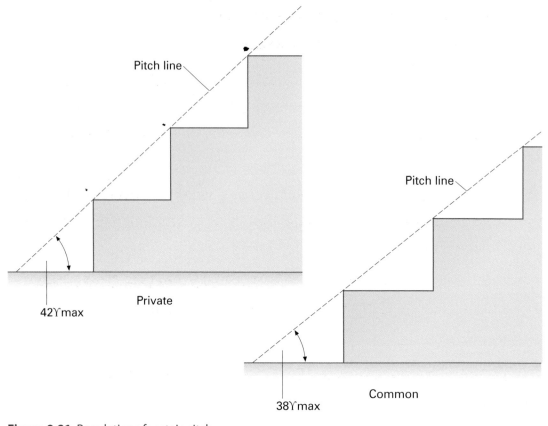

Figure 9.81 Regulations for stair pitch

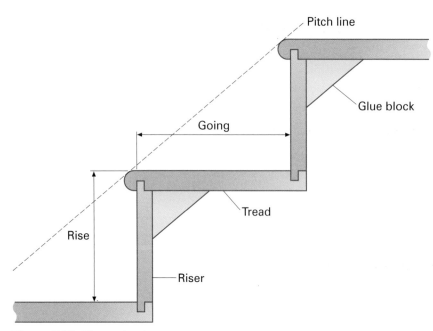

Figure 9.82 Rise and going

Figure 9.81 shows how the pitch or steepness is limited to a maximum of 42° for a private stair and a maximum of 38° for a common stair (i.e. where a stairway is used by more than one dwelling).

The steps for a straight flight of stairs should all have the same rise and going. See Figure 9.82. There are limits to these dimensions for different stairs. In all situations twice the rise plus the going should work out between 550–700 mm (2R+G).

Setting and marking out stairs
Calculating rise and going

The rise and going of a step needs to be determined before setting out can begin. The overall rise, from finished floor to finished floor, must first be measured then divided by the number of risers required to determine each rise.

The going for each step can be calculated by dividing the overall going, from top landing to nosing, by the number of treads needed. This will be one less than the number of risers.

The following is an example of how to calculate for a private flight of stairs where the overall rise is 2574 mm and the going 2805 mm.

Example:

The maximum rise for private stairs is 220 mm, found from Table 9.1 on page 296.

Minimum number of risers

   = total rise divided by maximum permitted rise for private stair

   = 2574 mm divided by 220 mm

   = 11.7

   = 12 risers (each measuring less than the maximum permitted)

Individual rise

   = total rise divided by number of risers

   = 2574 mm divided by 12

   = 214.5 mm (i.e. each less than 220 mm, the maximum permitted)

Individual going

   = total going divided by number of treads (one less than number of risers)

   = 2805 mm divided by 11

   = 255 mm

We know from *Building Regulations* that, in all situations, twice the rise plus the going should work out between 550–700 mm (2R+G). We have calculated the individual rise R = 214.5 and individual going G = 255. Hence 2R + G = (2 x 214.5) + 255 = 684 mm, which is between 550–700 mm. We therefore meet *Building Regulations*.

Setting out

After calculating the rise and the going you can begin to set them out.

A few templates are made in order to assist in manufacturing stairs, as shown in Figure 9.83.

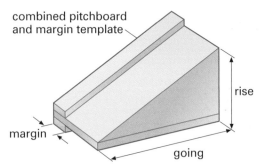

combined pitchboard and margin template

rise

margin

going

Figure 9.83 Stair templates

Tread template and wedge allowance

Riser template and wedge allowance

A **pitch board** is used to mark out the face side of the treads and risers on the string.

The tread and riser templates are used to mark out the housing for the treads and risers, with the width of wedges included.

Once marked out, a template can be used in conjunction with a portable router to form the housing into which the treads and risers will sit. This is a stopped joint, which does not go through the full thickness of the string.

Tread and riser assembly with wedges driven in

Template used with a portable router

Installation of stairs

Installing a staircase on a construction site is a major part in the construction of the building. The same basic procedures are followed, though there will be differences depending on what type of staircase is to be installed as well as variations due to the site.

A staircase is a large and fairly expensive item and should be handled with care when delivered to site and offloaded. They are normally delivered in completed form as far as possible, but components such as the handrail, balusters and newel posts will have to be fitted to suit the site requirements.

Step 1 Fix the wall string, cutting it off at floor level to suit the skirting height.

Step 2 Use a hand-saw to cut the plumb cut on the string at the foot of the stairs

Step 3 The staircase is now level on the floor

Step 4 Steps 1 and 2 can be repeated at the top with the underside cut out to sit on to the floor trimmer and the top tread is cut away so that it sits on the trimmer

Step 5 Mortise the outer string into the newel posts at each end. These are dowelled as shown

Step 6 Fix newel posts in place. The bottom newel can be held in position using various methods and this will depend on the composition of the floor. For rigidity and maximum strength the top newel should be notched over the trimmer joist and screwed or bolted to it

Step 7 Fix the wall string to the wall in approximately four places below the steps, usually with 75 mm screws and plugs. The balustrades and hand-rail can be fitted once the stairs are secure

Step 8 Once the staircase has been fitted, it should be protected to prevent damage. Strips of hardboard should be pinned to the top of each tread with a lath to ensure the nosing is protected. Use the same method to protect the newel posts

Timber studwork

Timber studwork covers partitions or walls, usually of light construction, used to divide a building or large area into compartments. The NVQ syllabus only covers non-load bearing walls.

This section will cover:

- basic construction

- in-situ partitions

- pre-made partitions

- holes and notches

- insulation.

Basic construction

Timber partitions are made up of a head and sole plate with studs at regular centres fixed between them. These are stiffened up with noggings, which also provide extra fixings for sheet material, usually plasterboard, and fixing points for heavy components such as wash basins, toilets etc. See Figure 9.84.

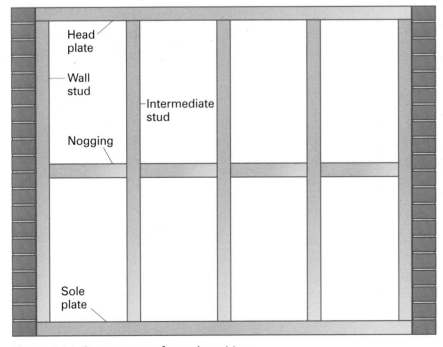

Figure 9.84 Components of a stud partition

The timber used is normally 75 mm × 50 mm for heights up to around 2.4 m and 100 mm × 50 mm for studwork above this height. Planed all round timber is preferred because its cross section is uniform and is better to handle.

Partitions are either made in-situ or pre-made. In-situ components are cut, fixed together and fitted on site. Pre-made partitions are assembled on site or in a factory, for erection on site later.

The intermediate studs are measured and fixed to suit the sheet material to be fixed. For 9.5 mm plasterboard studs are spaced at 400 mm centre to centre and for 12 mm plasterboard at 600 mm. These sheets should cover 2.4 m × 1.2 m. A sheet size of 2.4 m × 0.9 m would have studs spaced at 450 mm.

The majority of stud partitions are fixed together by butt joints and skew-nailed. Another method is to use framing anchors, which are strong and quick to fit.

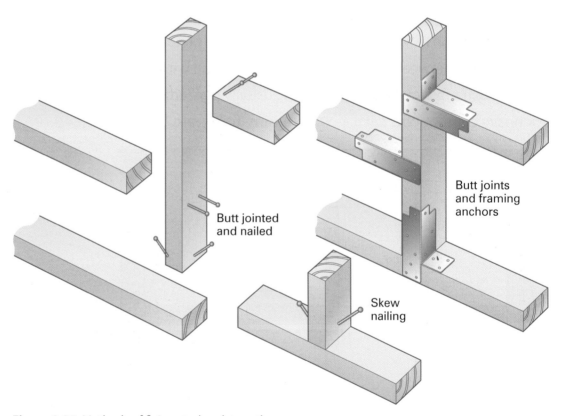

Butt jointed and nailed

Butt joints and framing anchors

Skew nailing

Figure 9.85 Methods of fixing studwork together

In-situ partitions
Fixing partitions in position

Step 1 Mark out positions for partitions on the floor. Then check the ceiling to see how to fix the head plate. Ideally it will run at a right angle to the joists but, if not, further noggings should be fixed between each joist to provide a fixing point. The head plate can now be fixed to the ceiling, usually with 100 mm wire nails or screws

Step 2 Plumb down from the head plate with a plumb bob, or a level and straight edge, and mark the position on the floor

Step 3 The sole plate can be fixed in the same way as the head plate. If on to a concrete floor it should be plugged and screwed

Step 4 Cut the wall studs and fix to the wall by plugs and screws. They should be skew-nailed to the head and sole plate

Step 5 Mark the position of intermediate studs on the side of the head and sole plates at the appropriate centres, i.e. 400, 450 or 600 mm depending on sheet material size and thickness

Step 6 Measure each stud individually, as they may vary in length between head and sole plate, then skew-nail with 100 mm wire nails. Studs should be a tight fit and, with the bottom in place, the tip should be forced over into position

Step 7 If overall partition height is greater than 2.4 m, position noggings centrally at the top edge of the boards. Through-nail one end and skew-nail the other

Step 8 Fix additional noggings at various heights from 600 mm, 1200 mm to 1800 mm to give extra strength and rigidity to the frame, and provide extra fixing points for the sheet material and any components that may have to be fixed to the walls

Noggings provide fixings for sheet materials

Forming openings

Where an opening is to be formed in a studwork partition, studs and noggings should provide fixing points for items such as door linings, windows, hatches etc. They also provide fixings for the edges of any sheet material to be used. Details are shown in Figures 9.86, 9.87 and photographs.

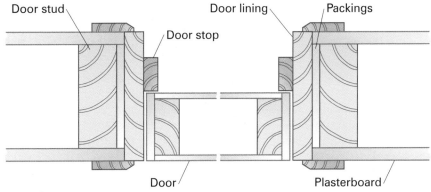

Figure 9.86 Section through a door opening

Opening formed to take a window lining

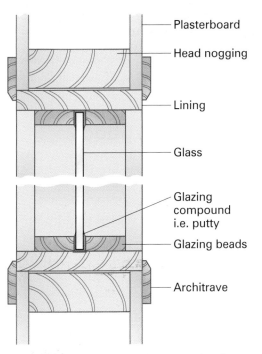

Figure 9.87 Section through a window lining

Corners and junctions

When a partition has to be returned at right angles or when a 'tee' junction is required, extra studs must be fixed to provide support and fixing for the covering material.

Corner detail with extra studs

Tee junction detail with extra studs

Pre-made partitions

Pre-made partitions are the same specification as in-situ partitions but can be made up either in a workshop or on site. They are made slightly under size in height and width to allow for the frame to be offered into position.

Joints are usually butt-jointed and nailed but can also be housed-in or framing anchors used.

Folding wedges can be used to keep the frame in position while fixing takes place.

Holes and notches

It is common practice for pipes and cables to be concealed within timber partitions, though it is recommended that they are kept to a minimum so as not to affect partition strength.

Holes for pipework

Notches with wire

Positioning is important. Holes for carrying cables, and notches for water pipes, should be kept away from areas where there is a possibility they may be punctured by a nail or screw. This includes areas where, for example, kitchen units, cupboards, skirting boards, dado or picture rails may be fixed.

Notches can be protected by fixing a metal plate over them.

Insulation

Certain situations may require studwork to have insulation between the wall coverings to form a sound or thermal barrier. *Building Regulations 1985* control the methods of achieving this and should be referred to for technical information.

Extra fire resistance can be achieved by double boarding the studwork or by using fire-lined board.

Fire-resistant insulation

Sound and thermal insulation

Mineral wool or glass fibre insulation are most commonly used for sound and thermal insulation.

Door frames and linings

The timber frames to which doors are hung may be divided into two main groups:

- linings (or casings)
- frames.

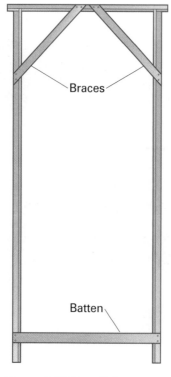

Braces

Batten

Figure 9.88 Door lining

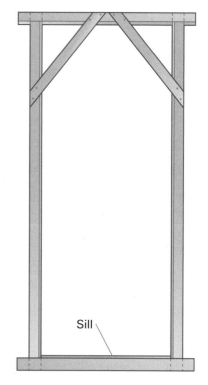

Sill

Figure 9.89 Door frame

Door frames are usually constructed from heavier material with solid rebates and generally used for external entrance doors. Linings are lighter with planted door stops and generally used for internal doors.

This section will look at doors under the following headings:

- door linings or casings

- door frames

- built-in frames

- storey frames.

Door linings or casings

Door linings or casings are lightweight internal frames that can be fixed into position by nailing through the jambs into fixing blocks, pads, plugs, or directly into a timber stud wall.

Blocks or pads are usually built into the door opening during construction by the bricklayer. Three or four will be needed on each jamb.

Where fixing blocks or pads have not been used, it may be necessary to plug the opening, using a plugging chisel to chase out four mortar joints on each side of the frame. Wooden plugs can be cut from scrap timber, driven into these slots and sawn off plumb. The sawn ends must be kept exactly in line and square. See Figure 9.90.

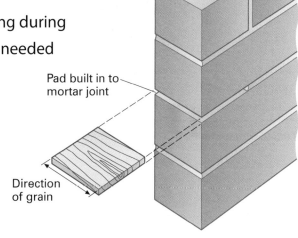

Pad built in to mortar joint

Direction of grain

Figure 9.90 Fixing blocks

The door opening should have been built with a clearance of about 20 mm, so that the lining fits loosely and can easily be plumbed and aligned with the walls. Packing will be needed between lining and brickwork so that it is held securely in place once fitted.

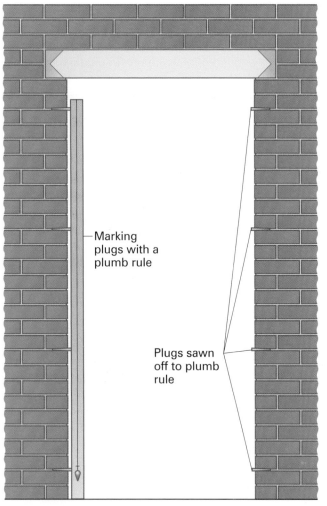

Figure 9.91 Plugging the joints for fixing a door lining

The lining can now be offered into the opening and checked that it is plumb and level. It is normal practice to fix one jamb first, making sure that it is plumb and straight and will suit the line of the finished plasterwork. Once this is done the second jamb can be fixed and sighted through to make certain that it is exactly parallel.

It is good practice to make a temporary fixing at the top and bottom of each jamb, leaving the fixing protruding. The lining can then be checked finally for accuracy and position, and adjustment made before it is finally fixed. See Figure 9.91.

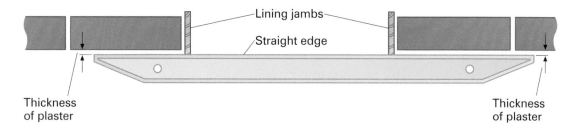

Figure 9.92 Checking alignment of a door lining

The following sequence of operations is recommended:

Step 1 Firstly remove the door stops, which should have been nailed lightly, and put to one side. The door is unfinished so check the finished floor level (FFL) in relation to the bottom of the lining. The most accurate way of doing this is to measure down from a datum line (usually 1 m or 900 mm above FFL) and pack the lining to suit

Step 2 Wedge the lining approximately in position by putting a wedge above each leg in the gap between the lintel and the head of the lining. The head should be checked with a spirit level to see that it is level. The lining can now be packed down the sides with either hardboard or plywood, at the top fixing positions. The top of the lining should be moved to ensure equal projection either side of the wall

Step 3 Fix the lining at the top, through the packing, with two nails at each fixing point

Step 4 Plumb the lining on the face side and edge using a level. Pack the bottom position as required and fix through one set of packing. Check that the fixed leg is square. Then complete the fixings on the same leg. The amount of fixing points should be about five (not less than four)

Step 5 Next remove the stretcher from the bottom of the lining, hold it at the head and mark the inside width to make a pinch rod

Step 6 The pinch rod can now be fitted in the bottom position of the lining and the lining packed to suit

Step 7 Check the leg to see that it is plumb and also the alignment of the frame. The bottom can be fixed, and then moving the pinch rod to ensure the frame is parallel, fix the intermediate positions. The head will only require fixing if the opening exceeds normal width. All nails should be punched to about 3 mm below the surface. The door stops can now be replaced and protection strips fixed if required

Door frames

Frames can be fixed to timber stud partitions using 75 mm oval nails or alternatively they can be screwed to solid walls using plastic plugs.

Built-in frames

The majority of frames are 'built-in' by the bricklayer as the brickwork proceeds. Prior to this the frame has to be accurately positioned, plumbed, levelled and struts temporarily inserted by the joiner.

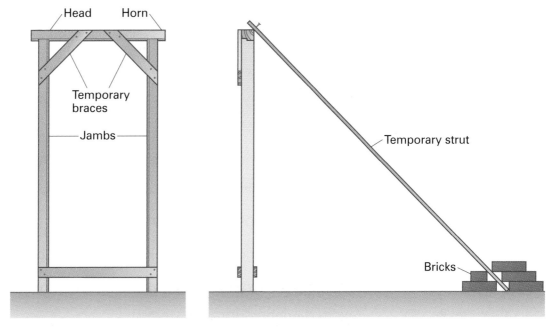

Figure 9.93 Temporary bracing and support

Storey frames

Storey frames are designed to give stability when doorways, or fanlights, occur in thin non-loading walls. They are known as storey frames because their height is from floor to floor (one storey).

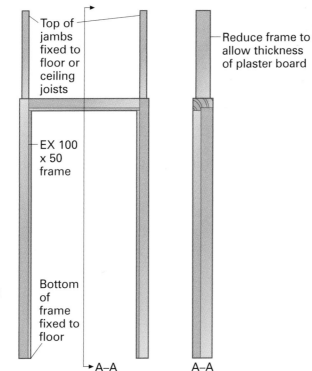

Figure 9.94 Plain storey frame

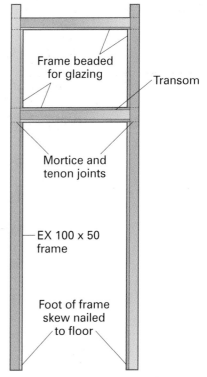

Figure 9.95 Fanlight storey frame

Ground lats

Ground lats (or just grounds) are timber battens which are fixed to the wall surface, particularly in high-class joinery work where hardwood skirting boards are to be used. They:

- provide a flat and level surface on which a covering (panelling, plasterboard, hardboard etc.) can be fixed to create a decorative finish

- provide a line for the plasterer to work to

- provide continuous fixing points for skirting boards

- enable these to be fixed during Second fixing (covered in Chapter 10) and avoid damage during plastering.

This section will look at:

- types of ground

- setting out of grounds

- fixing grounds.

Types of ground

Grounds are defined by their intended usage and include:

- grounds for skirting

- framed grounds

- counter battening

- separate grounds.

Setting out of grounds

Skirting grounds must be fixed carefully, keeping them straight and flush with the plaster line.

Grounds to which frames, sheets or panels are to be fixed need to be spaced to match their size.

The only requirements are a spirit level and straight edge, or snap chalk line, to mark their location.

Snap chalk line

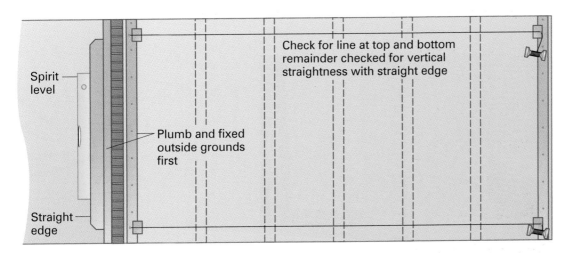

Elevation

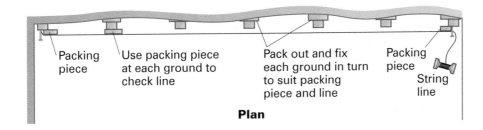

Plan

Figure 9.96 Setting out of grounds

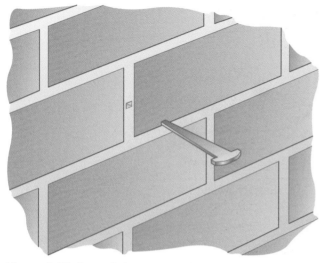

Figure 9.97 Cut nails in mortar joints

Fixing grounds

Grounds can be fixed in several ways, some of which are shown in the photographs. They include:

- screwing into timber plugs set into mortar joints
- screwing into plastic plugs set in masonry
- masonry nails
- adhesive.

Packing may be required at fixing points.

Masonry nails

Twisted timber plugs

Proprietary plastic plug

Panelling or sheet material fixed to grounds

Safety tip

Always wear goggles when driving in masonry nails

FAQ

My maths isn't very good and so I often struggle with the geometry and trigonometry skills needed, especially for roofing. What can I do?

Your training will include some basic numeracy skills lessons, which if you struggle with maths, you should take advantage of. Be patient and pay attention to any help and advice you are given regarding these sometimes complicated calculations. You will probably find that the more practical experience you get, the better your maths skills will become.

On the job: Roof trusses

Raoul is working on a new build house. The client has come to the site to see how things are progressing and asks Raoul if the position of the water tank in the roof can be altered to give more storage room. Moving the water tank will involve altering some of the roof trusses to accommodate the tank.

Do you think the water tank can be moved? Give a reason for your answer. If you were Raoul, what would you say to the client?

Knowledge check

1. State the reason for treating sawn ends of joists with preservative.

2. What is the purpose of a restraint strap?

3. At what centres are the restraint straps fixed?

4. State why strutting should be clear of the top and bottom edges of joists.

5. Describe a fascia board.

6. State the purpose of soffit ventilation.

7. What is the purpose of a wall plate?

8. State the purpose of notching and boring holes in joists.

9. Define a flat roof.

10. What is the slope on a flat roof for?

11. Name the most common way of producing a sloped roof.

12. Where are the triangle fillets used on a roof?

13. How do you construct an opening in a flat roof for a roof light?

14. Can you name five different types of suitable decking for flat roofs?

15. What is the purpose of trimming joists?

16. Why do you use profile frames?

17. Name the component parts of a window.

18. What is a mortar key used for in a window frame?

19. Why is it important to assemble windows flat?

20. How do you check a window frame is square as you assemble it?

21. Name two ways of fixing window board into position.

22. How do you level window board?

23. Name three materials used as window boards.

24. List five components you will find on a flight of stairs.

25. What is the minimum headroom allowed as stated in the *Building Regulations* covering stairs?

26. Name the vertical member used to provide support to a handrail and infill on an open balustrade.

27. After stairs have been fitted what three measures can be taken to prevent damage during building work?

28. Name three ways of fixing grounds.

29. What PPE should be worn when using masonry nails?

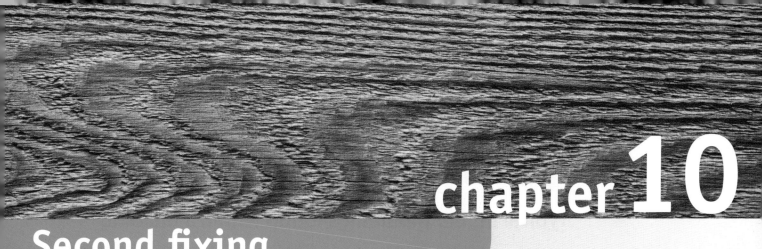

chapter 10

Second fixing

OVERVIEW

Second fixing covers all joinery work after plaster work is completed.

This chapter is designed to help you to identify the main activities associated with second fixing work. It is also designed to provide you with the knowledge and understanding required to carry out the associated work activities.

It will cover the following:

- Mouldings
- Internal doors
- Ironmongery
- Encasing services
- Wall and floor units.

Mouldings

This section will provide you with the knowledge and understanding required to enable you to select and fit internal mouldings.

Typical timber mouldings found within a building

Moulding refers to the pattern put on a length of timber. This is normally done by a machine such as a spindle moulder. However, specialist hand planes could be used to match existing patterns.

Common types of moulding that you will meet are:

- architrave
- skirting board
- plinth block
- picture rail
- dado rail
- cornice.

Where you will find these within a room is shown on Figure 10.1.

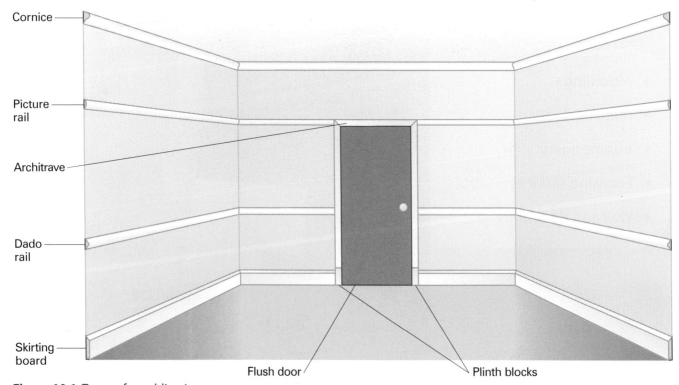

Cornice

Picture rail

Architrave

Dado rail

Skirting board

Flush door

Plinth blocks

Figure 10.1 Types of moulding in a room

Mouldings are usually produced using premium grade timber or MDF and should only be fixed at the 'second fixing' stage, once a building is weather tight and plastered.

Architrave

Architraves provide a decorative finish around internal openings, especially doors, and cover the joint between frame and wall finish. They are available in lengths ranging from 2.1 m – 5.1 m, increasing in 300 mm multiples; or as sets consisting of 2 × 2.1 m legs (the sides of the opening) and 1 × 900 mm head (the top of the opening). Architraves are between 50 mm – 75 mm wide and are usually 19 mm – 25 mm thick before they are planed. There is a range of commercially available architrave mouldings.

Commercially available architrave mouldings

The steps on page 324 and 325 show how to fit an architrave to a smooth surface. If the surface is not smooth, the back of the architrave may have to be scribed to fit to it before finally fixing in place. This is described in the second section 'Scribing to walls'.

How to fit an architrave

Step 1 Architraves are kept back from the front edge of a frame by 6 mm –10 mm, which is known as the margin. This is the line we work to when fitting architraves. Hence, as Step 1 shows, draw the margin on the front edge of the legs and head of the frame until they meet.

Step 2 With the heel (narrow point or inner edge) of the architrave to the margin, place the leg on the floor and mark the architrave where the margin marks intersect each other on the frame.

Step 3 Place the architrave into a mitre box and cut using a tenon saw. Alternatively, use a combination square to mark a 45° angle on the architrave and cut freehand.

Step 4 Position the cut leg against the margin marks and fix by nails. (When possible try and nail through the **quirks** in the moulding to help hide the nails.) If the surface is uneven you may need to shape the back of the architrave to fit to it before finally fixing, as described in the next section 'Scribing to walls'.

Definition

Quirk – the name used for the hollow in a moulding

Step 1 Drawing a working margin

Step 2 Marking the architrave

Step 3 Mitring the architrave legs

Step 4 Fixing the architrave legs

Step 5 Cut a 45° angle on the head piece and offer it to the angle of the leg that has just been fixed. If you have a good fit, repeat Step 2 with the head and then the remaining leg. Should the mitres not go together then the head piece will need planing until it does.

Step 6 Punch all nails below the surface and remove the **arris** from the toe (wide part of the architrave – its outer edge).

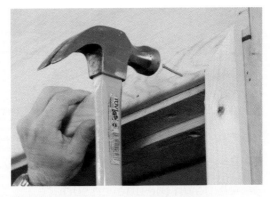

Step 5 Fixing the architrave head piece

Step 6 Finishing off the architrave

Remember

Use a block plane when planing end grain

Definition

Arris – the sharp edge formed when two flat or curved surfaces meet

Scribing to walls

Scribing is to mark the profile of something onto the surface against which it is to be butted. In the case of architraves (or skirting) it is used so that the back can be shaped to fit against an uneven surface.

Step 1 Lightly nail the architrave 20 mm – 25 mm in front of the door frame or lining of the opening, and parallel to it.

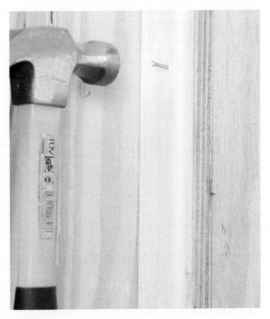

Step 1 Temporarily fix forward of the doorframe

Step 2 Measure the distance between the front edge of the architrave and the margin mark.

Step 3 Cut a block, or set a pair of compasses, to the measurement you have just worked out. Take the architrave off the frame. Copy the shape of the uneven surface onto its face by running a compass, or block and pencil, down the uneven surface.

Step 2 Measure to the margin mark

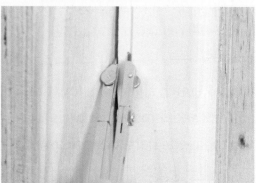

Step 3 Copy the surface shape onto the architrave

Step 4 Using a saw or a plane cut down to the line. Try in position, making sure the front of the architrave is level with the margin mark. Fix with nails.

Step 4 Shape the architrave

Remember

Skirting boards may have to be fitted clear of the floor to fit block flooring etc. so always check plans carefully

Skirting board

Skirting boards are used to provide a decorative finish between floor and walls. They also protect the wall finish from damage. Skirting boards are available in lengths ranging from 1.8 m up to 6.3 m, increasing by multiples of 300 mm. They are between 75 mm – 175 mm deep and 19 mm – 25 mm in thickness.

There are only ever three joints to cut when fitting skirting boards:

- internal joints, which should be scribed

- external joints, which should be mitred

- angle-lengthening joints.

How to fit skirting

Skirting boards can be fixed by:

- adhesive

- masonry nails

- screws and plugs

- oval/lost head nails (for internal stud walls).

Before starting, remove all obstructions from the floor, such as lumps of plaster. Then check lengths of timber and choose the most economical lengths.

The boards should be fixed on the top edge and at the bottom, and nails or screws made as inconspicuous as possible:

- Masonry nails should be **dovetailed**.

- Always plug the hole made by the screw or nail, using either a wooden plug or filler.

Safety tip

When fixing masonry nails always use protective glasses

Definition

Dovetailed nails – pairs of nails angled in towards each other

Dovetailed nails

Joiner using a kneeling board

To get a board tight to the floor it is a good idea to use a kneeling board.

Scribed joint

Skirting boards are shaped and frequently have mouldings to make them look attractive. Where they meet in a corner, the board butting up against the moulding needs to have its end shaped so that the boards fit neatly together. With one board fitted in place right into the corner, we now need to shape the board that will butt against it.

Method 1

Step 1 Place the square end of the board to be cut against the fixed board and copy the shape of the moulding onto the face of the board to be cut.

Step 2 Back cut with a coping saw and/or tenon saw to the line. Keep trying in place until a good joint has been achieved and then fit in place.

Step 1 Copy moulding shape to be scribed

Step 2 Back cut to the line

Method 2

Step 1 Using a mitre block, internally mitre across the width of the skirting board to be shaped. This will now show the end grain on the board.

Step 1 Mitred skirting board with end grain to be shaped

Step 2 Using a coping saw and/or tenon saw back cut the mitre by letting the saw blade follow the line where the straight grain on the fixed board meets the end grain that is showing on the face of the board being shaped. Try in position and fit when a good joint has been achieved.

Step 2 Back cut end grain to be shaped

Mitre joint

A completed mitre joint is shown in Figure 10.2. A step-by-step process for achieving this is as described on page 330.

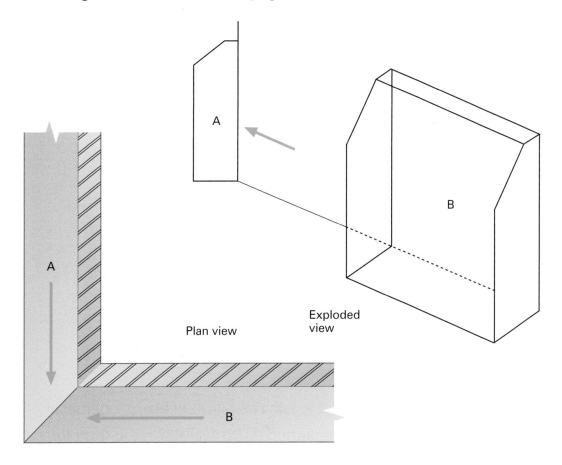

A

B

Plan view

Exploded view

A

B

Figure 10.2 Mitre joint on skirting board

Step 1 Lay the skirting board flat against the wall and draw a line on the floor where the board touches it, until the line reaches the adjoining wall. Repeat this with the board flat against the other wall. When the board is removed the lines on the floor should meet at a point near to the angle of the wall.

Step 1 Mark floor lines

Step 2 Place the stock of a sliding bevel right into the angle of the wall and move the blade around until it touches where the lines on the floor meet. You have just bisected the angle!

Step 2 Bisect the angle

Step 3 Place the bevel on the top edge of the skirting board and draw the line for the mitre. Cut accurately. Try in position and fit when a good joint has been achieved. Any adjustments can be made using a block plane.

Step 3 Mark the mitre angle on the skirting board

Angle-lengthening joint

Angle-lengthening joints are used to join two pieces of board together in length. This will be required if the skirting board available is too short for the wall.

Simply cut a 45° angle across the width of one board and do the opposite cut on the board to which it will be joined. Put them together and **skew-nail** through the joint to hold it in position. The finished joint is shown in Figure 10.3.

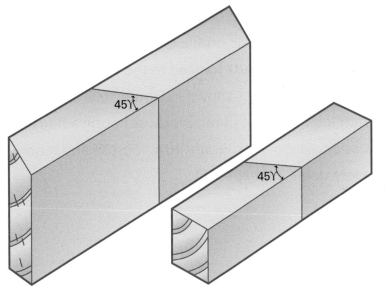

Figure 10.3 Angle-lengthening joint

Plinth block

Plinth blocks are also referred to as architrave blocks. They are fixed at the bottom of architraves and allow skirting to run up to them. See Figure 10.4.

They are used because:

- it is then possible to use skirting board that is thicker than the architrave

- skirting can have a moulded back edge

- they provide protection to the moulding on the architrave

- they look elegant.

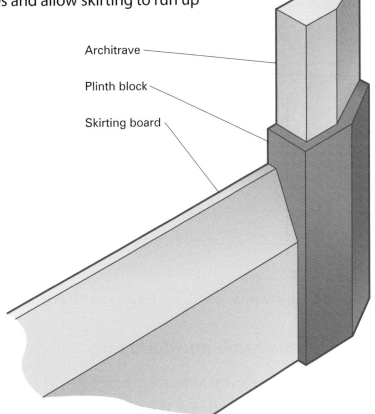

Architrave

Plinth block

Skirting board

Figure 10.4 Plinth block

Definition

Butt joint – the simplest joint between two pieces of wood, with the end grain of one meeting the long grain of the other and glued, screwed or nailed together

Plinth blocks should be approximately 15 mm taller than the skirting board and follow the basic profile of the architrave with at least a 6 mm excess. They should be **butt jointed** to the architrave or preferably fixed using a barefaced tenon as shown in Figure 10.5. The skirting board can also be butt jointed to the plinth block, although a housing joint would be a better option, as shown in Figure 10.6. Mortise and tenon joints are covered in more detail in Chapter 11.

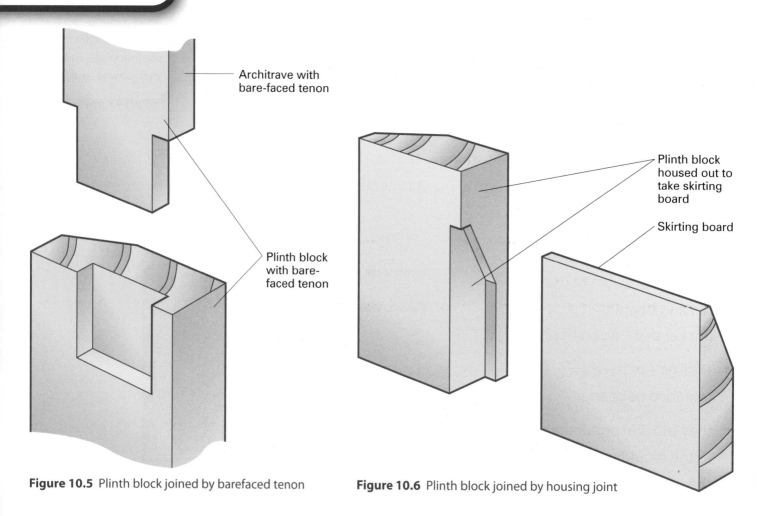

Architrave with bare-faced tenon

Plinth block with bare-faced tenon

Plinth block housed out to take skirting board

Skirting board

Figure 10.5 Plinth block joined by barefaced tenon

Figure 10.6 Plinth block joined by housing joint

Picture rails and dado rails

Pictures can be hung from a picture rail using special clips that are fastened to the picture frame, but the rails are often now just used for effect.

Dado is the name used for the lower part of a wall when it is visually different from the upper part. Dado rails run along the dividing line. They were originally designed to protect expensive hand printed wallpapers from chair and sofa backs but, like picture rails, are generally now used for effect.

Both dado and picture rails help reduce the visual height of rooms with high ceilings.

The same sequence and methods employed to fix skirting boards are used to fix dado and picture rails.

FAQ

What is a scribe?

A scribe is a copy of the surface it fits over.

What does bisecting an angle mean?

Cutting an angle equally in two, as when cutting a mitre to create an internal angle.

Do I scribe both ends of a length of skirting?

No. It looks neater if one end butts to the wall and the other end is scribed to the butted end of the next skirting.

Can I have a scribe and a mitre?

No. It would be very difficult to get the scribed edges to meet correctly.

Internal doors

This section has been designed to provide the knowledge and understanding to select and hang internal doors. It will cover:

- purpose of internal doors
- types of internal door
- choosing a door
- fitting a door.

Purpose of internal doors

The purpose of an internal door is to provide a means of privacy, a thermal, sound or security barrier, a means of access and egress (i.e. a way out) and, in some instances, a fire-resisting barrier.

Types of internal door

Framed doors

Framed doors are doors made from hardwood or softwood and are constructed using mortise and tenon joints (described in Chapter 11 Marking and setting out joinery products), or doweled joints. The frame is rebated or grooved, into which a board panel can be fitted; alternatively glass could be used and held in place with beading. Figure 10.7 shows an exploded view of a door including the types of joint used.

Figure 10.8 also shows types of sections used for door panels.

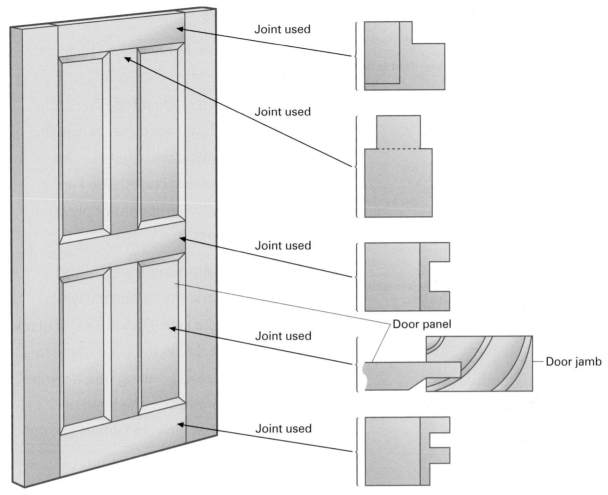

Figure 10.7 Framed door exploded view

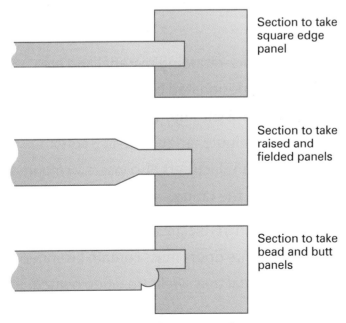

Figure 10.8 Sections used for door panels

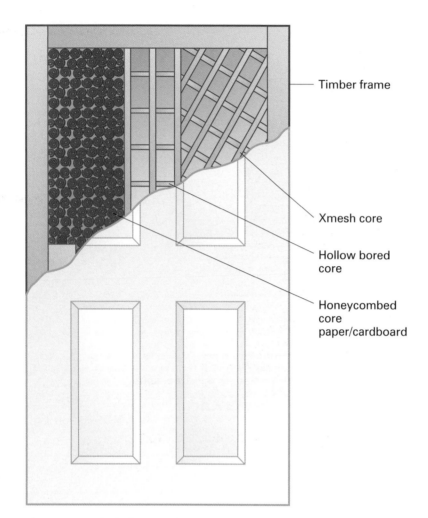

Timber frame

Xmesh core

Hollow bored core

Honeycombed core paper/cardboard

Figure 10.9 Flush door exploded view

Flush doors

Flush doors are lightweight, cheap and simply made. Most consist of a softwood frame, which is stapled together and houses a hollow-core material (usually cardboard honeycomb that has the appearance of egg crates). They are then faced with hardboard or plywood. See Figure 10.9.

Flush doors often come with fitting instructions and these indicate which **stile** contains a lock block (an extra block of wood included in the door frame to take the door lock). Failing this, a symbol is normally printed on the head or bottom rail that indicates where the lock block can be found.

Definition

Stile – the longest vertical timber in the frame of a door etc.

Fire-resisting doors

Fire-resisting doors having a core of solid, fire-retarding material and are frequently flush panelled. Their ratings are designated by their performance (resistance to penetration by flames or smoke through splits or gaps) with the prefix FD. For example, FD30 has a 30-minute rating, and an S suffix indicates the ability to resist smoke. The manufacturers also insert a coloured plastic plug into the door frame to indicate the rating.

Fire doors are available in standard sizes and in thicknesses of 44 mm for the FD30 and 54 mm for the FD60. Glazed fire doors must contain fire-rated plain or wired glass that is bedded in material that swells up when heated, hence increasing the resistance to smoke.

Fire door plugs – 30- and 60-minute (note that colours used differ between manufacturers)

Choosing a door

On a newly built property the door schedule (see Figure 10.10) and plans of the building will determine what door to use and which direction it shall operate; also how it should be furnished with ironmongery.

Description	D1	D2	D2	D2	D2	D2	D2	D2	D2	D10	NOTES
Type											
External gazed A1					●						
External panel A2	●										
Internal flush B1									●		
Internal flush B2		●				●	●	●		●	
Internal glazed B3			●	●							
Size											
813 mm x 2032 mm x 44 mm	●				●						
762 mm x 1981 x 35 mm		●	●	●		●	●	●		●	
610 mm x 1981 x 35 mm									●		
Material											BBS DESIGN
Hardwood	●										
Softwood			●	●	●						
Plywood/polished		●									JOB TITLE
Plywood/painted						●	●	●	●	●	
Infill											DRAWING TITLE Door Schedule/doors
6 mm tempered safety glass											JOB NO. DRAWING NO.
Clear			●	●	●						
Obscured	●										SCALE DATE DRAWN CHECKED

Figure 10.10 Example of a door schedule

Modern buildings tend to have standardised joinery throughout. Standard door heights are 2 m, 2.03 m and occasionally 2.17 m; widths range from 600 mm to 900 mm, usually in 75 mm increments. Thicknesses vary from 35 mm to 44 mm. Standard single door sizes that are available by type of door from a typical manufacturer are shown in Table 10.1. They include several that match the old imperial sizes (quoted in millimetres), as these are still required to replace existing doors. There are additional standard sizes available for double leaf, and single and double garage doors.

Height	1981	1981	1981	1981	2000	2032	2040	2040	2040
Width	610	686	762	838	807	813	626	726	826
External	*	*	*	*	*	*		*	*
Internal	*	*	*	*			*	*	*

Table 10.1 Standard single door sizes (mm)

Older properties often have relatively large doors to main rooms and may be of a non-standard size. In this case, the door will have to be made to measure; or the nearest available size, or larger, purchased and trimmed to fit by removing an equal amount from each stile to keep the frames symmetrical.

Fitting a door

Whenever possible doors should be stored flat for a few days prior to fitting in the location where they are to be hung. This is sometimes referred to as 'storing out of twist'. This gives the timber time to acclimatise to its new surroundings and any final shrinkage or reduction in moisture content can take place (which sometimes happens with modern central heating systems).

The following actions should be completed before starting to fit a door:

- Check building plans and door schedule to determine which type of door is to be used and in which direction it should operate. Failing this ask the supervisor or client.

- Check the frame is square and aligned properly.

- Measure the new door to make sure it will fit within the frame and check it is not twisted.

- Cut off horns, if fitted.

- Find where the lock block is located. The other stile is the hanging stile to which hinges will be attached.

Did you know?

Doors should normally conceal the largest area of the room when open to allow maximum privacy to those inside

Fitting is then carried out as follows:

Step 1 There must be a gap of 2 mm between the head of the door and the head of the frame and at least 6 mm clearance between the floor covering and the bottom of the door. If the door is too tall, always cut excess off the bottom rail.

Step 1 Make sure there is a gap between the door and the frame

Step 2 There must be a gap of 2 mm between both door styles and the frame. If necessary, plane evenly from both sides of the door. The door should now fit in the frame. With the hanging stile against the frame, wedge the door up so there is a 2 mm gap at the top and mark, if necessary, to shape the hanging style to match the frame. Plane off as necessary.

Step 2 Cut door to width and shape styles

Step 3 If necessary, mark and shape the opposite stile (containing the lock block), then slightly bevel the edge that will lead into the frame so that it will not catch when closing.

Step 3 Bevel the leading edge

Step 4 Mark hinges

Step 4 With the door fitting snugly in the frame and wedged up to give 2 mm clearance at the top, mark where the hinges are to go, on both door and frame at the same time. The top hinge normally sits 150 mm from the top of the door and the bottom hinge 225 mm from the bottom of the door.

Step 5 Remove the door from the frame and accurately mark where the hinges are to go, with the aid of a square and marking gauge. Do the same on the frame and then chop out recesses on both door and frame.

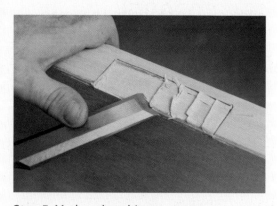

Step 5 Mark and cut hinge recesses

Step 6 Fit the hinges into the door recesses, putting in all the screws. Take the door to the frame and place the hinges into the frame recesses,

securing the hinges using only one screw. Check the door swings without binding. Alter or adjust until there is an equal gap on both sides and the correct clearance at the top, and no resistance is encountered when closing the door. Put in all remaining screws on the stile hinges.

Step 6 Fit hinges

Step 7 Fit all remaining ironmongery, or furniture, as instructed by the schedule or client. (Ironmongery is covered in the next section.)

Step 7 Fit all remaining ironmongery

Remember

When fitting a fire-resisting door all tolerances, as specified in *Building Regulations*, must be adhered to, so check with the supervisor

Ironmongery

This section has been designed to enable you to choose the correct fixtures and fittings for the work you are involved in.

It offers just a small guide to what is available and the range of ironmongery is continually increasing. As a carpenter it will be your responsibility to choose and supply the correct items to your client. Therefore you would be well advised to look around your local DIY superstore to see what is available. Also look at completed work to see what other people have used.

Functions of ironmongery

Ironmongery is also referred to as hardware and relates to the components used to fix or decorate work.

To fix a door into a frame a carpenter would require a minimum of hinges, screws and some form of lock or latch, unless the client specified otherwise. All are ironmongery and can be classified as:

- fixings that allow movement

- fixings that provide security

- fixings that penetrate timber.

Fixings that allow movement

These are principally hinges and made of metal, the main ones of which are described with photographs below.

Standard cranked butt hinges are fitted so that the knuckle of the hinge protrudes beyond the face of the door and the edge of the door jamb. These hinges are available in sizes from 25 mm – 100 mm, and produced in brass or steel.

Cast butt hinges are produced from cast iron and are classified as heavy duty. They will rust if left untreated.

Standard cranked butt hinges

Cast butt hinges

Rising butt hinges

Loose pin butt hinge

Rising butt hinges have a helical knuckle that allows the door to rise when opened, which assists the door in clearing carpets and uneven floors. The helical knuckle also allows the door to close under its own weight.

Loose pin butt hinges enable the door to be removed from the frame by removing the pin from the hinge knuckle.

Helical or double action hinges are light-duty hinges that do not require letting into the frame or door, provided the correct screws are used. This type of hinge also allows a door to open both ways and are commonly found in pubs and restaurants where there is two-way traffic.

Helical or double action hinge

Parliament hinge

Parliament hinges are used where extended movement is required; e.g. the door has to open through 180 degrees.

Storm-proof hinges are used in the manufacture of casement timber windows and have a cranked appearance.

Friction hinges are used on uPVC window systems and act as both a pivot and a stay.

Tee hinges are frequently used for hanging external doors on buildings like sheds. Light-duty versions are generally made from thin gauged steel and either galvanised or painted in a black epoxy lacquer. Heavy duty versions are made of stronger steel with a steel or brass pin.

Friction hinge

Tee hinges

Bands or straps of strong steel may be used instead of tee hinges for heavy-duty tasks, often doubled over and leaving a **gudgeon** to fit over a hinge pin welded to a plate on the frame; thus enabling the door or gate to be lifted off.

Bands and gudgeons

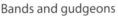

Definition

Gudgeons – tubes at the end of hinges to take the pin around which the hinge rotates

Fixings that provide security

Locks

Mortise dead locks have no latch and therefore they do not require standard handle furniture. Both the sash lock and dead lock versions can be obtained with hook bolts for use on sliding doors.

Mortise locks are available in 3-lever and 5-lever versions. 5-lever versions are stronger than their 3-lever counterparts and therefore more suitable for external door security. Good quality locks also have a reversible latch which means they can be fitted to LH (left hand) and RH (right hand) opening doors. Fitting instructions will be supplied with the locks and should be read thoroughly.

Mortise dead lock

Cylinder locks consist of a body, a cylinder containing the key mechanism and a staple into which the latch engages.

3- and 5-lever mortise locks

Cylinder lock

345

Bolts and other fastenings

A range of bolts and other fastenings is available on the market. A selection of those most frequently used in second fixing is listed below.

A hasp and staple comprise a hinged strap (the hasp) that closes over a strong wire staple; a padlock is then put through the staple. It is normally used to secure garages and sheds. However, it is versatile, being used for many applications.

Hasp and staple

Tower bolts consist of a long bar that is fixed to the door and is pushed to locate it in a keeper on the frame.

Pad bolts work on the same principle but when the bolt is closed, the handle locates over a staple to which a padlock can be fixed.

Tower bolt

Bow handle bolts are much longer and more suited to heavy-duty applications, such as garage doors. The long bow handle means that the bolt can be operated even when the locking point is out of normal reach. They are made from square section metal and are spring loaded to prevent the bolt slipping out, especially under its own weight, if fitted vertically.

Monkey tail bolts are very similar to bow handle bolts but have a ball on the end of the bolt, rather than a bow handle.

Pad bolt

Monkey tail bolt

Panic bar bolts are available for single and double doors. They incorporate a bolt that runs the length of the door, passing through a latch that is fixed at approximately waist height. When the latch is pulled the bolts locate in keepers positioned in the frame; when the latch is pushed the bolts disengage from the keepers. They are fitted on doors that are used as a means of escape, e.g. fire exits.

Panic bar bolt

Door closers

Door closers are mechanical devices that encourage a door to close on its own. There are three types in common use today, which are described below.

Overhead door closers are probably the most common type encountered and can be adapted to suit most hanging situations. The speed of closure can be adjusted, and they also have a check that stops the door from slamming. Overhead closers are the only type that uses hydraulic fluid.

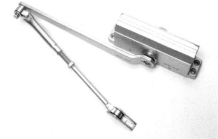

Overhead door closer

Concealed door spring closer

The concealed door spring type has a long barrel fitted into the door. This contains a strong spring and a chain. To the other end of the chain is a plate that is fixed to the door jamb. The mechanism is only visible when the door is open.

Surface door closers have a body fixed on to the door jamb and a tension arm that moves across a nylon guide fitted to the door. As the door is opened pressure is built up in the spring. When the door is released the spring pushes the door shut. Pressure adjustment is made via a detachable tommy bar.

Fixings that penetrate timber

Fixings are items of ironmongery that enable a carpenter to connect components together. When choosing a fixing we must consider certain factors, which include:

- What strength must the fixing have?

- Where will the fixing be used?

- Will the fixing need to be removed at a later date?

- Cost.

The best sources for finding out what fixings are available are trade catalogues, local builder's merchants or DIY superstores. New types of fixing are regularly added to an already extensive range.

Although there are many specialist fixings available the most common are:

- nails

- screws

- wall fixings for solid walls

- wall fixings for hollow walls

- adhesives.

Nails

Nails consist of a head and shank and are inserted by a hammer or mechanical tool. There are several types, made from either ferrous or non-ferrous metal. Ferrous metal contains iron and will therefore rust unless protected. The carpenter must decide the most appropriate nail for the required application.

Round wire nails are available in sizes from 25 mm to 150 mm. They should not be driven below the surface of the timber and are relatively easy to remove. They are used for low-quality work where they will not be seen, such as roofing, studwork etc.

Did you know?

Some hardwoods are acidic and when unprotected ferrous metals are inserted the process of oxidisation (rusting) is accelerated and they stain the timber

Round wire nails

Annular ring nails

Annular ring nails are available in sizes from 20 mm – 75 mm and also **sheradised** to prevent rusting. These nails are similar to the round wire nail but feature a series of rings along the shank that makes them much harder to remove, and also provides a stronger hold.

Oval wire nails are available in sizes from 25 mm – 100 mm. They are manufactured from ferrous metal and can be punched below the surface of the timber. They are less likely to split the grain of the timber and are usually used for higher-quality work than the round wire nail.

Lost head nails are available in sizes from 40 mm – 75 mm. The head can be punched below the surface of the timber for concealment.

Definition

Sheradising – a process of covering metal with zinc, a non-ferrous metal, to reduce rusting

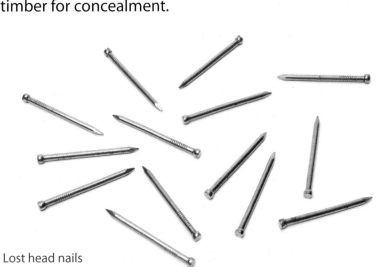

Oval wire nails

Lost head nails

Panel pins

Panel pins are available in sizes from 20 mm – 40 mm. They are easy to punch below the surface, causing little damage to the face of the work. They are used for fine applications. Variations include sheradised and brass versions that resist rust, and veneer pins for extra fine work.

Other nails include plasterboard, felt and clout nails, also plastic-headed nails for use with uPVC systems and double-headed nails for shuttering work. All are designed for specific applications.

Other nails

Screws

Most modern screws are computer designed. Like a nail, screws consist of a head and a shank. However, the shank is threaded and designed to pull the fixing into the material into which it is being inserted.

Screws are manufactured from both ferrous and non-ferrous materials and are defined by:

- head type

- length, measured from the tip to the part of the head that will be flush with the work surface, ranging from 12 mm – 150 mm

- gauge, the diameter of the shank, ranging from 2 mm – 6.5 mm.

Once again, it is the carpenter's responsibility to choose the correct screw for the application in which it is being used.

Remember

Screws are still sold by the old Imperial Measures gauge number (8, 10, 12 etc.) but these are being phased out

Head types

Screws with countersunk heads are used when the screw has to be flush with the work or below it.

Raised head screws are usually used for attaching metal components, such as door handles. Round heads are usually used for attaching sheet material to timber that is too thin to countersink.

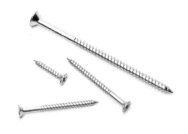

Countersunk

Mirror screws have a thread within the head to which a decorative dome can be attached. As the name suggests, these are used mainly for fixing mirrors.

Pan head and flange heads are commonly found on self-tapping screws where the fixing of sheet metal is involved.

Raised or round head screws   Mirror screw head   Pan head   Flange head

Screwdriver types

There are screwdrivers available, designed to fit each type of screw head and size of screw. A selection is shown in the following photographs:

Posidrive screwdriver

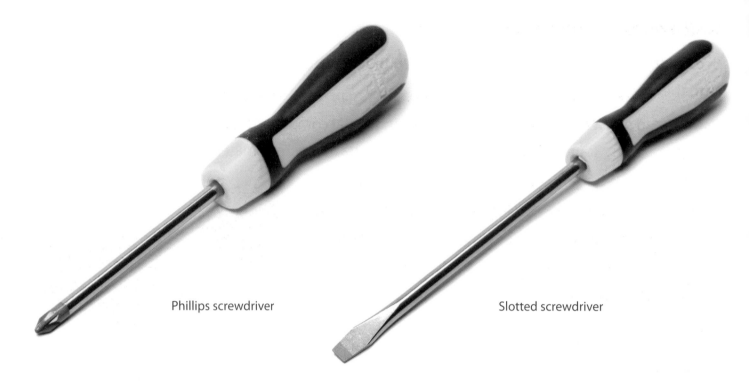

Phillips screwdriver

Slotted screwdriver

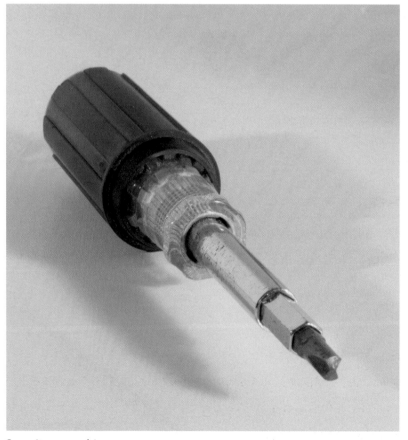

Security screwdriver

Wall fixings for solid walls

Plug fixings

Nails and screws can be used to fix components to masonry. However, the carpenter must first plug the masonry, which can either be done using a plugging chisel or an electric drill.

If a plugging chisel is used carpenters can make their own plugs, but this is time-consuming and not commonly done now. When using an electric hammer drill to plug a wall several plug types are available, which include:

- moulded plastic plugs
- hammer plugs
- frame fixings.

Moulded plastic plug

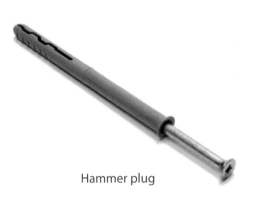
Hammer plug

Frame fixings

Remember

It is vital to use the correct size drill, as specified by the fixing manufacturer, and follow all instructions for use

All work on the same principle. A plastic segmented sleeve fits snugly into a hole that has been pre-drilled to the plug manufacturer's stated dimensions. A screw is then inserted into the plastic sleeve that push the segments apart to grip the side of the hole.

Anchor bolts

These are used for giving an extra strong fixing in concrete or masonry. They consist of a segmented metal sleeve that encases a conical plug on the end of a bolt. As the bolt is turned clockwise the conical plug rises up the thread of the bolt, expanding the metal sleeve.

Anchor bolt

Wall fixings for hollow walls

Hollow wall fixings work on the principle of the fixing opening out behind the wall panel and gripping it in some way. These include:

- nylon anchors
- plastic collapsible anchors
- metal collapsible anchors
- rubber sleeve anchors
- gravity toggles
- spring toggles.

Nylon anchors

Plastic collapsible anchors

Metal collapsible anchors

Rubber sleeve anchors

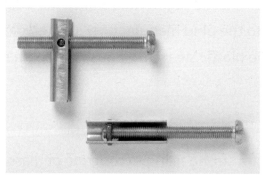

Gravity toggles

Spring toggles

Other fixings are available called EASI drivers™ but these are generally for use only in plasterboard, though they will support heavy items such as kitchen wall units or radiators. It is worth the effort to experiment with different types of fixing before deciding which one to use.

Adhesives

Adhesives, able to provide long-term fixing, are a relatively recent development within the building industry but already there are numerous products available. These range from dry lining adhesive through to expanding foam and trade name products such as No Nails™.

A selection of adhesives

Encasing services

This section has been designed to provide you with the knowledge and understanding to correctly encase a variety of services and structures.

The phrase 'encasing services' usually refers to the carcase, framework and trim that cover RSJs, service pipes, cables, steel and concrete columns or, in some instances, unsightly spaces such as where a bath is situated or where the bulkhead for a staircase cuts into a room.

Beams and columns

In some buildings RSJs have to be cladded to protect them from the effects of fire. The amount of protection required will depend upon the function and location of the beam.

Safety tip

With adhesive, or any other chemical, carefully read all instructions before use

Did you know?

RSJ stands for rolled steel joist, often used to provide load-bearing supports in a building because the shape is very resistant to bending

RSJ as load-bearing beam

How to clad a beam

If a beam to be clad is made of timber, or even concrete, it can have a frame fixed to it and then facing material put on to the frame, or the facing material can be fixed directly to it. The bigger problem is to clad a steel beam, often an RSJ used as a load-bearing support.

Step 1 Fix **noggings** between the rolled edges of the beam. This can be done by accurately cutting lengths of 50 mm x 50 mm timber to match the vertical gap in the side of the RSJ. Then drive them vertically into the gap on both sides of the beam so they wedge in place. They will provide attachment points for a cradle so should be no more than 600 mm apart.

Step 1 Fix noggings

Alternatively, timber supports can be fitted in the gap along the whole length of the beam and then bolted into place through holes in the beam (some come with them or they can be drilled). These similarly provide attachment points for a cradle.

Step 2 Create a cradle using 50 mm × 25 mm treated softwood and use a simple **halving joint** to fix the corners together. Screw the cradle to the bearers. (If the noggings or timber supports come flush with the sides of the metal beam it is possible to dispense with a cradle by fixing additional timber supports along the beam near the top and bottom as a support for facing material.)

Step 3 Run soffits along the length of the joist, fastening them into the cradle. The facing material can now be fixed to the soffits to conceal the sides of the beam.

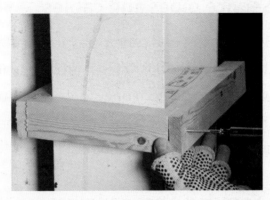
Step 2 Create a cradle

Definition

Halving joint – the same amount is removed from each piece of timber so that when fixed together the joint is the same thickness as the uncut timber

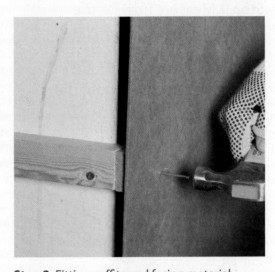
Step 3 Fitting soffits and facing material

How to clad a column

Concrete or steel columns are cladded by constructing a set of framed grounds (either two or four) slightly larger than the column itself. These are generally shaped like a ladder and made from rough sawn timber. They are assembled around the column and adjusted until plumb.

Any slackness is taken up, using wedges or packing pieces with a screw or nail driven into them to stop them slipping.

Facing material is then fixed to the framed grounds.

Did you know?

Plumb means vertical; hence, a plumb bob is used to check something is vertical

Service pipes and cables

Service pipes and cables are hidden from view whenever possible. However, there are occasions when it is not possible to do so; when the circuit of pipe work has to go from one storey to another for instance. When this occurs they should be encased behind a timber stud frame. The method is very similar to cladding a column.

Encasing pipes and wires

Step 1 Measure how far the services protrude. The framework that is about to be fitted should not stand excessively from the object to be encased.

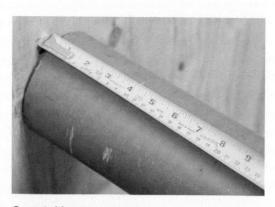

Step 1 Measure services

Step 2 By using halving joints or by butt nailing, construct two sets of framed grounds as shown in Figure 10.11.

Figure 10.11 Step 2 Construct frames

Step 3 Fix battens to the wall with plugs and screws or masonry nails.

Step 3 Fix battens to the wall

Step 4 Fix framed grounds

Step 4 Fix the framed grounds to the battens.

Step 5 Clad with 6mm ply or similar, scribing to the wall if necessary.

Step 5 Clad with ply

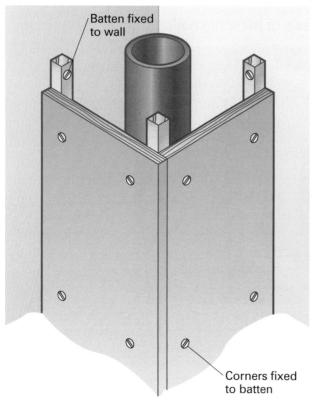

Figure 10.12 Corner casing for a large pipe

A corner casing for a large pipe is shown in Figures 10.12 and 10.13.

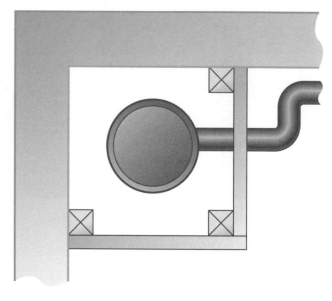

Figure 10.13 Plan view of casing

Alternative ways of encasing services are shown in Figures 10.14 –10.17.

Remember

Where there is a service valve or stop cock a removable panel must be fitted for maintenance and emergencies

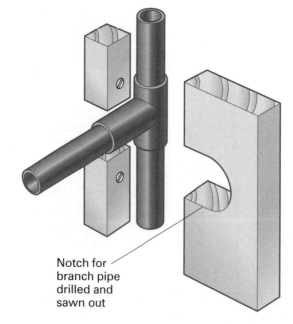

Figure 10.14 Branch pipe

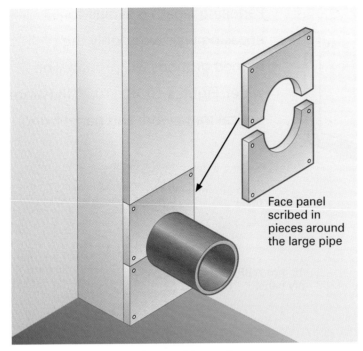

Figure 10.15 Face panel around large pipes

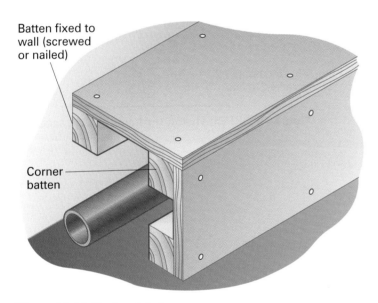

Figure 10.16 Horizontal pipes

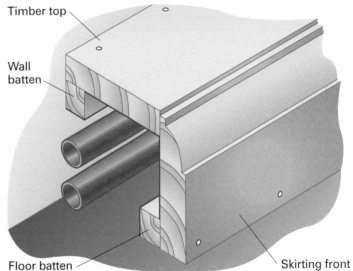

Figure 10.17 Horizontal pipes with skirting board

Baths

Baths are often panelled, but care should be taken to ensure that suitable materials are used that can cope with the heat and condensation associated with bathrooms. Also the plumbing should be easily accessible.

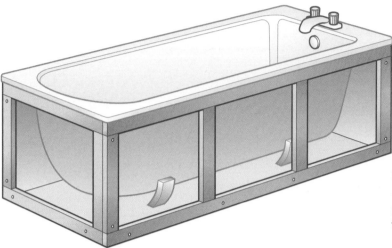

Figure 10.18 Framework for a bath panel

Panelling a bath is similar to encasing pipe work, only the framed grounds will probably be wider. Figures 10.18 –10.20 illustrate typical framework and panel fixing.

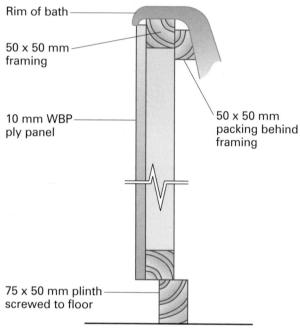

Rim of bath

50 x 50 mm framing

10 mm WBP ply panel

50 x 50 mm packing behind framing

75 x 50 mm plinth screwed to floor

Figure 10.19 Plinth below the frame as a toe space

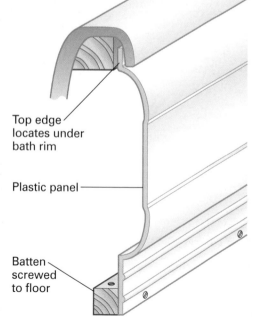

Top edge locates under bath rim

Plastic panel

Batten screwed to floor

Figure 10.20 Detail of a standard panel

Did you know?

Fitting loft insulation behind bath panels helps keep the bath water warmer longer and also provides some sound insulation

Wall and floor units

This section is designed to provide you with the knowledge and understanding to assemble and fix both wall and floor units. Normally you will be fitting these in kitchens and bedrooms. Kitchens are the most difficult and are described below. If you learn to follow these instructions they will enable you to fit wall and floor units in a bedroom or anywhere else.

Kitchen safety

Most household accidents happen in the kitchen. Thus, when planning a kitchen, safety is the number one priority. Always:

- Create a working triangle consisting of the sink, cooker and fridge, which avoids unnecessary movement and improves efficiency.

- Avoid a design that encourages people to use the working area of the kitchen as a cut through, to garden or living room for example.

- Try not to place a hob or sink at the end of a run of units; also make sure that children cannot easily reach either hob or sink.

- Try to design work surfaces either side of the hob and avoid placing the hob in front of a window.

A plan of a well laid out kitchen is shown in Figure 10.21.

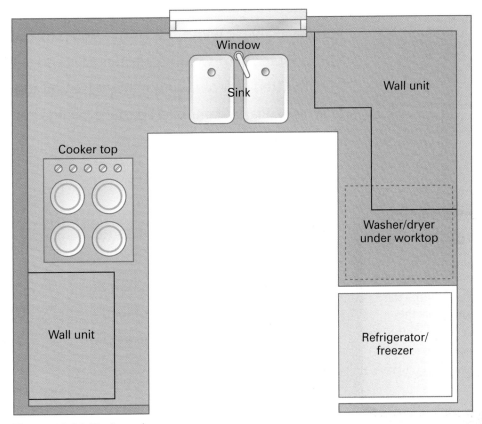

Figure 10.21 Kitchen plan

Kitchen units

The majority of kitchen units available today are constructed from melamine-faced particle board, and supplied as either base units or wall units. Base units are floor standing, whereas wall units are mounted on the wall.

Units are supplied ready-built or flat-pack. When supplied as flat-packs the assembly instructions must be followed with great care. Check whether shelves have to be fitted during assembly, rather than after installation, particularly in corner units.

Base units are available in widths 300 mm – 1200 mm, and normally 600 mm deep and 900 mm high. Corner units are available to match up with them. Most manufacturers incorporate adjustable height legs in their designs to allow for uneven floors.

Wall units are available in widths 300 mm – 1000 mm; typically 600 mm, 720 mm or 900 mm high and 300 mm deep.

Worktops are also mainly made from plastic-laminated particle board and available in widths 600 mm – 900 mm, but granite, stainless steel and proprietary, hard-wearing plastics are used in more expensive kitchens. The width fitted is dependant on the base unit used. Depth is usually 40 mm but can vary. Plastic-laminated particle boards have a square- or post-formed front edge.

Remember

When using a spirit level to mark a datum line always alternate the level along its length; this counteracts inaccuracies and prevents cumulative error

Fitting base units

Step 1 Carefully mark a horizontal datum line, approximately 1 metre from the floor, on the walls that are to have base or wall units placed against them. We now have a point to work up or down from.

Step 1 Mark a horizontal datum line

Step 2 Determine a user-friendly height for the units minus the worktop. Then, working down from the 1 metre datum, fix a back rail to the wall. We now have a datum that allows us to level across and along the units.

Step 2 Fixing a back rail

Remember

It may be worth fixing wall units at this stage before base units and worktops go in

Step 3 Adjust the unit's legs

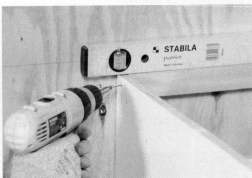

Step 4 Base units fixed in position

Step 3 Preferably working from a corner, place units where they should go, taking into consideration service pipes and cables. Adjust the legs so that all units are level and in line with the back rail.

Step 4 Once all units are in place they can be fixed together using connecting bolts and fixed to the wall or floor using screws.

Fitting worktops

Specialist tools and equipment are needed to cut and fix worktops. These include:

- jigsaw with downward cutting blades

- plunge router (minimum 1600 watt) capable of plunging more than the depth of the worktop, with 12.7 mm diameter collet and template guide

- 12.7 mm diameter straight-cutting router bits, minimum length equal to the depth of the worktop

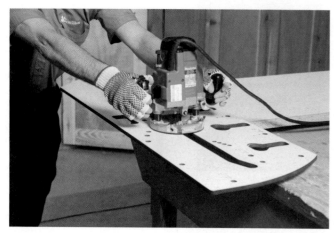

Joiner using router and jig

- worktop jig
- biscuit jointer
- clamps (G clamp or similar)
- contact adhesive
- varnish
- panel connectors.

Step 1 Cut to length and form an internal corner using a purpose-made jig. These are produced by a variety of manufacturers and, when used in conjunction with a powerful router, a clean accurate cut is achievable.

Step 1 Cut lengths and internal corners

Step 2 Strengthen joints with biscuit jointer

Step 2 Strengthen joints using a biscuit jointer.

Step 3 Cut worktops to house sink units etc.

Step 3 Cut worktops to house sink units or appliances using a jigsaw with a downward cutting blade. This prevents the plastic-laminated surface from being chipped. The chipboard that is exposed by the cut should be coated in varnish to prevent any moisture penetration.

Step 4 Fix worktops to the base units with screws and connectors.

Step 4 Fix worktops to base units

Fitting wall units

Most wall units are fastened to the wall by an adjustable bracket that hooks itself onto a steel hanger plate. The plans should show the clearance required between the worktop and base of the wall units. If not, check with a supervisor or the customer. It is normal to have the tops of all units at the same height.

Step 1 Measure the height of units and add this to the clearance from the work surface, which gives the height where the tops of the wall units should go. Measure and mark these, working upwards from our datum line.

Step 1 Mark the tops of wall units

Step 2 Mark the locations for the hanger plates and fix in place. Often the manufacturer of the wall units provides a template to help position them.

Step 3 Hang the wall units on the hanger plates and adjust for height by turning a screw housed within the adjustable bracket. Once done, another screw enables the bracket to be tightened on to the steel plate.

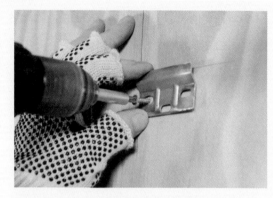

Step 2 Mark and fix hanger plates

Step 3 Hang and adjust wall units

Typical wall units in position

As with base units, wall units can be connected together by using connecting bolts.

Finishing off

Complete the job by fixing plinth boards, cornices, pelmets, doors, shelves and drawers. Details of how to do this should be provided with the kitchen units and often vary between manufacturers.

In general:

- Plinth boards are fixed to the legs of base units using clips supplied by the manufacturer. However, the boards may need scribing to the floor to avoid having any unsightly gaps.

- Cornices are often fitted on to wall units. This requires accurate marking out and either a chop saw or mitre saw used to give a clean, accurate cut. Care must be taken to ensure the cornice does not move or slip while it is being cut.

- Finally doors and shelves can be fitted to the units. This should be done last to avoid damage to the face of the work. The runners that hold the shelves, and hinges that hold the doors, both allow for adjustment. This ensures that an equal gap is seen between doors and shelves when the work has been completed.

Various plinths, cornices, doors and shelves

Completed kitchen

On the job: Fitting mouldings

Shauna has been asked to fit 300 mm x 30 mm skirting boards in a room. The architrave is 75 mm x 19 mm. What might be a problem at the junction where the architrave and the skirting board meet? How could Shauna get around this? The room is also to have a dado rail fitted. The rail is 5 mm thicker than the architrave. How could Shauna resolve this problem?

Knowledge check

1. Name three examples of mouldings.

2. How can architrave be fitted to a surface that is not smooth?

3. What are the different ways in which skirting can be fitted?

4. Briefly describe the two different methods of shaping skirting where it meets in a corner.

5. Why are plinth blocks used?

6. Describe in your own words the following types of door: a framed door; a flush door; a fire resisting door.

7. Why should a door be stored flat for a few days prior to fitting?

8. If a door is too tall for an opening, where should you cut excess wood from?

9. What is the special feature of a helical or double action hinge?

10. Why would a door closer be fitted to a door?

11. Why might a rolled steel joist (RSJ) need to be cladded?

12. What should you always consider when encasing service pipes or cables?

13. What is the number one priority when planning a kitchen?

14. When fitting kitchen wall units, how do you know how much clearance is required between the worktop and the base of the unit?

15. Why are the doors and shelves of kitchen units fitted last?

chapter 11

Marking and setting out joinery products

OVERVIEW

Many joinery items, such as doors, stairs and windows are now mass-produced under almost factory conditions using computer-programmed machinery. However, there will always be a place for bench joiners making small numbers of high-quality joinery items to a given specification. To do this, you must understand the main woodworking joints.

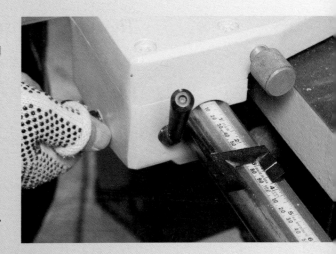

To turn the client's specification into a finished item of joinery, bench joiners must first produce detailed drawings. The information from the drawings can then be transferred to the timber in preparation for machining and assembly.

Production of the detailed drawings is known as 'setting out'. Transfer of this information to the timber is referred to as 'marking out'.

This chapter covers:

- Woodworking joints
- Setting out
- Marking out.

Woodworking joints

At the end of this section you should be able to:

- understand simple jointing methods used on doors and windows
- identify the main joints used in the assembly of units and fitments
- state the correct jointing methods used on a common staircase.

Joints used on doors and windows

During the manufacture of doors and windows the mortise and tenon joint is extensively used. The type of mortise and tenon will depend on its location. Examples of this joint are as follows:

Through mortise and tenon

In a through mortise and tenon joint a single rectangular tenon is slotted into a mortise. See Figure 11.1.

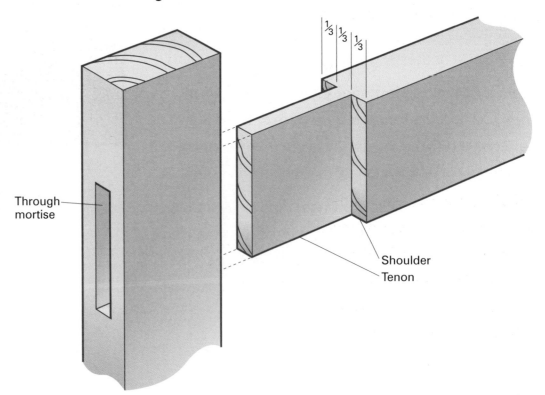

Figure 11.1 Through mortise and tenon

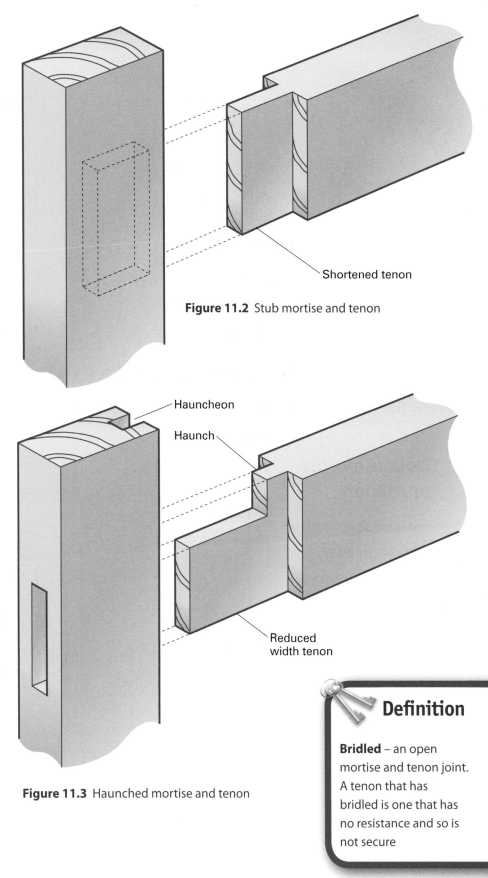

Stub mortise and tenon

In a stub mortise and tenon joint the tenon is stopped short to prevent it protruding through the member. See Figure 11.2.

Figure 11.2 Stub mortise and tenon

Shortened tenon

Haunched mortise and tenon

In a haunched mortise and tenon joint the tenon is reduced in width, leaving a shortened portion of the tenon protruding which is referred to as a haunch. See Figure 11.3. The purpose of the haunch is to keep the tenon the full width of the timber at the top third of the joint. This will prevent twisting. A haunch at the end of the member will aid the wedging-up process and prevent the tenon becoming **bridled**. For a detailed description of the wedging-up process look at Chapter 12 Assembling joinery products.

Hauncheon

Haunch

Reduced width tenon

Figure 11.3 Haunched mortise and tenon

Definition

Bridled – an open mortise and tenon joint. A tenon that has bridled is one that has no resistance and so is not secure

Twin mortise and tenon

In a twin mortise and tenon joint the haunch is formed in the centre of a wide tenon, creating two tenons, one above the other. See Figure 11.4.

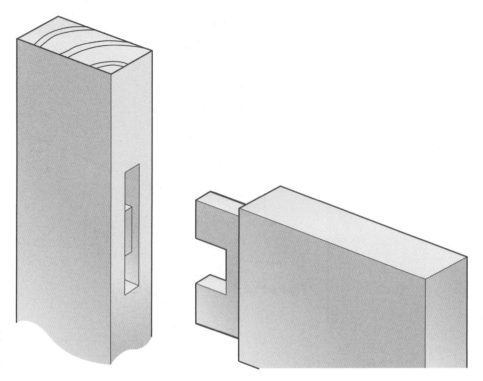

Figure 11.4 Twin mortise and tenon

Double mortise and tenon

For a double mortise and tenon, two tenons are formed within the thickness of the timber. See Figure 11.5.

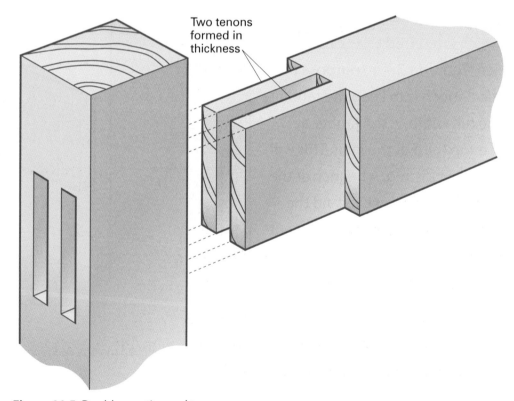

Two tenons formed in thickness

Figure 11.5 Double mortise and tenon

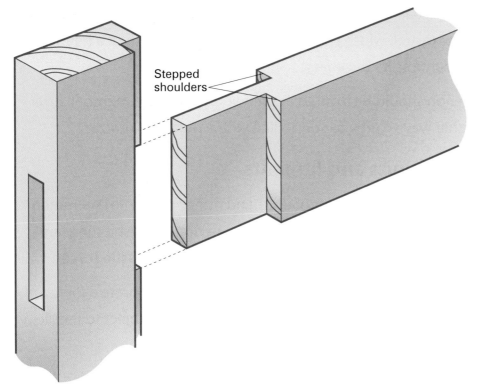

Figure 11.6 Stepped shoulder joint

Stepped shoulder joint

Used on frames with rebates, a stepped shoulder joint has a shoulder stepped the depth of the rebate. This joint can also be combined with haunched, twin or stub tenons. See Figure 11.6.

Twin tenon with twin haunch

A twin tenon with twin haunch joint is used on the deep bottom rails of doors. See Figure 11.7.

Basic rules on mortise and tenon joints

The proportions of mortise and tenon joints are very important to their strength. Some basic rules are as follows:

Tenon width should be no more than five times its thickness. This prevents shrinkage and movement in the joint. If more than five times then a haunch should be introduced.

The tenon should be one-third of the thickness of the timber. If a chisel is not available to cut a mortise at one-third, the tenon should be adjusted to the nearest chisel size.

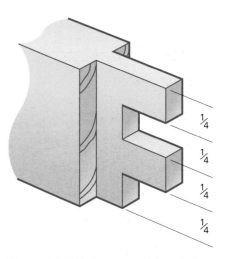

Figure 11.7 Twin tenon with twin haunch

When a haunch is being used to reduce the width of a tenon, then about one-third of the overall width should be removed. The depth of a haunch should be the same as its thickness.

Although a tenon should be located in the middle third of a member, it can be moved either way slightly to stay in line with a rebate or groove.

Joints used in units and fitments

During the design and setting out of units and fitments the most common joint used is the mortise and tenon, but these are not the best if there are forces likely to try to pull the joint apart. These are called **tensile forces**.

Parts of a unit or fitment subject to such forces must incorporate a joint design that will allow for this. A drawer on a unit is often subject to tensile forces, so a dovetail joint would be used.

The two most common types of dovetail joint are through and lapped. A through dovetail joint is shown in Figure 11.8 and a lapped dovetail at Figure 11.9.

Definition

Tensile forces – a force that is trying to pull something apart

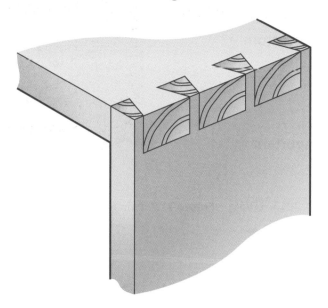

Figure 11.8 Through dovetail joint

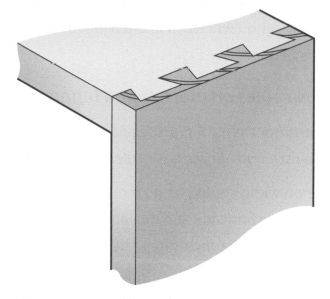

Figure 11.9 Lapped dovetail joint

Dovetail joints should have a slope (sometimes called the pitch) of 1:6 for softwoods, or 1:8 for hardwoods. If the slope of the dovetail is excessive then the joint will be weak due to short grain. If the slope is insufficient the dovetail will have a tendency to pull apart. The slope (or pitch) is shown in Figure 11.10.

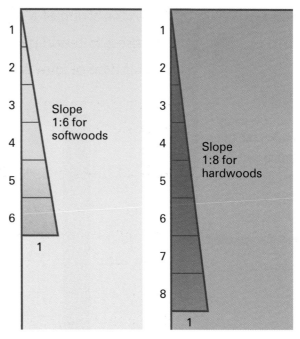

Figure 11.10 Slope of a dovetail joint

Correct jointing methods on staircases

The most common joint used in staircase construction is a **stopped housing joint**. This joint is used to locate or house the tread and riser of a step into the string. It will be stopped at the nosing of the tread. See Figure 11.11.

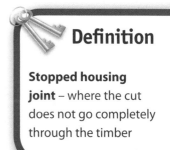

Definition

Stopped housing joint – where the cut does not go completely through the timber

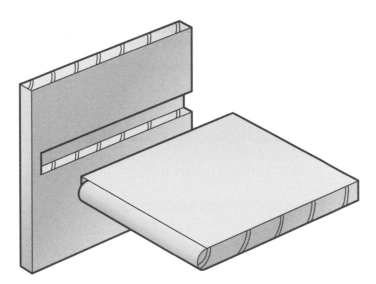

Figure 11.11 Stopped housing joint (staircase)

When the string of a stair meets a newel post, a stubbed and haunched mortise and tenon joint is used, as shown in Figure 11.12. More information on this type of joint can be found earlier in the chapter.

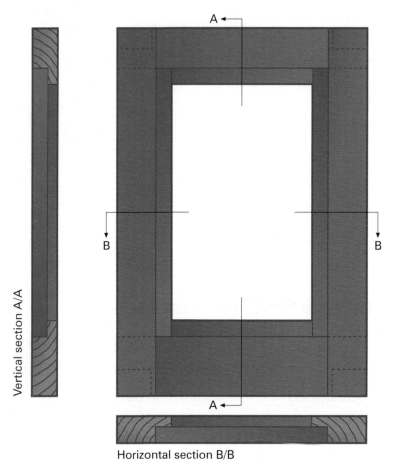

Figure 11.12 Housed string with mortise and tenon

Setting out

At the end of this section you will understand:

- the principles of a setting out rod and its uses

- the purpose of a cutting list.

Setting out rod

A setting out rod will usually be a thin piece of plywood, hardboard or MDF, on which can be drawn the full size measurements of the item to be made. It is quite often painted white in order to aid the clarity of drawing.

Rods can be used time and time again, simply by repainting the surface upon completion of a task. If marked rods are to be kept for reuse they must be referenced and stored safely.

Upon receipt of scale drawings, specification and any on-site measurements the **setter out** will produce a full size, horizontal and vertical section through the item by drawing it on a setting out rod. See Figure 11.14.

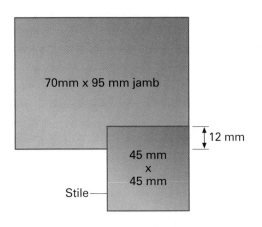

Figure 11.13 White setting out rod for small, four-pane sash

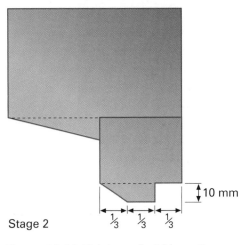

Figure 11.14 Height and width sections

Elevations may also be drawn on setting out rods. This is particularly valuable for shaped or curved work, as the setter out can get a 'true' visual image of a completed joinery item.

Safety tip

When painting rods or anything else, always refer to safety information on the paint tin and follow any guidelines given there

Definition

Setter out – an experienced bench joiner whose job is the setting out of joinery products

Although rods are marked up full size, certain critical dimensions can be added as a check against any errors or damage to the rod. These are usually:

- **sight size** – the size of the innermost edges of the component (usually the height and width of any glazed components and, therefore, sometimes referred to as 'daylight size')

- **shoulder size** – the length of any member between shoulders of tenons

- **overall size** – the extreme length and width of an item.

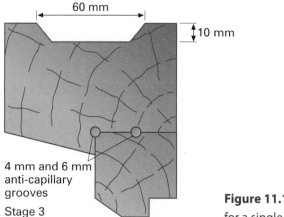

60 mm

10 mm

4 mm and 6 mm anti-capillary grooves

Stage 3

Figure 11.15 Rod with critical dimensions for a single-panel glazed door

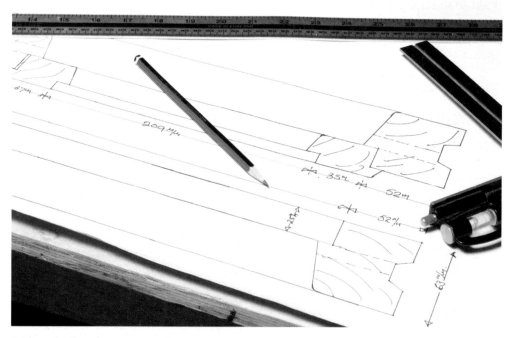

Rod marked up for a casement window

Developing drawn components

When producing workshop rods an inexperienced or apprentice joiner can sometimes have problems when building up a detailed section of timber. To overcome this, use the following step-by-step guidelines:

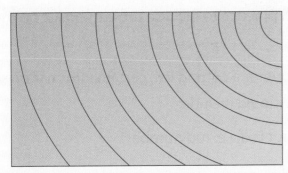

Figure 11.16 Step 1 Draw the components as a rectangular section

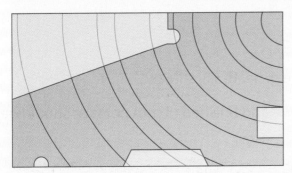

Figure 11.17 Step 2 Add any rebates, grooves and mouldings

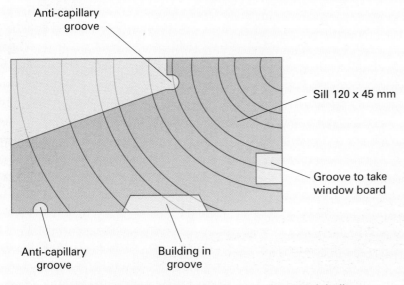

Anti-capillary groove

Sill 120 x 45 mm

Groove to take window board

Anti-capillary groove

Building in groove

Figure 11.18 Step 3 Add all other details, including any labelling

Cutting lists

Once the setting out rod has been completed the cutting list can be compiled. The cutting list is an accurate, itemised list of all the timber required to complete the job shown on the rod.

The cutting list will need to be referred to throughout the manufacturing process. It is, therefore, good practice to include the cutting list on the actual rod wherever possible.

Although there is no set layout for a cutting list, certain information should be clearly given in all lists. It should include:

- reference for the setting out rod, i.e. rod number
- date the list was compiled
- brief job description
- quantity of items required
- component description (e.g. head, sill, stile etc.)
- component size, both sawn and finished (3 mm per face should be allowed for machining purposes)
- general remarks.

An example cutting list is shown in Figure 11.19.

Timber cutting list

Job description: Two panel door

Date: 8 Sept 2006

Quantity	Description	Material	Length	Width	Thickness	Remarks
2	Stiles	S wood	1981	95	45	Mortise/groove for panel
1	Mid rail	"	760	195	45	Tenon/groove for panel
1	Btm rail	"	760	195	45	Tenon/groove for panel
1	Top rail	"	760	95	45	Tenon/groove for panel
1	Panel	Plywood	760	590	12	
1	Panel	"	600	590	12	

Figure 11.19 An example cutting list

Marking out

At the end of this section you will be able to:

- Select the correct sides of timber on which to mark out. These are known as the face and edge.

- Transfer information from setting out rod to timber.

Marking out is the transfer of the information on a setting out rod to the timber. It is a very important process and should be checked thoroughly. Wrong information transferred on to the timber at this stage will result in errors during assembly, which are likely to be time-consuming and costly.

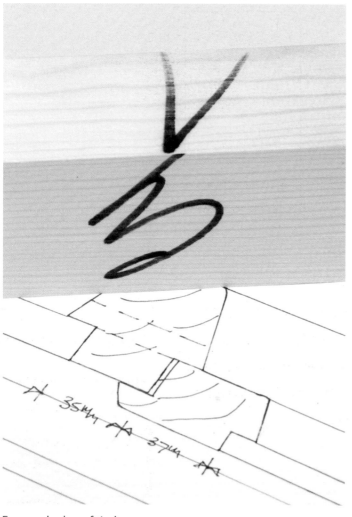

Face and edge of timber

Face and edge marks

The face and edge are the two most important of the four sides of a piece of timber. They are, therefore, usually selected as the two best adjacent sides.

The position and severity of any defects present in the timber should also be noted at this point. If these can be removed when cutting rebates or grooves then the sides containing them may still be the best sides to become the face and edge.

Face and edge marks are clearly applied to the relevant sides after careful inspection of the timber. They are used as a reference point from which all marking out is completed.

Items such as door stiles must be marked out in pairs, since they are not reversible. In this case the face and edge marks must always be opposite to each other.

Paired members

Face side and edge are normally the front and inside edges of the framework. However, where one side of the frame is not flush with the other, such as a casement window and sill, then the flush side should be chosen as the face.

Transferring information from a setting out rod

Marking out on the timber should be as clear and simple as possible with no unnecessary lines, as these cause confusion and possible errors. Pencil lines should be clear, sharp and made with a hard pencil. Wherever possible all marking out should be completed in a single operation and any wrongly placed or double lines should be rectified immediately.

Did you know?

A 2H pencil is suitable for marking out, with the nib sharpened to a chisel point for better accuracy

Find out

What tools would be used in the marking out process?

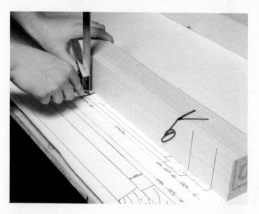

These two photos show a piece of timber being marked out from a door rod.

Note how the shoulder and mortise lines are directly transferred and that a completed section of timber is drawn across the member.

On the job: Marking out mix-up

Molly, a second-year apprentice, has been given a task to manufacture a number of replacement sashes for a housing redevelopment project in the local area. All setting out rods had been drawn up by Phil, a recently-qualified bench joiner. Molly was given all the rods with a range of component drawings referenced to the specific rod. After marking out the first sash, Molly realised that the size written on the drawings did not match the size on the rod as drawn, but did however match another sash to be made.

1   What do you think has happened?

2   What action should Molly take to overcome this problem?

3   What should be done to prevent this happening again?

FAQ

Why use a double tenon joint? Would it not be easier to just put in a thicker single tenon?

Yes, it would be easier but it would not be as strong. Putting in a double tenon will increase the surface area of the joint. This will give the joint a larger area for adhesion (gluing), thus producing a stronger, well-proportioned joint.

When a stair string tenon is jointed into a newel post would you use a twin tenon or a twin tenon with a twin haunch?

Both. At the top of the stair the newel post will be deeper than the string, therefore a twin tenon should be used. At floor level the newel post will be cut flush, therefore a twin tenon with twin haunch would be the strongest joint.

Why would you need sawn sizes on a cutting list?

By putting on sawn sizes the machinist will quickly be able to determine the most cost-effective sections of stock to use from the timber rack.

When marking out for repetitive items of joinery, for example a large number of standard-size doors, would you need to mark each piece of stock from the rod separately?

No. If you transfer the information to one piece of stock you can then clamp all the pieces that will be the same size together. From there you can transfer joint lines to all pieces. You must remember to ensure that all pieces are in pairs using your face and edge marks.

Knowledge check

1. What is a haunch and why is it used?

2. When should a tenon with a stepped shoulder be used?

3. A door stile has a finished section of 95 mm x 44 mm. What size chisel would be used to cut the mortise?

4. What pitch should be used for a dovetail in softwood?

5. State the joints used in the following: stair tread to string; string to newel post; middle rail of a two panel door; drawer on a kitchen unit.

6. What is the purpose of setting out?

7. Describe the purpose of cutting lists.

8. Explain the following: sight size; shoulder size; overall size.

9. What is the purpose of face and edge marks?

10. Explain what marking out entails.

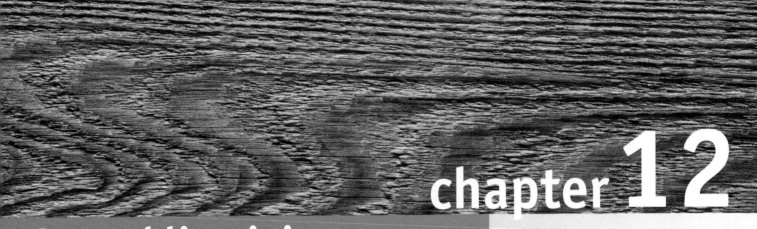

chapter **12**

Assembling joinery products

OVERVIEW

Once a bench joiner has produced the setting out details for the specified task and transferred the information onto the timber stock to be used, a joiner can begin the task of cutting and assembling the required item of joinery.

This chapter will cover the following aspects of assembling joinery products:

- Frames and linings
- Doors
- Stairs
- Units.

Frames and linings

Window and door frames/linings are fitted into openings left in masonry and hold the window or door in place. It is very important to make sure the frame or lining fits the opening well and that it is level. If this is not done, you will end up with doors and windows that don't hang properly and don't open and close properly.

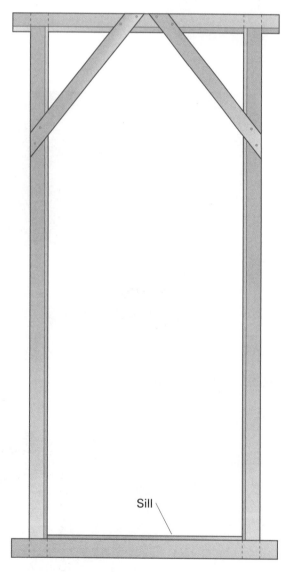

Sill

Figure 12.1 Door frame

Door frames and linings

Door frames are usually of a substantial and solid construction. They are mortised and tenoned and comprise heads, jambs and sills. They usually have a rebate cut from the solid timber. See Figure 12.1.

Door linings are of much lighter construction than frames and are used exclusively for internal doors. They don't usually have sills and are normally jointed between head and jambs with a form of housing joint, such as tongued housing (see Figure 12.2). Door linings usually have planted (nailed on) stops.

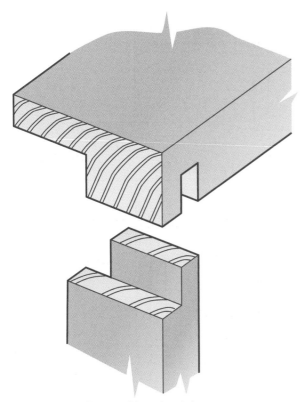

Figure 12.2 Tongued housing joint

Door frames and linings are usually assembled in the joiner's shop using a through mortise and tenon style of joint (see Chapter 11 Marking and setting out for more information on joints). To give additional strength and to pull the joint tight, a timber **dowel** is fixed through the face of the frame's head and into the tenon. The hole should be previously drilled in the face and then slightly off-centre in the tenon. When the dowel is knocked home the joint is pulled tight. This method is known as draw boring.

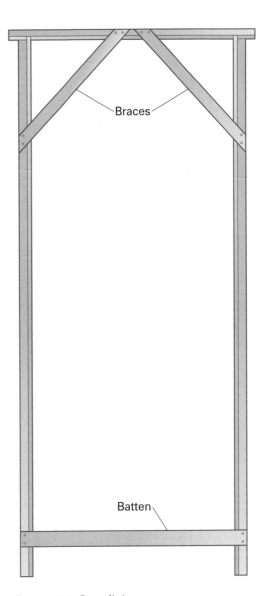

Figure 12.3 Door lining

Definition

Dowel – a headless wood or metal pin used to join timber together

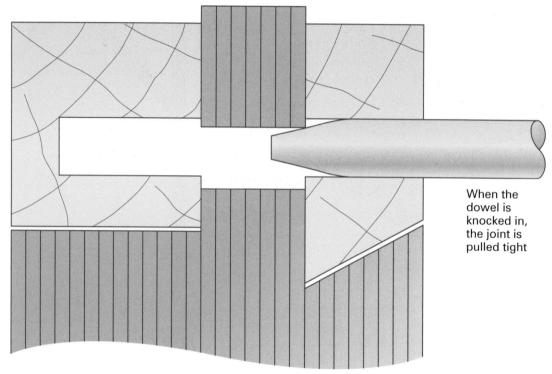

When the dowel is knocked in, the joint is pulled tight

Figure 12.4 Draw boring

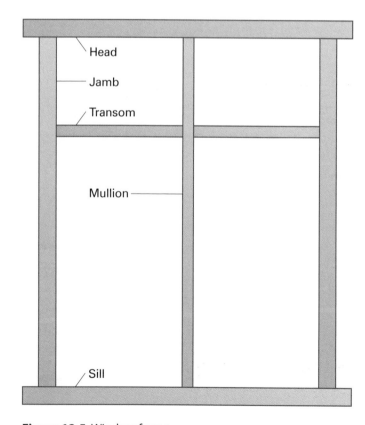

Head

Jamb

Transom

Mullion

Sill

Figure 12.5 Window frame

Window frames

The majority of modern windows are casement windows, which means that they are hinged on the side allowing them to swing open vertically (similar to the way a door opens). A casement window is made up of two main components:

- the frame

- the opening casement.

The frame

Like a door frame, a window frame consists of a head, sill and jambs. When the frame is to be divided, members called **mullions** (vertical dividers) and **transoms** (horizontal dividers) are included (see Figure 12.5).

The opening casement

The opening part of the window, known as the sash, consists of a top rail, bottom rail and two **stiles**. When the opening of the casement sash is to be divided up further, glazing bars are used (see Figure 12.6). The procedure for hanging a casement sash is exactly the same as for a door, only usually on a smaller scale. The procedure is summarised below, but look back at Chapter 10 Second fixing for the full door hanging procedure (page 338).

Definition

Stiles – the vertical parts of a window frame. The hinges are fitted on to one of them

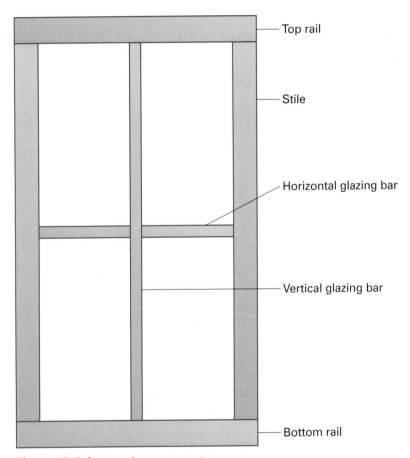

Figure 12.6 An opening casement

Hanging casement window sashes

- Mark the hanging side on both the frame and the sash.

- Cut off any horns (these are waste stock left overhanging on the stiles to aid cleaning up and prevent damage to sash corners prior to installation).

- Plane to fit the hanging stile.

- Plane the sash to the required width, running parallel with the side of the frame.

- Plane to fit the top and bottom of the frame.

- Mark out and cut the hinges.

- Screw one leaf of each hinge to the sash.

- Offer up the sash to the opening and screw the other leaves of the hinges to the frame.

- Make fine adjustments if needed and fit specified ironmongery.

General assembly procedure

There are some general points you should be aware of when assembling a door or window frame:

- dry assembly

- squaring up

- checking for winding

- wedging up.

We will look at each of these in turn over the next few pages.

Dry assembly

All the timber making up the frame should be knocked together dry prior to final assembly. 'Dry', in this situation, doesn't mean in dry conditions (i.e. out of the rain), but rather without the use of adhesive (i.e. a dry or practice run). This ensures that all joints are a good fit and that the frame is:

- the correct size

- square

- not **winding**.

Definition

Winding – twisted

Remember

Once the frame is assembled dry, check the sizes one more time. As soon as the frame is glued together it will be too late to adjust anything

Squaring up

When the frame has been assembled, glued and cramped up (held together whilst drying with clamps – see Figure 12.7), it should be tested to make sure that it is square, i.e. that the corners are at right angles. The most accurate way of doing this is to compare the diagonals using a squaring rod, which is a piece of rectangular timber with a small nail or panel pin knocked into the end (see Figure 12.8). The protruding nail is placed in one corner of the frame and the corner of the opposite diagonal is marked on the rod with a pencil. This procedure is repeated for the two other corners of the frame. If both pencil lines match up, then the frame is square (see Figure 12.9).

If the pencil lines do not match up, the frame needs to be adjusted by angling the cramps and pushing the frame. This should be done until the two pencil marks match up, meaning that the diagonals are the same length and the frame is square.

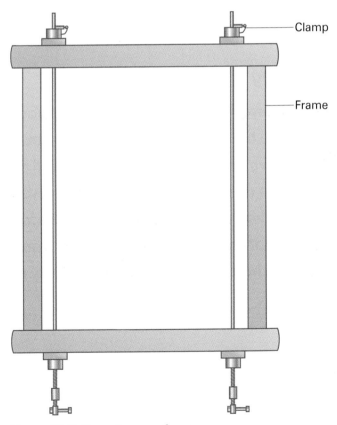

Figure 12.7 Cramping up a frame

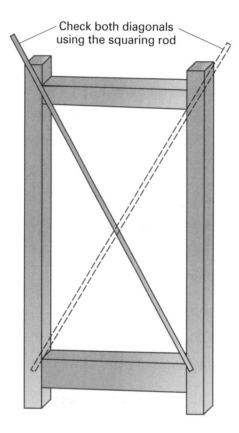

Check both diagonals using the squaring rod

Figure 12.8 Squaring up with a squaring rod

Checking for winding

Winding is a term that describes a frame that is twisted. You will need to check that the frame you have assembled is not twisted by using winding rods. These are simply two pieces of timber which are laid parallel across the frame when it is lying flat on the workbench. Close one eye and look across the winding rods. They should be parallel. If they are, the frame has no twist. If the winding rods are not parallel, the frame is winding and adjustments will have to be made to the joints before further assembly is carried out.

Remember

When you have made any adjustments to remove winding, go back and make sure the the frame is still square

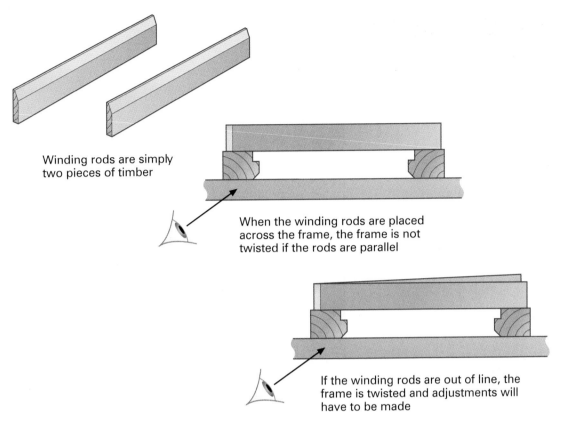

Winding rods are simply two pieces of timber

When the winding rods are placed across the frame, the frame is not twisted if the rods are parallel

If the winding rods are out of line, the frame is twisted and adjustments will have to be made

Figure 12.9 Checking for winding

Wedging up

The haunched mortise and tenon joints you have used in the assembly of your door or window frame are not only held in place by glue but also wedged. This should be done after the frame has been glued, squared and checked for winding. Wedging up involves placing a small wedge on either side of the tenon and carefully driving it into ensure a good tight joint. To help keep the frame square and the joints pulled in tight, it is best to drive in the external wedge (the haunch side) first. Look back at Chapter 11 Marking and setting out joinery products to remind yourself about haunched mortise and tenon joints.

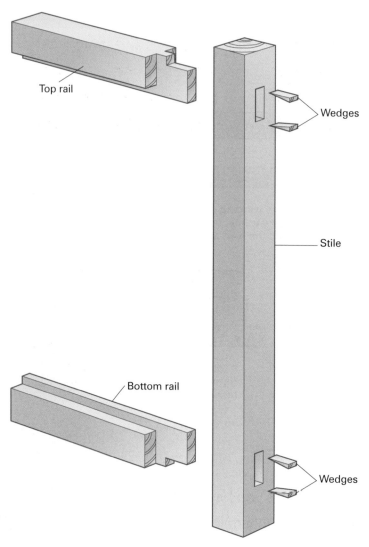

Figure 12.10 Wedging up a frame

Find out

How many different types of door are available?

Why do you think there are so many?

Doors

There are a number of different types of door assembled by carpenters and joiners. In this section we will only look at panelled and glazed doors, since they incorporate all the principles that you need to know about to be able to assemble any door.

Panelled doors

Panelled doors have a frame made from solid timber rails and styles (see Figure 12.11). When made by the bench joiner in the workshop, they will almost certainly incorporate a mortise and tenon type of joint. The frame will either be grooved or rebated to receive a number of either plywood or timber panels.

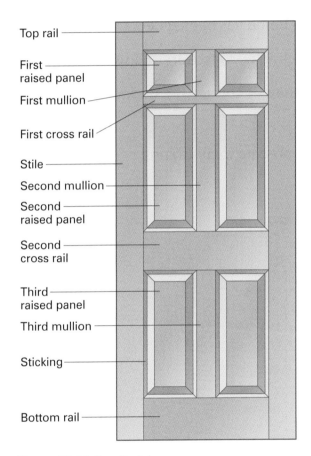

Figure 12.11 Panelled door

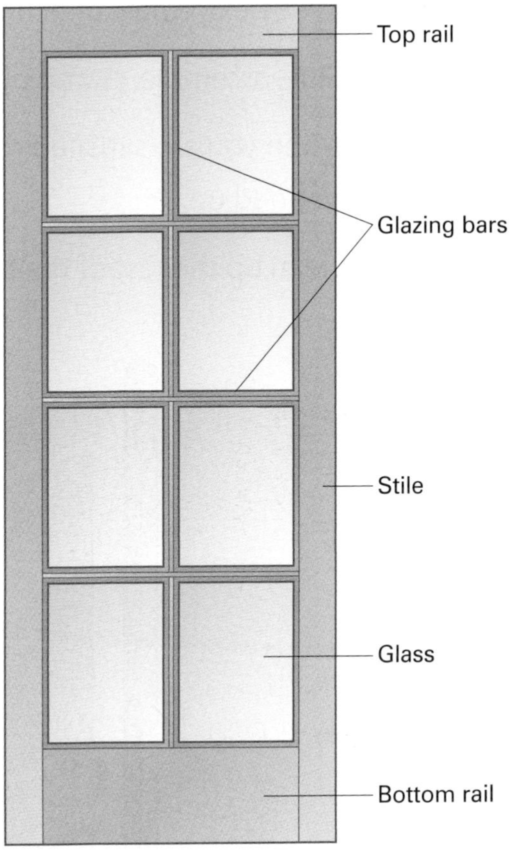

Figure 12.12 Glazed door

Glazed doors

Glazed doors are made in a similar fashion to panelled doors, however one or more of the panels is replaced by glass.

General assembly procedure

The following assembly procedure can be carried out for all types of framed door.

- Assemble the frame dry to ensure that all joints are tight, the right size, square and not winding.

- Before final assembly, clean up the inside edges of all components as this will be extremely difficult once the frame has been glued.

- Glue, assemble, cramp up and check again for square and winding.

- When you are satisfied that everything is correct, the door can be wedged up.

- Clean up the rest of the frame and prepare for finishing.

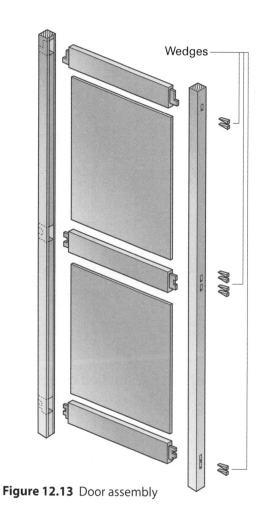

Figure 12.13 Door assembly

Stairs

We have already looked in some detail at stairs and their installation in Chapter 9 First fixing. Look back at page 293 to remind yourself of the terminology and regulations governing the construction and installation of stairs. You may also want to look back at Chapter 11 Marking and setting out to refresh your understanding before reading on (see page 377).

The next section covers the following tasks:

- marking out

- cutting out housings

- assembly.

Marking out

The following procedure should be followed for marking out the strings and newel:

Step 1 After making face and edge marks, place strings in pairs on the workbench (i.e. pairs made up of the wall and outer string or left and right string).

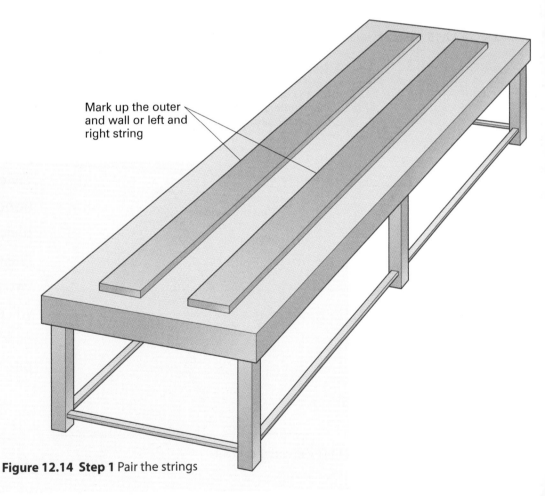

Mark up the outer and wall or left and right string

Figure 12.14 Step 1 Pair the strings

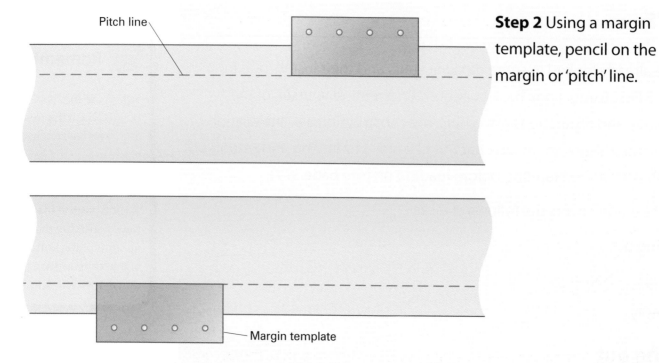

Step 2 Using a margin template, pencil on the margin or 'pitch' line.

Figure 12.15 Step 2 Marking the pitch line using a margin template

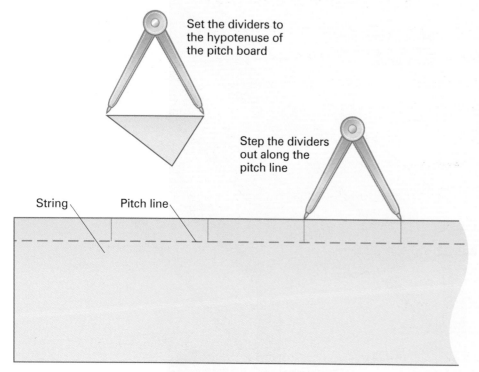

Step 3 Take the pitch board made during the marking out process and set a pair of dividers to the hypotenuse (longest side). Step the dividers out along the pitch line of the stair string. The two points of intersection will establish the tread and riser points relevant to the pitch line.

Figure 12.16 Step 3 Marking the tread and riser points

Step 4 The pitch board can now be used to mark out the rise (height) and going (depth) of each step. Using a template of the tread and riser, you can now mark out the actual position of each step in preparation for cutting.

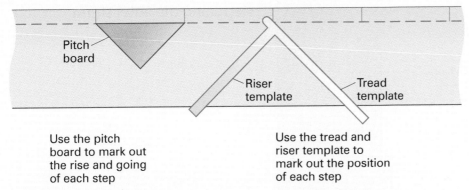

Use the pitch board to mark out the rise and going of each step

Use the tread and riser template to mark out the position of each step

Figure 12.17 Step 4 Marking the rise and going and the position of the treads and risers

Step 5 Mark out a tenon for housing the newel at the bottom of the outer string. The step used at the bottom of a staircase is usually a **bull nose step**, which means that the riser is shaped to curve slightly around the newel. The face of the second riser from the bottom of the stair should be in line with the centre line of the newel. With the newel post at a right angle to the second riser, mark the thickness of half the newel post on the second riser, which will give the shoulder line for the tenon. This process should be repeated at the top of the outer string if an upper newel post is being incorporated.

The tenon should be three-quarters of the newel post thickness and divided up, which will give you a stub twin tenon with a central haunch (note that the bottom joint has an additional haunch). The design and angle of the tenons avoids undercutting the joint, which will keep it as strong as possible. Mark any handrail details on the newel post.

Newel

Step 3

Step 2

Step 1

Figure 12.18 Step 5 Marking out the newel

Finished floor level (FFL)

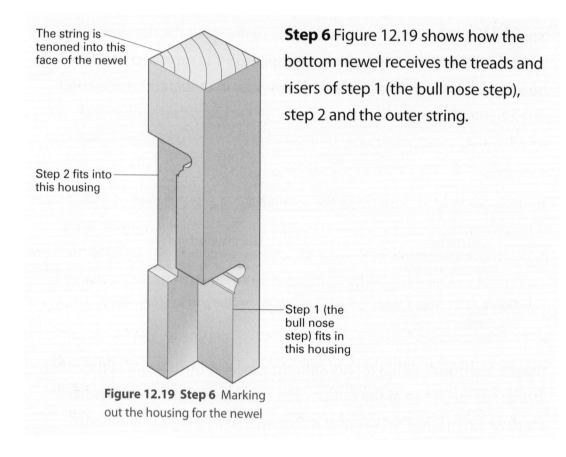

The string is tenoned into this face of the newel

Step 2 fits into this housing

Step 1 (the bull nose step) fits in this housing

Step 6 Figure 12.19 shows how the bottom newel receives the treads and risers of step 1 (the bull nose step), step 2 and the outer string.

Figure 12.19 Step 6 Marking out the housing for the newel

Cutting out housings

The strings will need housings to receive the stairs and the newel(s) will need housings to receive the strings. The stair housings are usually cut using a router together with a stair-housing template or jig.

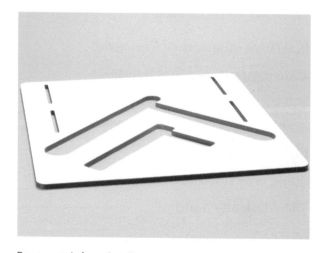

Router stair-housing jig

Assembly

When all the work has been carried out on the strings and newels, the assembly can be carried out. Although the assembly procedure can be carried out using a proprietary cramping system, it is more often than not carried out on an adapted workbench. The bench must be sturdy and level as it is essential that the strings are totally straight and parallel.

The stairs are held in position in the string housing with adhesive and timber wedges. First, the treads and risers should be slid into the string housing. Adhesive is then applied to the wedges, which are then pushed into both the tread and riser housing. Wedging must be done in a methodical order. It is easiest to start with the first riser and wedge both sides. Next the first tread can be fitted and wedged. This process continues until all risers and treads are fitted and wedged. During this process it is important that only the wedges are glued, not the treads and risers. Finally, the risers should be screwed to the back of the tread to prevent movement when the step is being used.

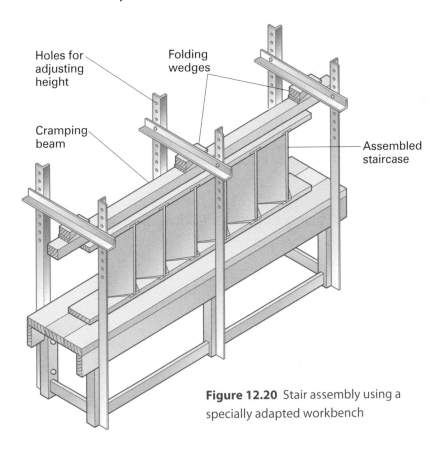

Holes for adjusting height

Folding wedges

Cramping beam

Assembled staircase

Figure 12.20 Stair assembly using a specially adapted workbench

On the job: Assembling a door

Thomas and Laura are both second-year apprentices and have been tasked with assembling a door that has been made by an experienced joiner. They glue and cramp up the door and leave it to go to lunch. When they return, their supervisor is not happy with them as the door is out of square and the joints are not tight-fitting.

How could this have happened and what could have been done to prevent it?

Units

The most common type of unit you will probably work with is kitchen units, although if you understand the basic principles of assembling these, you will find that the assembly of other types of unit (e.g. bathroom, bedroom) can easily follow a similar procedure. Most types of unit are made from melamine faced chipboard, MDF, block board, plywood and, sometimes, solid timber. See Chapter 4 Timber technology for more information on these materials (page 79).

There are a number of different methods of unit construction but we will only look at probably the two most common: box and framed. We will also briefly look at different types of knock-down fittings, which are often used in unit assembly.

See Chapter 10 Second fixing for further information about kitchen units and their fitting (page 321).

Box construction

This is also known as 'slab construction'. The unit is composed of vertical standards, rails and shelves and the plinth and bottom shelf are often an integral part of the unit. The back panel holds the frame square.

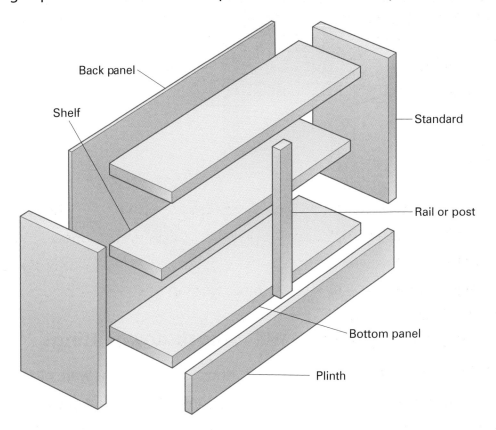

Figure 12.21 Box construction

Framed construction

This is also known as 'skeleton construction'. The units are composed of either a pair of frames (a front and a back frame) joined together with rails, or cross-frames joined together by rails at the front and back. See Figure 12.22. The plinths and draws are usually built separately in this type of unit. The frames are mortise and tenoned and assembly follows the same procedure as doors or casement window sashes (see pages 394–398 and 400).

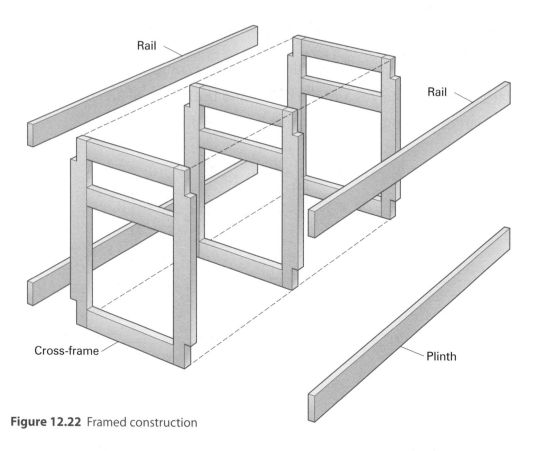

Figure 12.22 Framed construction

Example of knock-down fitting

Knock-down fittings

Knock-down fittings were originally designed as temporary fittings, although they are often used as permanent fittings on units. The fittings are normally quite simple (a block with drilled holes) and often made from plastic. Because of their simplicity and the fact that they usually only need a few screws, they can be easily undone and the unit quickly dismantled. They are ideal for flat-pack self-assembly furniture and the joints they provide are relatively strong.

FAQ

What causes a door or window frame to wind and can it be fixed?

Winding can be caused by the frame not sitting flat when it is assembled and can also be caused by using timber with a high moisture content which warps when it dries out. Winding can only be prevented by ensuring the frame is flat when clamped up.

Why do frames always have to be dry assembled?

Every frame you make needs to be dry assembled to check that the joints are tight and that the frame is square. If a frame is not checked in this way and it is glued and clamped and then found to have gaps in the joints, it will be difficult to put right.

Knowledge check

1. What type of joint is used in door frames?

2. What is draw boring?

3. What are mullions and transoms?

4. What is winding and how can you check for it?

5. Describe the general assembly procedure for doors.

6. What is the minimum going and maximum rise of a step allowed by *Building Regulations*?

7. Describe the use of a margin template and a pitch board.

8. Give a brief account of stair assembly.

9. Explain the difference between box and framed unit construction.

10. What are the advantages of using knock-down fittings?

adhesive glue

aggregates sand, gravel and crushed rock

architrave a decorative moulding, usually made from timber, that is fitted around door and window frames to hide the gap between the frame and the wall

arris the sharp edge formed when two flat or curved surfaces meet

balusters vertical members forming the infill between the string and the handrails in stairs

balustrade unit comprising handrail, newels and the infill between it and the string, which provides a barrier for the open side of the stair

barge boards fascia boards inclined like a pair of rafters and fixed to the face of the verge on a gable-ended roof; sometimes with soffit boards added if the barge boards project from the wall

barrier cream a cream used to protect the skin from damage or infection

beads the shaped pieces of timber added to the end of other pieces of timber to give a desired finish

binders timbers fixed on edge in the roof space, at right angles to ceiling joists, to give support if the span is greater than 2.5 m

birdsmouth notch cut out of the rafter to form a seating on the outside edge of the wall plate

botanical the classification of trees based upon scientific study

brick-on-edge a way of laying bricks to form an attractive, projecting window or door sill

bridled an open mortise and tenon joint. A tenon that has bridled is one that has no resistance and so is not secure

bull nose step quarter-rounded step at the bottom of a stair

butt joint the simplest joint between two pieces of wood, with the end grain of one meeting the long grain of the other and glued, screwed or nailed together

cap shaped top of a newel post, which can be fixed on or turned on the solid newel

capping fixed on the top edge of strings to take the fixing of a balustrade

carded scaffolder someone who holds a recognised certificate showing competence in scaffold erection

cement bonded chipboard a type of chipboard bonded with cement to make it stronger and more durable

chipboard material made in rigid sheets from compressed wood chips and resin

clear span the distance between joist supports

close couple a roof structure whereby the rafters are closed with a ceiling joist

collars sawn timber ties, sometimes used to give extra strength to prevent a roof spreading out at purlin level

common rafters load-bearing ribs that pitch up opposite each other from the wall plate on each side of the roof span, and fixed to the ridge board

conservation preservation of the environment and wildlife

contamination when harmful chemicals or substances pollute something (e.g. water)

corrosive a substance that can damage things it comes into contact with (e.g. material, skin)

coving a decorative moulding that is fitted at the top of a wall where it meets the ceiling

cradling L-shaped brackets use to provide fixing for the soffit

crawling board	a board or platform placed on roof joists which spread the weight of the worker allowing the work to be carried out safely	**egress**	an exit or way out
cripple rafters	pairs of rafters similar to jacks, spanning from the ridge to the valley rafter	**employer**	the person or company you work for
		enforced	making sure a law is obeyed
crown rafter	the centre rafter that meets the hip	**evergreen**	a type of tree that keeps its leaves all year round
cube units	the product of a number multiplied by its square, represented by a 3 after the unit (*see* **square units**)	**fascia board**	board of about 175 mm x 20 mm p.a.r. (plane all round timber) fixed to the plumb (i.e. vertical) cuts of the rafters at the eaves to provide a finish and a fixing board for guttering
damp proof course	a substance that is used to prevent damp from penetrating a building	**FIFO**	first in first out (a system of using stock whereby the oldest material is used first so that it doesn't perish)
deciduous	the name given to a type of tree that sheds its leaves every year	**firring**	a long wedge, tapered where joists are parallel to the fall, or of variable depth for joists at right angles
denominator	the bottom number in a fraction		
dermatitis	a skin condition where the affected area is red, itchy and sore	**frame**	a main frame consists of a head sill and two vertical jambs
detached	a building that stands alone and is not connected to any other building	**gable**	the triangular part of end walls
		gable-ends	the triangular ends of a roof
dovetailed nails	pairs of nails angled in towards each other	**galvanised steel frame cramps**	a fixing component which is screwed to a frame
dowel	a headless wood or metal pin used to join timber together	**gang-nailed**	galvanised plate with spikes used to secure butt joints
dry rot safety line	when the moisture content of damp timber reaches 20 per cent. Dry rot is likely if the moisture content exceeds this	**going**	the depth of a step (the measurement from a step's riser to the edge of the step)
dust mask	a form of respiratory protection that covers the mouth and nose and is used when working in a dusty environment	**gudgeons**	tubes at the end of hinges to take the pin around which the hinge rotates
eaves	lowest part of the roof surface where it meets the outside walls	**halving joint**	the same amount is removed from each piece of timber so that when fixed together the joint is the same thickness as the uncut timber
edge cut	the angled cut on top of the jack rafter where it meets the hip	**hazard**	a danger or risk
effective span	the distance between centres of joist bearings	**Health and Safety Executive**	the government organisation that enforces health and safety law in the UK

hip — part of the roof where two external sloping surfaces meet

hip rafters — pitched up from the wall plate corners of a hipped end to the saddle board at the ridge; acting as a spine for the heads of the jack rafters

horns — these are extensions to the frame that protect it during storage or transport, cut off before installation

hypotenuse — the longest side of a right-angled triangle

induction — a formal introduction you will receive when you start any new job, where you will be shown around, shown where the toilets and canteen etc. are, and told what to do if there is a fire

jack rafters — fixed in pairs on each side of the hip rafter, diminishing in size from ridge to wall plate

jig — any device made to hold a specific piece of work and help guide the tools being used

joint — a point at which parts are joined

landings — used between floor levels to break up the overall length of a flight and can be used to change the direction of a flight of stairs

LPG — liquefied petroleum gas

manual handling — using the body to lift, carry, push or pull a load

MDF — medium density fibreboard, used to form skirting boards and mouldings

metal decking — a decking material using aluminium or galvanised steel

moulding — decorative finishes around door openings and at floor and wall junctions

mullions — vertical dividers in a window frame

muster points — fire assembly points

newel — heavy vertical member at each end of the stair to which the handrail is fixed

nogging — a short length of timber, most often found fixed in a timber frame as a brace

nosing — front edge of a tread, or loose narrow top tread which sits on the trimmer joist at the top of the stairs

noxious — harmful or poisonous

numeracy skills — abilities that demonstrate a good basic knowledge of arithmetic

numerator — the top number in a fraction

opening casement — consists of top and bottom rails with two stiles

oriented strand board (OSB) — oriented strand board is made by coating wood chips (known as strands) with MDI and/or phenol formaldehyde, then arranging consecutive strand layers roughly perpendicular to each other, and finally pressing the strands under high temperature and high pressure to form boards

overall size — the extreme length and width of an item

p.a.r. — a term used for timber that has been 'planed all round'

packing — any material, generally waste wood, used to fill a gap

perpendicular — at right angles to

pitch or pitch angle — the rise and run gives the pitch angel or, knowing the pitch angle and the run, we can calculate the rise and basic rafter length

pitch board — a template of the rise and going

pitch line	plumb line marked at the base of the setting out rafter (pattern rafter), marked down two-thirds of its depth to the top of the birdsmouth cut, which acts as a reference or datum point for the rafter's length
plant	industrial machinery
plaster skim	a thin layer of plaster that is put on to walls to give them a smooth and even finish
plumb cut	the vertical cut at the top of the rafter where it meets the ridge
plywood	a material made from thin layers of timber called veneers
PPE	personal protective equipment, which might include a helmet, safety glasses and gloves
proactive	taking action before something happens (e.g. an accident)
proportionately	in proportion to the size of something else
prosecute	to accuse someone of committing a crime, which usually results in being taken to court and, if found guilty, being punished
purlins	horizontal beams that support the rafters mid-way between the ridge and the wall plate when the rafters are longer than 2.5 m
quirk	the name used for the hollow in a moulding
ratio	something that describes a relationship between quantities
reactive	taking action after something happens
ridge	acts as a spine at the apex of the roof structure, running horizontally and against which the uppermost ends of the rafters are fixed

rise	distance measured from the outside of the wall plates at wall plate level to the apex of the pitch lines, which run at two-thirds of the depth of the rafters
riser	vertical part of a step
rising	the height of a step (the measurement from the top of one step to the top of another)
run	equal to half of the span, it is used to reduce the roof shape to a right-angled triangle
saddle board	a timber board that is fixed to the common rafter and used as a bearing for the crown and hip rafters to fix to
seat cut	the 90° cut in a rafter where it meets the horizontal wall plate
semi-detached	a building that is joined to one other building and shares a dividing wall called a party wall
setter out	an experienced bench joiner whose job is the setting out of joinery products
setting out, or pattern, rafter	rafter selected as the basic rafter from which all setting out is done
shelf life	how long something will remain fit for its purpose whilst being stored
sherardised holdfast	a fixing component that is fixed quickly and easily driven in by hammer
sherardising	a process of covering metal with zinc, a non-ferrous metal, to reduce rusting
shoulder size	the length of any member between shoulders of tenons
side cut	the angled cut at each end of the purlin where it meets the hip
sight size	the size of the innermost edges of the component (usually the height and width of any glazed components and, therefore, sometimes referred to as 'daylight size')

skew-nailing knocking nails in at angles so that the wood cannot be pulled away easily

skirting a decorative moulding that is fitted at the bottom of a wall to hide the gap between the wall and the floor

soffit board board, similar to a fascia, fixed to the underside of the cradling in closed-eaves design

span the distance measured in the direction of ceiling joists, from the outside of one wall plate to the other; known as the overall (O/A) span

spandrel framing where the triangular area is formed under stairs, which can be framed to form a cupboard

sprocket pieces long, wedge-shaped pieces of rafter material fixed on top of each rafter so that the eaves create an upward tilt, thus reducing the slope on a steep roof to ease flow of rainwater into guttering

square units a unit of measurement equal to the area of a square whose side is of the unit given

squaring rod any piece of straight timber long enough to lie across the diagonal

stair well opening formed in a floor layout to accommodate a staircase

step combination of one tread and one riser

stile the longest vertical timber in the frame of a door, window etc.

stiles the side pieces of a stepladder into which the steps are set

still green mortar that is unset and not at full strength

stopped housing joint where a cut does not go completely through the timber

straining pieces sole plates fixed to the ceiling joists between the base of struts

string main board to which treads and risers are fixed

struts timbers that support purlins at every fourth or fifth pair of rafters, used to transfer roof load to ceiling joists and onto a load-bearing wall or partition

symptom a sign of illness or disease (e.g. difficulty breathing, a sore hand or a lump under the skin)

tensile forces a force that is trying to pull something apart

terraced a row of three or more buildings that are joined together, of which the inner buildings share two party walls

tie-rods metal rods underneath the rungs of a ladder that give extra support to the rungs

tile or slate battens sawn battens fixed at regular intervals on top of the lapped roofing felt; usually fixed by a slater and tiler, not the carpenter

tilting fillet triangular-shaped timber fixed behind a raised fascia to give it support

tongued and grooved board a decking material, rarely used these days

tongues the projecting piece of timber that fits into a groove in a tongue and groove joint

toxic poisonous

translucent sheeting corrugated or flat decking material

transoms horizontal dividers in a window frame

tread flat, horizontal part of a step

trimmer/ trimming/ trimmed joists joists affected by an opening in the floor such as a stairwell

truss a prefabricated component of a roof which spreads the load of a roof over the outer walls and forms its shape

valley part of a roof where two sloping surfaces meet

valley boards	used to form a gutter in the valley	**volume**	the amount of space taken up by a 3-D or solid shape
valley rafters	like hip rafters but forming an internal angle, acting as a spine for fixing cripple rafters	**wall plates**	timber plates laid flat and bedded on mortar, running along a wall to carry the feet of all rafters and ceiling joists; anchored down with restraint straps to prevent movement
veneer	a very thin layer of wood used as a ply (usually the finishing layer)		
verge	where a roof overhangs at the gable	**weather proofing**	to make something resistant to the effects of bad weather, especially rain
vibration white finger	a condition that can be caused by using vibrating machinery (usually for very long periods of time). The blood supply to the fingers is reduced which causes pain, tingling and sometimes spasms (shaking)	**winding**	twisted (wood)
		zinc-plated screw tie	a fixing component that is screwed to a frame; use avoids vibration from hammering